Military Aircraft Markings 1988

LONDON

IAN ALLAN LTD

Peter R. March

Contents

Photographs by Andrew March (APM), Daniel March (DJM), and Peter R. March (PRM)

This ninth edition published 1988

ISBN 0 7110 1764 6

Published by Ian Allan Ltd
and phototypeset and printed by Ian Allan Printing Ltd at their works
at Coombelands in Runnymede, England

Cover: Tornado GR1 ZA608 'Z' of No 617 Squadron. *John Oaten courtesy No 617 Squadron*

Introduction

This ninth edition of *abc Military Aircraft Markings*, a companion to *abc Civil Aircraft Markings*, again sets out to list in alphabetical and numerical order all the aircraft which carry a United Kingdom military serial, and which are based, or might be seen, in the UK. The term 'aircraft' used here covers powered, manned aeroplanes, helicopters and gliders. Included are all the current Royal Air Force, Royal Navy, Army Air Corps, Ministry of Defence (Procurement Executive), manufacturers' test aircraft and civilian-owned aircraft with military markings, together with gliders of the services' gliding associations.

Aircraft withdrawn from operational use but which are retained in the UK for ground training purposes or otherwise preserved by the Services and in museums and collections are listed. The serials of some incomplete aircraft have been included, such as the cockpit sections of machines displayed by the RAF Exhibition Flight, aircraft used by airfield fire sections and for service battle damage repair training (BDRT), together with significant parts of aircraft held by preservation groups and societies. Many of these aircraft are allocated, and sometimes wear, a secondary identity, such as an RAF Support Command 'M' or a Royal Navy 'A' maintenance number. These numbers are listed against those aircraft to which they have been allocated, and cross-references are included.

A serial 'missing' is either because it was never issued as it formed part of a 'black-out block', or because the aircraft is written off, scrapped, sold, abroad or allocated an alternative marking. Aircraft used as targets on MoD ranges to which access is restricted, and un-manned target drones, are omitted.

In the main, the serials listed are those markings presently displayed on the aircraft. Aircraft which bear a **false** serial are quoted in *italic* type. The manufacturer and aircraft type are given, together with any alternative, previous, secondary or civil identity shown in brackets. The operating unit and its based location, along with any known unit and base code markings in square brackets, are given as accurately as possible. The unit markings are normally carried boldly on the sides of the fuselage or on the aircraft's fin. In the case of RAF and AAC machines currently in service, they are usually one or two letters or numbers, while the RN continues to use a well-established system of three-figure codes between 000 and 999 together with a fin letter code denoting the aircraft's operational base. RN squadrons, units and bases are allocated blocks of numbers from which individual aircraft codes are issued. To help identification of RN bases and landing platforms on ships, a list of tail-letter codes with their appropriate name, helicopter code number, ship pennant number and type of vessel is included; as is a helicopter code number/ships' tail-letter code grid cross-reference.

Codes change, for example when aircraft move between units, and therefore the markings currently painted on a particular aircraft might not be those shown in this edition because of subsequent events. Those airframes which may not appear in the next edition because of sale, accident, etc, have their fates, where known, given in the 'Locations' column.

The Irish Army Air Corps fleet is listed, together with the serials of other overseas air arms whose aircraft might be seen visiting the UK from time to time. The serial numbers are as usually presented on the individual machine or as they are normally identified. Where possible, the aircraft's base and operating unit have been shown.

USAF, US Army and US Navy aircraft based in the UK and in Western Europe, and of types which regularly visit the UK from the USA, are listed in separate sections by type. The serial number actually displayed on the aircraft is shown in full, with additional Fiscal Year (FY) or full serial information also provided. Where appropriate, details of the operating wing, squadron allocation and base are added. Veteran and Vintage aircraft which carry overseas military markings but which are based in the UK have been separately listed showing the identity carried as a principal means of identification.

Information shown is believed to be correct at 31 January 1988, and significant changes can be monitored through the monthly 'Military Markings' column in *Aircraft Illustrated.*

Acknowledgements

The compiler wishes to thank the many people who have taken trouble to send comments, criticism and other useful information following the publication of the previous edition of *abc Military Aircraft Markings*. In particular the following correspondents: G. Beattie, P. H. Butler, CU Friends, J. R. Cross, J. Cottingham, D. P. Curtis, P.-J. Martin, T. Poole, M. C. Powney, L. P. Robinson, K. Sloper, R. Symes, M. Thompson and G. Turner.

This compilation has relied heavily on the publications of the following aviation groups and societies: *Air* (West London Aviation Group), *Air North, British Aviation Review* (British Aviation Research Group), *Humberside Air Review* (Humberside Aviation Society), *Irish Air Letter, Norfolk Air Review* (Norfolk Aviation Society), *North-West Air News* (Air Britain, Merseyside), *Osprey* (Solent Aviation Society), *Prestwick Airport Letter* (Prestwick Airport Aviation Group), *Scotland Scanned* & *Scottish Air News* (Central Scotland Aviation Group), *Skyward* (Westcountry Aviation Society), *South West Aviation News* (South West Aviation Society), *Stansted Aviation Newsletter* (The Stansted Aviation Society), *Ulster Airmail* (Ulster Aviation Society), together with these publications: *British Military Aircraft Serials* (Midland Counties Publications), *Euromil — Foreign Military Air Arms to Europe* (Seefive Publications); *NATO to the UK 1987* (West London Aviation Group); *United States Military Aircraft to Europe* (Seefive Publications) and *Wrecks and Relics* (Midland Counties Publications/ Merseyside Aviation Society).

The new edition of *abc Military Aircraft Markings* would not have been possible without considerable research and checking by Howard Curtis and Wal Gandy to whom I am indebted.

PRM

Abbreviations

AAC Army Air Corps
A&AEE Aeroplane & Armament Experimental Establishment
AAS Aeromedical Airlift Squadron
ABS Air Base Squadron
ABW Air Base Wing
ACCGS Air Cadets Central Gliding School
ACCS / ACCW Airborne Command and Control Squadron/Wing
ACR Armoured Cavalry Regiment
AEF Air Experience Flight
AES Air Engineering School
AETW Air Engineering Training Wing
AEW Airborne Early Warning
AFRES Air Force Reserve
AFSC Air Force System Command
AHB Attack Helicopter Battalion
AIU Accident Investigation Unit
AKG Aufklarüngs Geschwader (Reconnaissance Wing)
AMS Air Movements School
ANG Air National Guard
APS Aircraft Preservation Society
ARF Aircraft Restoration Flight
ARG Air Refuelling Group
ARRS / ARRW Aerospace Rescue and Recovery Squadron/Wing
ARS Air Refuelling Squadron
ARW Air Refuelling Wing
ARW/LCF Advanced Rotary Wing/Lynx Conversion Flight
ARWS Advanced Rotary Wing Squadron
AS Aggressor Squadron
ASF Aircraft Servicing Flight
AS&RU Aircraft Salvage and Repair Unit
ATC Air Training Corps
ATCC Air Traffic Control Centre
ATS Aircrewman Training Squadron
AvCo Aviation Company
AW Armstrong Whitworth Aircraft/ Aircraft Workshops
AW&CS / AW&CW Airborne Warning & Control Squadron/ Wing
BAC British Aircraft Corporation
BAe British Aerospace Company
BAOR British Army of the Rhine
BAPC British Aircraft Preservation Council
BATUS British Army Training Unit Support
BBMF Battle of Britain Memorial Flight
BDRF Battle Damage Repair Flight
BDRT Battle Damage Repair Training
BFWF Basic Fixed Wing Flight
BGA British Gliding & Soaring Association
BHC British Hovercraft Corporation
BP Boulton & Paul
B-V Boeing-Vertol
BW Bomber Wing
CAARP
CARG Cotswold Aircraft Restoration Group
CASA Construcciones Aeronautics SA
CATCS Central Air Traffic Control School
CBAS Commando Brigade Air Squadron
CCF Combined Cadet Force
CDE Chemical Defence Establishment
CFS Central Flying School
CIC
CinC Commander in Chief
Co Company

CSDE Central Servicing Development Establishment
CTE Central Training Establishment
CTTS Civilian Technical Training School
CV Chance-Vought
D-BD Dassault-Breguet Dornier
Det Detachment
DH De Havilland
DHC De Havilland Canada
D&TS Development and Trials Squadron
DTI Department of Trade and Industry
ECS } Electronic Countermeasures
ECW } Squadron/Wing
EE English Electric
EFTS Elementary Flying Training Squadron/Wing
EMA East Midlands Airport
EoN Elliot's of Newbury
ETPS Empire Test Pilots' School
ETS Engineering Training School
EWAU Electronics Warfare Avionics Unit
FAA Fleet Air Arm/Federal Aviation Authority
FBS Flugbereitschaftsstaffel
FBW Fly by wire
FCS Facility Checking Squadron
FE Further Education
FF&SS Fire Fighting & Safety School
FGF Flying Grading Flight
FI Falkland Islands
FIS Fighter Interceptor Squadron
Flt Flight
FMA Fabrica Militar de Aviones
FOL Forward Operating Location
FONAC Flag Officer Naval Air Command
FRADU Fleet Requirements and Direction Unit
FRL Flight Refuelling Ltd
FRSB Fleet Reserve Storage Base
FTS Flying Training School
FW Foster Wikner
FY Fiscal Year
GAL General Aircraft Ltd
GD General Dynamics
HFWS Heeresflieger Waffenschule
HMS Her Majesty's Ship
HP Handley-Page
HQ Headquarters
HS Hawker Siddeley
IAF Israeli Air Force
IAM Institute of Aviation Medicine
IWM Imperial War Museum
JATE Joint Air Transport Establishment
JbG Jagd Bomber Geschwader (Fighter Bomber Wing)
JG Jagd Geschwader (Fighter Wing)
JMU Jaguar Maintenance Unit
JTU Joint Trials Unit
LCF Lynx Conversion Flight
LTG Luft Transport Geschwader (Air Transport Wing)
LVG Luftwaffen Versorgungs Geschwader (Air Force Maintenance Wing)
MAC Military Airlift Command
MAG Military Airlift Group
MAAG Military Air Advisory Group
MAS Military Airlift Squadron
MAW Military Airlift Wing
McD McDonnell Douglas
MFG Marine Flieger Geschwader (Naval Air Wing)
MGSP Mobile Glider Servicing Party
MH Max Holste
MIB Military Intelligence Battalion
MoD(PE) Ministry of Defence (Procurement Executive)
Mod Modified
MR Maritime Reconnaissance
MS Morane-Saulnier
MU Maintenance Unit
NA North American
NACDS Naval Air Command Driving School
NAF Naval Air Facility
NASU Naval Air Support Unit
NE North-East
NHTU Naval Hovercraft Trials Unit
NI Northern Ireland
OCU Operational Conversion Unit
OEU Operation Evaluation Unit
OPITB Offshore Petroleum Industry Training Board
OTD Overseas Training Division
PAX Passenger procedural trainer
PRU Photographic Reconnaissance Unit
RAE Royal Aircraft Establishment
RAeS Royal Aeronautical Society
RAF Royal Aircraft Factory/ Royal Air Force
RAFC Royal Air Force College
RAFGSA Royal Air Force Gliding and Soaring Association
RAOC Royal Army Ordnance Corps
RCAF Royal Canadian Air Force
RE Royal Engineers
REME Royal Electrical & Mechanical Engineers
RM Royal Marines
RMC of S Royal Military College of Science
RN Royal Navy
RNAS Royal Naval Air Station
RNAY Royal Naval Aircraft Yard
RNEC Royal Naval Engineering College
RNEFTS Royal Naval Elementary Flying Training School
RNGSA Royal Navy Gliding and Soaring Association
ROC Royal Ordnance Corps
ROF Royal Ordnance Factory
R-R Rolls-Royce
RS Reid & Sigrist/Reconnaissance Squadron
RS&RE Royal Signals and Radar Establishment
RW Reconnaissance Wing
SA Scottish Aviation
SAC Strategic Air Command
SAH School of Air Handling
SAL Scottish Aviation Limited
SAR Search and Rescue
Saro Saunders-Roe
SAREW Search & Rescue Engineering Wing
SARTU Search and Rescue Training Unit
SCF Scout Conversion Flight
SEPECAT Société Européenne de Production de l'avion Ecole de Combat et d'Appui Tactique
SHAPE Supreme Headquarters Allied Forces Europe
SHSU Sea Harrier Servicing Unit
SKTU Sea King Training Unit
SNCAN Société Nationale Aeronautique du Nord
SOS Special Operations Squadron
SoTT School of Technical Training
Sqn Squadron
SRW Strategic Reconnaissance Wing
SSF Station Servicing Flight
SW Strategic Wing
TAS Tactical Airlift Squadron
TASS Tactical Air Support Squadron
TAW Tactical Airlift Wing
TCW Tactical Control Wing
TDCS Tactical Deployment Control Squadron
Tech Coll Technical College
TFS Tactical Fighter Squadron
TFW Tactical Fighter Wing
TMTS Trade Management Training School
TOEU Tornado Operational Evaluation Unit

TRS	Tactical Reconnaissance Squadron
TRW	Tactical Reconnaissance Wing
TSLW	Technische Schule der Luftwaffe
TTTE	Tri-national Tornado Training Establishment
TW	Test Wing
TWCU	Tornado Weapons Conversion Unit
TWU	Tactical Weapons Unit
UAS	University Air Squadron
UK	United Kingdom
UKAEA	United Kingdom Atomic Energy Authority
US	United States
USAF	United States Air Force
USAFE	United States Air Forces in Europe
USAREUR	US Army Europe
USEUCOM	United States European Command
USN	United States Navy
VGS	Volunteer Gliding School
VQ	Air Reconnaissance Squadron
VR	Logistic Support Squadron
VS	Vickers-Supermarine
WRG	Weather Reconnaissance Group
WRS	Weather Reconnaissance Squadron
WS	Westland
WW2	World War II

British Military Aircraft Serials

The Committee of Imperial Defence through its Air Committee introduced a standardised system of numbering aircraft in November 1912. The Air Department of the Admiralty was allocated the first batch 1-200 and used these to cover aircraft already in use and those on order. The Army was issued with the next block from 201-800, which included the number 304 which was given to the Cody Biplane now preserved in the Science Museum. By the outbreak of World War 1 the Royal Navy was on its second batch of serials 801-1600 and this system continued with alternating allocations between the Army and Navy until 1916 when number 10000, a Royal Flying Corps BE2C, was reached.

It was decided not to continue with five digit numbers but instead to start again from 1, prefixing RFC aircraft with the letter A and RNAS aircraft with the prefix N. The RFC allocations commenced with A1 an FE2D and before the end of the year had reached A9999 an Armstrong Whitworth FK8. The next group commenced with B1 and continued in logical sequence through the C, D, E and F prefixes. G was used on a limited basis to identity captured German aircraft, while H was the last block of wartime ordered aircraft. To avoid confusion I was not used, so the new postwar machines were allocated serials in the J range. A further minor change was made in the serial numbering system in August 1929 when it was decided to maintain four numerals after the prefix letter, thus omitting numbers 1 to 999. The new K series therefore commenced at K1000, which was allocated to an AW Atlas.

The Naval N prefix was not used in such a logical way. Blocks of numbers were allocated for specific types of aircraft such as seaplanes or flying boats. By the late 1920s the sequence had largely been used up and a new series using the prefix S was commenced. In 1930 separate naval allocations were stopped and subsequent serials were issued in the 'military' range which had by this time reached the K series. A further change in the pattern of allocations came in the L range. Commencing with L7272 numbers were issued in blocks with smaller blocks of serials between not used. These were known as blackout blocks. As M had already been used as a suffix for Maintenance Command instructional airframes it was not used as a prefix. Although N had previously been used for naval aircraft it was used again for serials allocated from 1937.

With the build-up to World War 2 the rate of allocations quickly accelerated and the prefix R was being used when war was declared. The letters O and Q were not allotted, and nor was S which had been used up to S1865 for naval aircraft before integration into the RAF series. By 1940 the serial Z9999 had been reached, as part of a blackout block, with the letters U and Y not used to avoid confusion. The option to recommence serial allocation at A1000 was not taken up; instead it was decided to use an alphabetical two-letter prefix with three numerals running from 100 to 999. Thus AA100 was allocated to a Blenheim IV.

This two-letter, three-numeral serial system which started in 1940 continues today with the current issue being in the ZH range. The letters C, I, O, Q, U and Y were, with the exception of NC, not used. For various reasons the following letter combinations were not issued: DA, DB, DH, EA, GA to GZ, HA, HT, JE, JH, JJ, KR to KT, MR, NW, NZ, SA to SK, SV, TN, TR and VE. The first postwar serials issued were in the VP range while the end of the WZs had been reached by the Korean War. At the current rate of issue the Z range should last out the remainder of this century.

Note: Whilst every effort has been made to ensure the accuracy of this publication, no part of the contents has been obtained from official sources. The compiler will be pleased to continue to receive comments, corrections and further information for inclusion in subsequent editions of *Military Aircraft Markings*. A monthly up-date of additions, amendments and cancellations is published in *Aircraft Illustrated*.

British Military Aircraft Markings

A serial in *italics* denotes that it is not the genuine marking for that airframe.

Serial	Type (alternative identity)	Owner, Operator or Location	Notes
164	Bleriot Type XI (BAPC 106)	RAF Museum, Hendon	
168	Sopwith Tabloid Scout Replica (G-BFDE)	Bomber Command Museum, Hendon	
304	Cody Biplane (BAPC 62)	Science Museum, South Kensington	
433	Bleriot Type XXVII (BAPC 107)	RAF Museum, Hendon	
2345	Vickers FB5 Gunbus Replica (G-ATVP)	RAF Museum, Hendon	
2699	RAF BE2C	Imperial War Museum, Duxford	
3066	Caudron GIII (G-AETA)	RAF Museum, Hendon	
5964	DH2 Replica (G-BFVH)	Privately owned, Duxford	
5964	DH2 Replica (BAPC 112)	Museum of Army Flying, Middle Wallop	
6232	RAF BE2C Replica (BAPC 41)	RAF St Athan Historic Aircraft Collection	
8151	Sopwith Baby Replica (BAPC 137)		
8359	Short 184	FAA Museum, RNAS Yeovilton	
A1325	RAF BE2e	Mosquito Aircraft Museum, London Colney	
A1742	Scout D Replica (BAPC 38)	RAF, St Mawgan	
A4850	RAF SE5A Replica (BAPC176)	South Yorkshire APS, Firbeck	
A8226	Sopwith 1½ Strutter Replica (G-BIDW)	RAF Museum, Hendon	
B1807	Sopwith Pup (G-EAVX) [A7]	Privately owned, Keynsham, Avon	
B4863	RAF SE5A Replica (BAPC 113) [G]		
B4863	Eberhardt SE5E (G-BLXT) [G]	Privately owned, Booker	
B6401	Sopwith Camel F1 Replica (G-AWYY/C1701)	FAA Museum, RNAS Yeovilton	
B7270	Sopwith Camel F1 Replica (G-BFCZ)	Privately owned, St Just	
C1904	RAF SE5A Replica (G-PFAP) [Z]	Privately owned, Bicester	
C4912	Bristol M1C Replica (G-BLWM)	RAF Museum, Hendon	
C4912	Bristol M1c Replica (BAPC 135)		
D3419	Sopwith Camel F1 Replica (BAPC 59)	RAF, St Mawgan	
D5329	Sopwith Dolphin	RAF Museum Store, Cardington	
D7560	Avro 504K	Science Museum, South Kensington	
D7889	Bristol F2b Fighter (G-AANM/BAPC 166)	Privately owned, St Leonards	
D8096	Bristol F2B Fighter (G-AEPH) [D]	Shuttleworth Collection, Old Warden	
E373	Avro 504K Replica (BAPC178)	RAF Museum Store, Henlow	
E449	Avro 504K (G-EBJE)	RAF Museum, Hendon	
E2466	Bristol F2b (BAPC165)	RAF Museum, Hendon	
E2581	Bristol F2b Fighter	Imperial War Museum, Duxford	
E6452	SNCAN Stampe SV4C (G-AXNW)	Privately owned, St Merryn	
F344	Avro 504K Replica	RAF Museum Store, Henlow	
F760	SE5A Microlight Replica [A]	Privately owned, Redhill	
F904	RAF SE5A (G-EBIA)	Shuttleworth Collection, Old Warden	
F938	RAF SE5A (G-EBIC)	RAF Museum, Hendon	
F939	RAF SE5A (G-EBIB/F937) [6]	Science Museum, South Kensington	
F943	RAF SE5A Replica (G-BIHF) [S]	Privately owned, Booker (*Lady Di*)	
F943	RAF SE5A Replica (G-BKDT)	Privately owned, Elvington	
F1010	DH9A [19]	Bomber Command Museum, Hendon	
F3556	RAF RE8	Imperial War Museum, Duxford	
F4013	Sopwith Camel Replica	To La Ferte Alais	
F5447	RAF SE5A Replica (G-BKER) [N]	Privately owned, Strathallan/ Strathallan Aircraft Collection	
F5459	RAF SE5A Replica (BAPC 142) [11-Y]	Cornwall Aero Park, Helston	
F-5459	RAF SE5A Replica (G-INNY) [Y]	Privately owned, Old Sarum	
F6314	Sopwith Camel F1 [B]	RAF Museum, Hendon	
F8010	RAF SE5A Replica (G-BDWJ) [Z]	Privately owned, Booker	

Notes	Serial	Type (alternative identity)	Owner, Operator or Location
	F8614	Vickers Vimy Replica (G-AWAU)	Bomber Command Museum, Hendon
	G1381	Avro 504K Replica [G] (BAPC 177)	Brooklands Museum, Weybridge
	H1968	Avro 504K Replica (BAPC 42)	RAF St Athan Historic Aircraft Collection
	H2311	Avro 504K (G-ABAA)	RAF Museum Store, Henlow
	H5199	Avro 504K (G-ACNB, G-ADEV)	Shuttleworth Collection, Old Warden
	J7326	DH Humming Bird (G-EBQP)	Privately owned, Hemel Hempstead
	J8067	Pterodactyl 1a	Science Museum, South Kensington
	J9941	Hawker Hart 2 (G-ABMR)	RAF Museum, Hendon
	K1786	Hawker Tomtit (G-AFTA)	Shuttleworth Collection, Old Warden
	K1930	Hawker Fury Replica (G-BKBB)	Privately owned, Booker
	K2050	Hawker Fury Replica (G-ASCM)	Privately owned, Stapleford
	K2059	Isaacs Fury (G-PFAR)	Privately owned, Dunkeswell
	K2060	Isaacs Fury II (G-BKZM)	Privately owned, Huddersfield
	K2567	DH Tiger Moth (G-MOTH)	Russavia Collection, Duxford
	K2568	DH Tiger Moth (G-APMM)	Privately owned, Bedford
	K2571	DH Tiger Moth	Privately owned, Lutterworth
	K2572	DH Tiger Moth (G-AOZH) (really NM129)	Privately owned, Shoreham
	K3215	Avro Tutor (G-AHSA)	Shuttleworth Collection, Old Warden
	K3584	DH 82B Queen Bee (BAPC 186)	Mosquito Aircraft Museum, London Colney
	K3731	Isaacs Fury Replica (G-RODI)	Privately owned, Exeter
	K4232	Avro Rota I (SE-AZB)	RAF Museum, Hendon
	K4235	Avro Rota I (G-AHMJ)	Shuttleworth Collection, Old Warden
	K4972	Hawker Hart Trainer IIA (1764M)	RAF Museum Restoration Centre, Cardington
	K5054	Supermarine Spitfire Replica	Privately owned, Swindon
	K5414	Hawker Hind (G-AENP/ BAPC 78) [XV]	Shuttleworth Collection, Old Warden
	K6038	Westland Wallace II (2365M)	RAF Museum Store, Cardington
	K7271	Hawker Fury II Replica (BAPC 148)	RAF Cosford Aerospace Museum
	K8042	Gloster Gladiator II (8372M)	Battle of Britain Museum, Hendon
	K9942	VS Spitfire IA (8383M) [SD-V]	RAF Museum, Hendon
	L1592	Hawker Hurricane I [KW-Z]	Science Museum, South Kensington
	L1592	Hawker Hurricane I Replica (BAPC 63) [KW-Z]	Torbay Aircraft Museum, Paignton
	L2301	VS Walrus I (G-AIZG)	FAA Museum, RNAS Yeovilton
	L2940	Blackburn Skua I	FAA Museum, RNAS Yeovilton
	L5343	Fairey Battle I	RAF St Athan Historic Aircraft Collection
	L6906	Miles Magister (G-AKKY) (BAPC 44)	Berkshire Aviation Group, Woodley
	L7245	HP Halifax	*See HR792*
	L7775	Vickers Wellington (fuselage)	South Yorkshire Aircraft Museum, Firbeck, Notts
	L8032	Gloster Gladiator (G-AMRK)	Shuttleworth Collection, Old Warden
	L8756	Bristol Bolingbroke IVT (RCAF 10001) [XD-E]	Battle of Britain Museum, Hendon
	N220	Supermarine S5 Replica (G-BDFF)	Crashed 23 May 1987, Falmouth
	N248	Supermarine S6A	Southampton Hall of Aviation
	N1671	Boulton Paul Defiant I (8370M) [EW-D]	Battle of Britain Museum, Hendon
	N1854	Fairey Fulmar II (G-AIBE)	FAA Museum, RNAS Yeovilton
	N2078	Sopwith Baby	FAA Museum, RNAS Yeovilton
	N2276	Gloster Gladiator II (really N5903) [H]	FAA Museum, RNAS Yeovilton
	N2980	Vickers Wellington IA [R]	Brooklands Museum, Weybridge
	N3788	Miles Magister (G-AKPF) (really G-ANLT)	Privately owned, Bassingbourn
	N4389	Fairey Albacore I [4M] (really N4172)	FAA Museum, RNAS Yeovilton
	N4877	Avro Anson I (G-AMDA) [VX-F]	Skyfame Collection, Duxford
	N5180	Sopwith Pup (G-EBKY)	Shuttleworth Collection, Old Warden
	N5182	Sopwith Pup Replica (G-APUP)	RAF Museum, Hendon
	N5195	Sopwith Pup (G-ABOX)	Museum of Army Flying, Middle Wallop
	N5419	Bristol Scout Type D Replica	RAF Museum restoration centre, Cardington
	N5445	DH Tiger Moth	*To D-EHXH*
	N5492	Sopwith Triplane Replica (BAPC 111)	FAA Museum, RNAS Yeovilton

Serial	Type (alternative identity)	Owner, Operator or Location	Notes
N5628	Gloster Gladiator II	RAF Museum, Hendon	
N5912	Sopwith Triplane (8385M)	RAF Museum, Hendon	
N6004	Short Stirling 1	RAeS Medway Branch, Rochester	
N6160	Sopwith Pup	Privately owned, Tattershall Thorpe	
N6452	Sopwith Pup Replica (G-BIAU)	FAA Museum, RNAS Yeovilton	
N6466	DH Tiger Moth (G-ANKZ)	Privately owned, Barton	
N6720	DH Tiger Moth (7014M) [RUO-B]	No 1940 Sqn ATC, Levenshulme	
N6812	Sopwith Camel	Imperial War Museum, Lambeth	
N6847	DH Tiger Moth (G-APAL)	Privately owned, Little Gransden	
N6848	DH Tiger Moth (G-BALX)	Privately owned, Sedlescombe	
N6985	DH Tiger Moth (G-AHMN)	Museum of Army Flying, Middle Wallop	
N9191	DH Tiger Moth (G-ALND)	Privately owned, Shipdham	
N9238	DH Tiger Moth (G-ANEL)	Privately owned, Oxford	
N9389	DH Tiger Moth (G-ANJA)	Privately owned, Shipmeadow, Suffolk	
N9510	DH Tiger Moth (G-AOEL)	Royal Scottish Museum of Flight, East Fortune	
N9899	Supermarine Southampton I	RAF Museum Store, Cardington	
P2183	Fairey Battle I	RAF St Athan Historic Aircraft Collection	
P2617	Hawker Hurricane I (8373M) [AF-F]	Battle of Britain Museum, Hendon	
P3175	Hawker Hurricane I	Battle of Britain Museum, Hendon	
P6382	Miles Magister (G-AJRS)	Shuttleworth Collection, Old Warden	
P7350	VS Spitfire IIA (G-AWIJ) [EB-Z]	RAF Battle of Britain Memorial Flight, Coningsby	
P7540	VS Spitfire IIA [DU-W]	Dumfries & Galloway Aviation Museum, Tinwald Downs	
P9390	VS Spitfire I Replica (BAPC 71) [KL-B]	Norfolk & Suffolk Aviation Museum, Flixton	
P9444	VS Spitfire IA [RN-D]	Science Museum, South Kensington	
R1914	Miles Magister (G-AHUJ)	Strathallan Aircraft Collection	
R3950	Fairey Battle I (RCAF 1899)	Privately owned, Duxford	
R4907	DH Tiger Moth (G-ANCS)	Privately owned, Moulton St Mary	
R4959	DH Tiger Moth (G-ARAZ) [59]	Privately owned, Goodwood	
R5086	DH Tiger Moth (G-APIH)	Privately owned, Little Gransden	
R5250	DH Tiger Moth (G-AODT)	Privately owned, Swanton Morley	
R5868	Avro Lancaster I (7325M) [PO-S]	Bomber Command Museum, Hendon	
R6915	VS Spitfire I	Imperial War Museum, Lambeth	
R9125	Westland Lysander III (8377M) [LX-L]	Battle of Britain Museum, Hendon	
S1287	Fairey Flycatcher Replica (G-BEYB) [5]	Privately owned, Stockbridge	
S1595	Supermarine S6B	Science Museum, South Kensington	
S1595	Supermarine S6B Replica (BAPC 156)		
S3398	Spad XIII Replica (G-BFYO)	FAA Museum, RNAS Yeovilton	
S4523	Spad XIII [I] (N4727V)	Imperial War Museum, Duxford	
T5424	DH Tiger Moth (G-AJOA)	Privately owned, Chiseldon	
T5493	DH Tiger Moth (G-ANEF)	Privately owned, Cranwell	
T5672	DH Tiger Moth (G-ALRI)	Privately owned, Chalmington	
T5854	DH Tiger Moth (G-ANKK)	Privately owned, Halfpenny Green	
T5968	DH Tiger Moth (G-ANNN)	Privately owned, Ayr	
T5879	DH Tiger Moth (G-AXBW)	Privately owned, Tongham	
T6099	DH Tiger Moth (G-AOGR/ XL714)	Privately owned, Clacton	
T6296	DH Tiger Moth (8387M)	RAF Museum, Hendon	
T6313	DH Tiger Moth (G-AHVU)	Privately owned, Denham	
T6553	DH Tiger Moth (G-APIG) [N]	Privately owned, Avignon	
T6645	DH Tiger Moth (G-AIIZ)	Sold to SE	
T6818	DH Tiger Moth (G-ANKT)	Shuttleworth Collection, Old Warden	
T7281	DH Tiger Moth (G-ARTL)	Privately owned, Egton, nr Whitby	
T7404	DH Tiger Moth (G-ANMV)	Privately owned, Booker	
T7909	DH Tiger Moth (G-ANON)	Privately owned, Sherburn-in-Elmet	
T7997	DH Tiger Moth (G-AOBH)	Privately owned, Benington	
T8191	DH Tiger Moth	RN Historic Flight, RNAS Yeovilton	
T9707	Miles Magister (G-AKKR/8378M/T9708)	Greater Manchester Museum of Science and Industry	
T9738	Miles Hawk Trainer III (G-AKAT)	Privately owned, Hillam	
V3388	Airspeed Oxford (G-AHTW)	Skyfame Collection, Duxford	
V6028	Bristol Blenheim IV (G-MKIV) [GB-D] (really RCAF 10038)	Crashed 21 June 1987, Denham	

Notes	Serial	Type (alternative identity)	Owner, Operator or Location
	V7350	Hawker Hurricane I	Robertsbridge Aviation Society
	V7767	Hawker Hurricane Replica (BAPC 72)	Air Museum, North Weald
	V9281	Westland Lysander III (G-BCWL) [RU-M] (really RCAF 1244)	Privately owned, Middle Wallop
	V9300	Westland Lysander III (G-LIZY)	British Aerial Museum, Duxford
	V9441	Westland Lysander IIIA (RCAF2355/G-AZWT) [AR-A]	Strathallan Aircraft Collection
	W1048	HP Halifax II (8465M) [TL-S]	Bomber Command Museum, Hendon
	W4041	Gloster E28/39 [G]	Science Museum, South Kensington
	W4050	DH Mosquito 1	Mosquito Aircraft Museum, London Colney
	W5856	Fairey Swordfish II (G-BMGC)	Strathallan Aircraft Collection
	W5984	Fairey Swordfish II (really HS618/A2001) [5H]	FAA Museum, RNAS Yeovilton
	X4590	VS Spitfire I (8384M) [PR-F]	Battle of Britain Museum, Hendon
	Z2033	Fairey Firefly I (G-ASTL)	Skyfame Collection, Duxford
	Z7015	Hawker Sea Hurricane IB (G-BKTH)	Shuttleworth Collection, Duxford
	Z7197	Percival Proctor III (G-AKZN/ 8380M)	RAF St Athan Historic Aircraft Collection
	Z7258	DH Dragon Rapide (G-AHGD) (really NR786)	Privately owned, Old Warden
	AB910	VS Spitfire VB [BP-O]	RAF Battle of Britain Memorial Flight, Coningsby
	AL246	Grumman Martlet I	FAA Museum, RNAS Yeovilton
	AP507	Cierva C30A (G-ACWP) [KX-P]	Science Museum, South Kensington
	AR213	VS Spitfire IA (G-AIST) [PR-D]	Privately owned, Booker
	AR501	VS Spitfire VC (G-AWII) [NN-D]	Shuttleworth Collection, Duxford
	BB807	DH Tiger Moth (G-ADWO)	Wessex Aviation Society, Wimborne
	BB814	DH Tiger Moth (G-AFWI)	RN Gliding Club, Lee-on-Solent
	BL614	VS Spitfire VB (4354M) [ZD-F]	Greater Manchester Museum of Science and Industry
	BM597	VS Spitfire VB (5718M) [PR-O]	RAF Church Fenton, on gate
	DE208	DH Tiger Moth (G-AGYU)	Privately owned, Nayland
	DE363	DH Tiger Moth (G-ANFC)	Military Aircraft Preservation Group, Hadfield, Derbyshire
	DE373	DH Tiger Moth T2 (A680/ A2127)	Privately owned
	DE623	DH Tiger Moth (G-ANFI)	Privately owned, St Athan
	DE673	DH Tiger Moth (G-ADNZ/ 6948M)	Privately owned, Hampton
	DE992	DH Tiger Moth (G-AXXV)	Privately owned, Wellesbourne Mountford
	DF128	DH Tiger Moth (G-AOJJ) [RCO-U]	Privately owned, Abingdon
	DF130	DH Tiger Moth (G-BACK)	Privately owned, Laindon
	DF155	DH Tiger Moth (G-ANFV)	Privately owned, Lossiemouth
	DF198	DH Tiger Moth (G-BBRB)	Privately owned, Biggin Hill
	DG202	Gloster F9/40 Meteor (5758M) [G]	RAF Cosford Aerospace Museum
	DG590	Miles Hawk Major (G-ADMW/8379M)	RAF Museum Store, Henlow
	DP872	Fairey Barracuda II	FAA Museum, St Just on rebuild
	DR613	FW Wicko GM1 (G-AFJB)	Privately owned, Berkswell
	DR628	Beech D.17s (N18V) [PB-1]	Privately owned, Duxford
	DV372	Avro Lancaster I (nose only)	Imperial War Museum, Lambeth
	EE416	Gloster Meteor III (nose only)	Science Museum, South Kensington
	EE531	Gloster Meteor F4 (7090M)	Midland Air Museum, Coventry
	EE549	Gloster Meteor F4 (7008M)	RAF St Athan Historic Aircraft Collection
	EJ693	Hawker Tempest V [SA-J]	Privately owned
	EM727	DH Tiger Moth (G-AOXN)	Privately owned, Yeovil
	EM903	DH Tiger Moth (G-APBI)	Privately owned, Audley End
	EN398	VS Spitfire IX Replica (BAPC184) [JE-J]	Aces High, North Weald
	EP120	VS Spitfire VB (5377M/8070M) [QV-H]	RAF Wattisham
	EX280	NA Harvard IIA (G-TEAC) [G]	Privately owned, North Weald
	EX976	NA Harvard III	FAA Museum, RNAS Yeovilton
	EZ259	NA Harvard III (G-BMJW)	Privately owned, Bracknell
	EZ407	NA Harvard III	RN Historic Flight, Lee-on-Solent
	FE905	NA Harvard IIB (LN-BNM/12392)	RAF Museum Store, Cardington

Serial	Type (alternative identity)	Owner, Operator or Location	Notes
FE992	NA Harvard IIB (G-BDAM)	Privately owned, Lee-on-Solent	
FH153	NA Harvard IIB (G-BBHK) [GW-A]	Privately owned, Cardiff	
FR870	Curtiss Kittyhawk III (NL1009N) [GA-S]	Privately owned, Duxford	
FS728	NA Harvard IIB (G-BAFM)	Privately owned, Booker	
FS890	NA Harvard T2 (T554M)	A&AEE, stored Boscombe Down	
FT239	NA Harvard IV (G-BIWX)	Privately owned, White Waltham	
FT323	NA Harvard III	Privately owned, Cranfield	
FT375	NA Harvard IIB	MoD(PE) A&AEE Boscombe Down	
FT391	NA Harvard IIB (G-AZBN)	Privately owned, Duxford	
FX301	NA Harvard III (G-JUDI) [FD-NQ] (really EX915)	Privately owned, RAF Binbrook	
FX442	NA Harvard IIB	Privately owned, Bournemouth	
HB275	Be.C-45 Expeditor II (N5063N)	Privately owned, White Waltham	
HB751	Fairchild Argus III (G-BCBL)	Privately owned, Little Gransden	
HD368	NA B-25J Mitchell (N9089Z/ G-BKXW) [VO-A]	Aces High, Duxford	
HH379	GAL48 Hotspur II (rear fuselage only)	Museum of Army Flying, Middle Wallop	
HJ711	DH Mosquito NFII [VI-C]	Privately owned, York	
HM354	Percival Proctor III (G-ANPP)	Privately owned, Stansted	
HR792	HP Halifax GR II	Yorkshire Air Museum, Elvington	
HS503	Fairey Swordfish IV (BAPC 108)	RAF Museum Store, Henlow	
HS649	VS Spitfire XVIII	*See Historic Aircraft Section, India*	
HX922	DH Mosquito TT35 (G-AWJV) [EG-F] (really TA634)	Mosquito Aircraft Museum, London Colney	
JV482	Grumman Wildcat V	Ulster Aviation Society, Newtownards	
JV928	PBY-5A Catalina (G-BLSC) [Y]	Plane Sailing, Duxford	
KB889	Avro Lancaster B10 (G-LANC)	Imperial War Museum, Duxford	
KB976	Avro Lancaster B10 (G-BCOH) [LQ-K]	Privately owned, Woodford *Extensively damaged 12 August 1987*	
KD431	CV Corsair IV [E2-M]	FAA Museum, RNAS Yeovilton	
KE209	Grumman Hellcat II	FAA Museum, RNAS Yeovilton	
KE418	Hawker Tempest (rear fuselage)	RAF Museum Store, Cardington	
KF183	NA Harvard IIB	MoD(PE) A&AEE Boscombe Down	
KF388	NA Harvard IIB (nose only)	Wessex Aviation Society, Wimborne	
KF423	NA Harvard II	Booker Aviation Museum	
KF435	NA Harvard IIB	Privately owned, Booker	
KF594	NA Harvard IIB (cockpit section)	Newark Air Museum, Winthorpe	
KG374	Douglas Dakota C-4 [YS] (really KN645/8355M)	RAF Cosford Aerospace Museum	
KG874	Douglas Dakota C-4 (really TS423/G-DAKS) [YS-L]	*See 100884, Historic Aircraft, US*	
KK995	Sikorsky Hoverfly I [E]	RAF Museum, Hendon	
KN448	Douglas Dakota C4 (nose only)	Science Museum, South Kensington	
KN751	Consolidated Liberator VI [K]	RAF Cosford Aerospace Museum	
KP208	Douglas Dakota C-4 [YS]	Airborne Forces Museum, Aldershot	
KX829	Hawker Hurricane IV [JV-I]	Birmingham Museum of Science & Industry	
LA198	VS Spitfire F21 (7118M) [RAI-G]	RAF Leuchars, on display	
LA226	VS Spitfire F21 (7119M)	RAF Memorial Chapel, Biggin Hill	
LA255	VS Spitfire F21 (6490M) [JX-U]	RAF Wittering	
LA564	VS Seafire F46	Privately owned, Newport Pagnell	
LB294	Taylorcraft Plus D (G-AHWJ)	Museum of Army Flying, Middle Wallop	
LB312	Taylorcraft Plus D (G-AHXE)	Privately owned, Shoreham	
LB375	Taylorcraft Plus D (G-AHGW)	Privately owned, Coventry	
LF363	Hawker Hurricane IIC [NV-L]	RAF Battle of Britain Memorial Flight, Coningsby	
LF738	Hawker Hurricane IIC (5405M)	RAF, RAeS Medway Branch, Rochester	
LF751	Hawker Hurricane IIC (5466M)	RAF Manston, Memorial Hall	
LF858	DH Queen Bee (G-BLUZ)	Privately owned, Little Gransden	
LH208	Airspeed Horsa I (parts only)	Museum of Army Flying, Middle Wallop	
LS326	Fairey Swordfish II (G-AJVH) [L2]	RN Historic Flight, RNAS Yeovilton	
LZ551	DH Sea Vampire I [G]	FAA Museum, RNAS Yeovilton	
LZ766	Percival Proctor III (G-ALCK)	Skyfame Collection, Duxford	
MD497	WS 51 Widgeon (G-ANLW) [NE-X]	Privately owned, Wellingborough	
MF628	Vickers Wellington T10	Bomber Command Museum, Hendon	
MH434	VS Spitfire IX (G-ASJV) [ZD-B]	Privately owned, Duxford	
MJ627	VS Spitfire TIX (G-ASOZ/ G-BMSB)	Privately owned, Kenilworth	

Notes	*Serial*	*Type (alternative identity)*	*Owner, Operator or Location*
	MJ730	VS Spitfire IX (G-BLAS)	Privately owned, East Midlands Airport
	MK356	VS Spitfire IX (5690M) [21-V]	RAF St Athan Historic Aircraft Collection
	ML407	VS Spitfire T9 (G-LFIX) [OU-V]	Privately owned, Middle Wallop
	ML417	VS Spitfire LFIXe (G-BJSG) (2I-T]	Privately owned, Duxford
	ML427	VS Spitfire IX (6457M) [I-ST]	Birmingham Museum of Science & Industry
	ML796	Short Sunderland V	Imperial War Museum, Duxford
	ML824	Short Sunderland V [NS-Z]	Battle of Britain Museum, Hendon
	MN235	Hawker Typhoon IB	RAF Museum, Hendon
	MP425	Airspeed Oxford (G-AITB)	RAF Museum Store, Cardington
	MT360	Auster 5 (G-AKWT)	*To G-AKWT*
	MT438	Auster III (G-AREI)	Privately owned, Chessington
	MT847	VS Spitfire XIV (6960M)	RAF Cosford Aerospace Museum
	MV154	VS Spitfire HF VIII (G-BKMI/ A58-671)	Privately owned, Huntingdon
	MV262	VS Spitfire XIV [42-G]	Privately owned, Winchester
	MV363	VS Spitfire XIV (G-SPIT/G-BGHB) (really MV293)	Privately owned, Duxford
	MV370	VS Spitfire XIV (G-FXIV) [AV-L]	Privately owned, North Weald
	MW100	Avro York C1 (G-AGNV/TS798)	RAF Cosford Aerospace Museum
	NF370	Fairey Swordfish II	Imperial War Museum, Duxford
	NF389	Fairey Swordfish III [5B]	FAA Museum, Lee-on-Solent
	NF875	DH Dragon Rapide 6 (G-AGTM) [603/CH]	Russavia Collection, Duxford
	NH238	VS Spitfire IX (N238V/ G-MKIX) [D-A]	Warbirds of GB, Biggin Hill
	NH799	VS Spitfire XIV	Privately owned, Duxford
	NJ673	Auster 5D (G-AOCR)	Privately owned, Saltby
	NJ695	Auster 4 (G-AJXV)	Privately owned, Leicester East
	NJ703	Auster 5 (G-AKPI)	Privately owned, Doncaster
	NL879	DH Tiger Moth (G-AVPJ)	Privately owned, Wellesbourne Mountford
	NL985	DH Tiger Moth (7015M)	Vintage Aircraft Team, Cranfield
	NP181	Percival Proctor IV (G-AOAR)	Privately owned, Biggin Hill
	NP184	Percival Proctor IV (G-ANYP) [K]	Torbay Aircraft Museum, Paignton
	NP294	Percival Proctor IV [TS-M]	Lincolnshire Aviation Museum, East Kirkby
	NP303	Percival Proctor IV (G-ANZJ)	Privately owned, Byfleet, Surrey
	NR747	DH Dragon Rapide (G-AJHO)	Privately owned, near Bassingbourn
	NV778	Hawker Tempest V (8386M)	RAF Museum, Hendon
	NX611	Avro Lancaster VII (G-ASXX/ 8375M) [YF-C]	Privately owned, RAF Scampton
	PA474	Avro Lancaster I [SR-D]	RAF Battle of Britain Memorial Flight, Coningsby
	PG617	DH Tiger Moth (G-AYVY)	Privately owned, Langham
	PG651	DH Tiger Moth (G-AYUX)	Privately owned, Booker
	PG671	DH Tiger Moth (N82AM) [26]	Privately owned
	PK624	VS Spitfire F22 (8072M) [RAU-T]	RAF Abingdon, at main gate
	PK664	VS Spitfire F22 (7759M) (V6-B)	RAF Binbrook, at main gate
	PK683	VS Spitfire F24 (7150M)	Southampton Hall of Aviation
	PK724	VS Spitfire F24 (7288M)	RAF Museum, Hendon
	PL344	VS Spitfire IX	Privately owned, Winchester
	PL965	VS Spitfire XI [3-W]	RAeS, Rochester
	PL983	VS Spitfire XI (G-PRXI)	Privately owned, Biggin Hill
	PM631	VS Spitfire XIX	RAF Battle of Britain Memorial Flight, Coningsby
	PM651	VS Spitfire XIX (7758M)	RAF Benson, at main gate
	PN323	HP Halifax VII (nose only)	Imperial War Museum, Duxford
	PS853	VS Spitfire XIX	RAF Battle of Britain Memorial Flight, Coningsby
	PS915	VS Spitfire XIX (7548M/7711M)	RAF Battle of Britain Memorial Flight, Coningsby
	PT462	VS Spitfire T9 (G-CTIX)	Privately owned, Micheldever, Hants
	PV202	VS Spitfire TIX (G-TRIX)	Privately owned, Battle, Sussex
	PV260	VS Spitfire IX (really BR601) [DB-P]	Privately owned, Bitteswell

Serial	Type (alternative identity)	Owner, Operator or Location	Notes
PZ865	Hawker Hurricane II (G-AMAU)	RAF Battle of Britain Memorial Flight, Coningsby	
RA848	Slingsby Cadet TX1	Privately owned, Leeds	
RA854	Slingsby Cadet TX1	The Aeroplane Collection store, Wigan	
RA897	Slingsby Cadet TX1	Newark Air Museum store, Hucknall	
RD253	Bristol Beaufighter TF10 (7931M)	RAF Museum, Hendon	
RF342	Avro Lincoln B2 (G-29-1/ G-APRJ)	Aces High, North Weald	
RF398	Avro Lincoln B2 (8376M)	RAF Cosford Aerospace Museum	
RG333	Miles Messenger IIA (G-AIEK)	Privately owned, Filton, Bristol	
RG333	Miles Messenger IIA (G-AKEZ)	Torbay Aircraft Museum, Paignton	
RH377	Miles Messenger 4A (G-ALAH)	The Aeroplane Collection, RAF Henlow	
RH746	Bristol Brigand TF1	North East Aircraft Museum, Usworth	
RL962	DH Dragon Rapide (G-AHED)	RAF Museum Store, Cardington	
RM221	Percival Proctor IV (G-ANXR)	Privately owned, Biggin Hill	
RM689	VS Spitfire XIV (G-ALGT) [MN-E]	Rolls-Royce, Filton	
RR232	VS Spitfire IXC	Privately owned, Winchester	
RR299	DH Mosquito T3 (G-ASKH) [HT-E]	British Aerospace, Hatfield	
RT520	Auster 4 (G-ALYB)	South Yorkshire Air Museum, Firbeck	
RT610	Auster 5A (G-AKWS)	Privately owned, Exeter	
RW382	VS Spitfire XVIe (7245M/ 8075M)	RAF Uxbridge, London	
RW386	VS Spitfire XVIe (6944M/ G-BXVI) [RAK-A]	Warbirds of GB, Bitteswell	
RW388	VS Spitfire XVIe (6946M) [U4-U]	Stoke-on-Trent City Museum, Hanley	
RW393	VS Spitfire XVIe (7293M) [XT-A]	RAF Turnhouse, at main gate	
SL542	VS Spitfire XVIe (8390M) [4M-N]	RAF Coltishall, at main gate	
SL674	VS Spitfire XVIe [RAS-H] (8392M)	RAF Memorial Chapel, Biggin Hill	
SM832	VS Spitfire XIV (G-WWII)	Privately owned, Micheldever, Hants	
SM969	VS Spitfire XVIII (G-BRAF)	Warbirds of GB, Bitteswell	
SX137	VS Seafire XVII	FAA Museum, RNAS Yeovilton	
SX300	VS Seafire XVII (A646/A696/ A2054)	Privately owned, Warwick	
SX336	VS Seafire XVII (A2055)	Privately owned, Twyford, Bucks	
TA122	DH Mosquito FBVI [UP-G]	Mosquito Aircraft Museum, London Colney	
TA634	DH Mosquito B35 (G-AWJV)	Mosquito Aircraft Museum, London Colney	
TA639	DH Mosquito TT35 (7806M)	RAF Cosford Aerospace Museum	
TA719	DH Mosquito TT35 (G-ASKC) [6T]	Skyfame Collection, Duxford	
TB252	VS Spitfire XVIe (7257M/7281M/ 8073M) [GW-H]	RAF Bentley Priory, on display	
TB382	VS Spitfire XVIe (7244M)	RAF Exhibition Flight, Abingdon	
TB752	VS Spitfire XVIe (7256M/ 7279M/8086M) [KH-Z]	RAF Manston, Memorial Hall	
TB863	VS Spitfire XVIe (G-CDAN)	Privately owned, Duxford	
TB885	VS Spitfire LFXVIE	Shoreham Aircraft Preservation Society	
TD248	VS Spitfire XVIe (7246M) [DW-A]	RAF Sealand, at main gate	
TE311	VS Spitfire XVIe (7241M)	RAF Exhibition Flight, Abingdon	
TE356	VS Spitfire XVIe (7001M) (G-SXVI)	Privately owned, East Midlands	
TE392	VS Spitfire XVIe (7000M/8074M)	Warbirds of GB, Biggin Hill	
TE462	VS Spitfire XVIe (7243M)	Royal Scottish Museum of Flight, East Fortune	
TE476	VS Spitfire XVIe (7451M/ 8071M)	RAF Northolt at main gate	
TE517	VS Spitfire LFIX (2046/G-BIXP/ G-CCIX)	Privately owned, Micheldever, Hants	
TE566	VS Spitfire IX (G-BLCK)	Privately owned, Ludham	
TF956	Hawker Sea Fury FB11 [123/T]	RN Historic Flight, RNAS Yeovilton	
TG263	Saro SRA1 (G-12-1) [P]	Skyfame Collection, Duxford	
TG511	HP Hastings T5 (8554M)	RAF Cosford Aerospace Museum	
TG517	HP Hastings T5 [517]	Newark Air Museum, Winthorpe	
TG528	HP Hastings C1A	Skyfame Collection, Duxford	
TG568	HP Hastings C1A	RAE Bedford Fire Section	

Notes	Serial	Type (alternative identity)	Owner, Operator or Location
	TJ118	DH Mosquito TT35 (nose only)	Mosquito Aircraft Museum store
	TJ138	DH Mosquito B35 (7607M) [VO-L]	RAF St Athan Historic Aircraft Collection
	TJ343	Auster 5 (G-AJXC)	Privately owned, Popham
	TJ398	Auster AOP5 (BAPC 70)	Aircraft Preservation Society of Scotland, East Fortune
	TJ569	Auster 5 (G-AKOW)	Museum of Army Flying, Middle Wallop
	TJ672	Auster 5 (G-ANIJ)	Privately owned, Thruxton
	TK777	GAL Hamilcar I	Museum of Army Flying, Middle Wallop
	TL615	Airspeed Horsa II	Robertsbridge Aviation Society
	TL659	Airspeed Horsa (BAPC 80) [74]	Museum of Army Flying, Middle Wallop
	TP298	VS Spitfire XIV (fuselage)	Privately owned, Ludham
	TS291	Slingsby Cadet TX1 (BGA852)	Museum of Flight, East Fortune
	TV959	DH Mosquito T3 [AF-V]	Imperial War Museum, Lambeth
	TW117	DH Mosquito T3 (7805M)	Bomber Command Museum, Hendon
	TW385	Auster 5 (G-ANFU)	North East Aircraft Museum, Usworth
	TW439	Auster 5 (G-ANRP)	Privately owned, Dorchester
	TW467	Auster 5 (G-ANIE)	Privately owned, Cranfield
	TW511	Auster 5 (G-CMAL/G-APAF)	Privately owned, Southampton
	TW536	Auster AOP6 (7704M/G-BNGE)	AAC Historic Aircraft Flight, Middle Wallop
	TW591	Auster 6A (G-ARIH) [N]	Privately owned, Burnaston
	TW641	Auster AOP6 (G-ATDN)	Privately owned, Biggin Hill
	TX183	Avro Anson C19	Privately owned, Arbroath
	TX192	Avro Anson C19	Guernsey Airport Fire Section
	TX213	Avro Anson C19 (G-AWRS)	North East Aircraft Museum, Usworth
	TX214	Avro Anson C19 (7817M)	RAF Cosford Aerospace Museum
	TX226	Avro Anson C19 (7865M)	Imperial War Museum, Duxford
	TX228	Avro Anson C19	City of Norwich Aviation Museum
	TX235	Avro Anson C19	Torbay Aircraft Museum, Paignton
	VF301	DH Vampire F1 (7060M) [RAL-B]	Midland Air Museum, Coventry
	VF516	Auster AOP6 (G-ASMZ) [T]	Museum of Army Flying, Middle Wallop
	VF548	Beagle Terrier 1 (G-ASEG)	Privately owned, Liverpool
	VH127	Fairey Firefly TT4	FAA Museum, RNAS Yeovilton
	VL348	Avro Anson C19 (G-AVVO)	Newark Air Museum, Winthorpe
	VL349	Avro Anson C19 (G-AWSA)	Norfolk & Suffolk Aviation Museum, Flixton
	VM325	Avro Anson C19	Midland Air Museum, Coventry
	VM360	Avro Anson C19 (G-APHV)	Royal Scottish Museum of Flight, East Fortune
	VM791	Slingsby Cadet TX3 (really XA312) (8876M)	No 135 Redhill & Reigate Sqn ATC, RAF Kenley
	VN148	Grunau Baby IIb (BAPC 33) (BGA 2400)	Russavia Collection, Duxford
	VP293	Avro Shackleton T4	Strathallan Aircraft Collection
	VP519	Avro Anson C19 (nose only) (G-AVVR)	Military Aircraft Preservation Group, Hadfield, Derbyshire
	VP952	DH Devon C2 (8820M)	RAF Cosford Aerospace Museum
	VP953	DH Devon C2	CTE, RAF Manston
	VP955	DH Devon C2 (G-DVON)	Privately owned, Staverton
	VP956	DH Devon C2	CTE, RAF Manston
	VP957	DH Devon C2 (8822M)	RAF Bishop's Court NI, BDRT
	VP958	DH Devon C2 [DC] (8795M)	RAF CTTS, St Athan
	VP959	DH Devon C2 [L]	MoD(PE) RAE West Freugh
	VP960	DH Devon C2	CTE, RAF Manston
	VP961	DH Devon C2 (G-ALFM)	Privately owned, Leavesden
	VP962	DH Devon C2 (G-BLRB)	Privately owned, RAF Kemble
	VP963	DH Devon C2	CTE, RAF Manston
	VP965	DH Devon C2 [DE] (8823M)	CTE, RAF Manston
	VP967	DH Devon C2 (G-KOOL)	East Surrey Technical College, Redhill
	VP968	DH Devon C2	A&AEE Boscombe Down Fire Section
	VP971	DH Devon C2 (8824M)	RAF FF&SS, Catterick
	VP975	DH Devon C2 [M]	Science Museum, Wroughton
	VP976	DH Devon C2 (8784M)	RAF Northolt Fire Section
	VP977	DH Devon C2 (G-ALTS)	RAE West Freugh Fire Section
	VP981	DH Devon C2	RAF Battle of Britain Flight, Coningsby
	VR137	Westland Wyvern TF1	FAA Museum, RNAS Yeovilton
	VR192	Pervical Prentice T1 (G-APIT)	Second World War Aircraft Preservation Society, Lasham
	VR249	Percival Prentice T1 (G-APIY) [FA-EL]	Newark Air Museum, Winthorpe
	VR930	Hawker Sea Fury FB11 (8382M)	FAA Museum, stored Lee-on-Solent

Serial	Type (alternative identity)	Owner, Operator or Location	Notes
VS356	Percival Prentice T1 (G-AOLU)	Scottish Aircraft Collection Trust, Perth	
VS562	Avro Anson T21 (8012M)	Privately owned, Portsmouth	
VS610	Percival Prentice T1 (G-AOKL) [K-L]	Privately owned, Southend	
VS623	Percival Prentice T1 (G-AOKZ) [KQ-F]	Midland Air Museum, Coventry	
VT229	Gloster Meteor F4 (7151M) [60]	Newark Air Museum, Winthorpe	
VT260	Gloster Meteor F4 (8813M) [67]	Imperial War Museum, Duxford	
VT409	Fairey Firefly AS5 (really WD889)	North East Aircraft Museum, Usworth	
VT812	DH Vampire F3 (7200M) [N]	RAF Museum, Hendon	
VT921	Grunau Baby	Privately owned, Honington	
VT935	Boulton Paul P111A (VT769)	Midland Air Museum, Coventry	
VV106	VS517 (7175M)	RAF Cosford Aerospace Museum	
VV119	Supermarine 535 (nose only) (7285M)	Lincolnshire Aviation Museum, East Kirkby	
VV217	DH Vampire FB5 (7323M)	No 301 Sqn ATC, Bury St Edmunds	
VV901	Avro Anson T21	Pennine Aviation Museum, Bacup	
VV950	Avro Anson T21	RAF Kinloss Fire Section	
VW453	Gloster Meteor T7 (8703M)	Cotswold Aircraft Restoration Group, RAF Innsworth	
VW985	Auster AOP6 (G-ASEF)	Privately owned, Upper Arncott, Oxon	
VX118	Auster 6A (G-ASNB)	Privately owned, Keevil	
VX185	EE Canberra B(I)8 (nose only) (7631M)	Science Museum, South Kensington	
VX250	DH Sea Hornet 21 [48] (rear fuselage)	Mosquito Aircraft Museum, London Colney	
VX272	Hawker P1052 (7174M)	RAF Cosford Aerospace Museum	
VX275	Slingsby Sedbergh TX1 (8884M) (BGA 572)	RAF Museum Store, Cardington	
VX461	DH Vampire FB5 (7646M)	RAF Museum Store, Henlow	
VX573	Vickers Valetta C2 (8389M)	RAF Cosford Aerospace Museum	
VX577	Vickers Valetta C2	North East Aircraft Museum, Usworth	
VX580	Vickers Valetta C2	Norfolk & Suffolk Aviation Museum Flixton	
VX595	WS51 Dragonfly HR1 [29]	RAF Museum Store, Henlow	
VX653	Hawker Sea Fury FB11	RAF Museum, Hendon	
VZ304	DH Vampire FB5 (7630M)	Vintage Aircraft Team, Cranfield	
VZ345	Hawker Sea Fury T20S	A&AEE Boscombe Down (Damaged)	
VZ462	Gloster Meteor F8	Second World War Aircraft Preservation Society, stored	
VZ467	Gloster Meteor F8 [01]	RAF, stored Shawbury	
VZ477	Gloster Meteor F8 (nose only) (7741M)	Kimbolton School CCF, Cambs	
VZ608	Gloster Meteor FR9	Newark Air Museum, Winthorpe	
VZ634	Gloster Meteor T7 (8657M)	Newark Air Museum, Winthorpe	
VZ638	Gloster Meteor T7 (G-JETM)	Aces High, North Weald	
VZ728	RS4 Desford Trainer (G-AGOS)	Scottish Aircraft Collection Trust, Perth	
VZ962	WS51 Dragonfly HR1	British Rotorcraft Museum, Weston-super-Mare	
VZ965	WS51 Dragonfly HR5	FAA Museum, at RNAS Culdrose	
WA473	VS Attacker F1 [102/J]	FAA Museum, RNAS Yeovilton	
WA576	Bristol Sycamore 3 (G-ALSS/ 7900M)	Dumfries & Galloway Aviation Museum, Tinwald Downs	
WA577	Bristol Sycamore 3 (G-ALST/ 7718M)	North East Aircraft Museum, Usworth	
WA591	Gloster Meteor T7 (7917M) [W]	RAF Woodvale, on display	
WA634	Gloster Meteor T7/8	RAF Cosford Aerospace Museum	
WA638	Gloster Meteor T7	Martin Baker Aircraft, Chalgrove	
WA662	Gloster Meteor T7	MoD(PE) Marshalls, Cambridge	
WA984	Gloster Meteor F8 [A]	Wessex Aviation Society, Wimborne	
WB188	Hawker Hunter F3 (7154M)	RAF Cosford Aerospace Museum	
WB271	Fairey Firefly AS5 [204/R]	RN Historic Flight, RNAS Yeovilton	
WB440	Fairey Firefly AS6	Greater Manchester Museum of Science and Industry	
WB491	Avro Ashton 2 (nose only) (TS897/G-AJJW)	Wales Aircraft Museum, Cardiff	
WB530	DH Devon C2 (8825M)	RAF Swinderby Fire Section	
WB531	DH Devon C2 (G-BLRN)	Privately owned, Staverton	
WB533	DH Devon C2 (G-DEVN) [DA]	British Air Reserve, Lympne	

Notes	Serial	Type (alternative identity)	Owner, Operator or Location
	WB550	DH Chipmunk T10 [F]	RAF EFTS, Swinderby
	WB556	DH Chipmunk T10	RAFGSA, Bicester
	WB560	DH Chipmunk T10	RAF No 4 AEF, Exeter
	WB565	DH Chipmunk T10 [X]	AAC BFWF, Middle Wallop
	WB567	DH Chipmunk T10	RAF No 12 AEF, Turnhouse
	WB569	DH Chipmunk T10 [2]	RAF No 1 AEF, Manston
	WB575	DH Chipmunk T10 [907]	RN Flying Grading Flt, Plymouth
	WB584	DH Chipmunk T10 PAX (7706M)	No 327 Sqn ATC, Kilmarnock
	WB585	DH Chipmunk T10 (G-AOSY) [RCU-X]	Privately owned, Blackbushe
	WB586	DH Chipmunk T10 [A]	RAF No 6 AEF, Abingdon
	WB588	DH Chipmunk T10 (G-AOTD) [D]	Shuttleworth Collection, Old Warden
	WB615	DH Chipmunk T10 [E]	AAC BFWF, Middle Wallop
	WB624	DH Chipmunk T10 PAX	The Aeroplane Collection, Warmingham
	WB626	DH Chipmunk T10 PAX	Privately owned, Swanton Morley
	WB627	DH Chipmunk T10 [N]	RAF No 5 AEF, Cambridge
	WB647	DH Chipmunk T10 [R]	AAC BFWF, Middle Wallop
	WB652	DH Chipmunk T10 [V]	RAF No 5 AEF, Cambridge
	WB654	DH Chipmunk T10 [14]	RAF No 10 AEF, Woodvale
	WB657	DH Chipmunk T10 [908]	RN Flying Grading Flt, Plymouth
	WB660	DH Chipmunk T10 (G-ARMB)	Privately owned, Teesside
	WB670	DH Chipmunk T10 (8361M)	Newark Air Museum, Winthorpe
	WB671	DH Chipmunk T10 [910]	RN Flying Grading Flt, Plymouth
	WB685	DH Chipmunk T10 PAX	North East Aircraft Museum, Usworth
	WB693	DH Chipmunk T10 [S]	AAC BFWF, Middle Wallop
	WB697	DH Chipmunk T10 [O]	RAF No 3 AEF, Shawbury
	WB732	DH Chipmunk T10 (G-AOJZ/ *G-ASTD*)	Air Service Training, Perth
	WB739	DH Chipmunk T10 [8]	RAF No 8 AEF, Shawbury
	WB754	DH Chipmunk T10 [H]	AAC BFWF, Middle Wallop
	WB758	DH Chipmunk T10 (7729M) [P]	Torbay Aircraft Museum, Paignton
	WB763	DH Chipmunk T10 (G-BBMR) [14]	Southall Technical College
	WD289	DH Chipmunk T10 [N]	RAF EFTS, Swinderby
	WD293	DH Chipmunk T10 PAX (7645M)	No 2308 Sqn ATC, Cwmbran
	WD305	DH Chipmunk T10 (G-ARGG)	Privately owned, Meppershall
	WD310	DH Chipmunk T10 [H]	RAF EFTS, Swinderby
	WD318	DH Chipmunk T10 PAX (8207M)	No 145 Sqn ATC, Timperley
	WD325	DH Chipmunk T10 [N]	AAC BFWF, Middle Wallop
	WD331	DH Chipmunk T10 [A]	RAF EFTS, Swinderby
	WD335	DH Chipmunk T10 PAX	No 1955 Sqn ATC, Wells, Somerset
	WD355	DH Chipmunk T10 PAX (8099M)	Scrapped Reading October 1987
	WD356	DH Chipmunk T10 (7625M)	Privately owned, Huntingdon
	WD363	DH Chipmunk T10 (G-BCIH) [5]	Privately owned, Stansted
	WD373	DH Chipmunk T10 [12]	RAF No 2 AEF, Hurn
	WD374	DH Chipmunk T10 [903]	RN Flying Grading Flt, Plymouth
	WD379	DH Chipmunk T10 (really WB696/G-APLO) [K]	Privately owned, Jersey
	WD390	DH Chipmunk T10 [68]	RAF No 9 AEF, Finningley
	WD413	Avro Anson C 21 (G-BFIR/ 7881M)	Privately owned, Edinburgh
	WD496	HP Hastings C2	A&AEE Boscombe Down Fire Section
	WD646	Gloster Meteor TT20 (8189M) [R]	No 2030 Sqn ATC, Sheldon
	WD686	Gloster Meteor NF11	Imperial War Museum, Duxford
	WD790	Gloster Meteor NF11 (8743M) (nose only)	North East Aircraft Museum, Usworth
	WD889	Fairey Firefly AS6	North East Aircraft Museum, Usworth
	WD931	EE Canberra B2 (nose only)	No 425 Sqn ATC, Aldridge, W Midlands
	WD935	EE Canberra B2 (8440M)	RAF St Athan Historic Aircraft Collection
	WD954	EE Canberra B2 (nose only)	Lincolnshire Aviation Museum, East Kirkby
	WD955	EE Canberra T17A	RAF No 360 Sqn, Wyton
	WE113	EE Canberra B2 [BJ]	RAF No 231 OCU, Wyton
	WE122	EE Canberra TT18 [845]	MoD(PE) RAE Llanbedr
	WE139	EE Canberra PR3 (8369M)	RAF Museum, Hendon
	WE146	EE Canberra PR3 (cockpit only)	MoD(PE) RAE Farnborough

Serial	Type (alternative identity)	Owner, Operator or Location	Notes
WE168	EE Canberra PR3 (8049M)	RAF Manston, on display	
WE173	EE Canberra PR3 (8740M)	RAF Coltishall, BDRT	
WE188	EE Canberra T4	BAe, stored Samlesbury	
WE192	EE Canberra T4 [92]	BAe, stored Samlesbury	
WE569	Auster T7 (G-ASAJ)	Privately owned, Oakington	
WE600	Auster T7 (mod) (7602M)	RAF St Athan Historic Aircraft Collection	
WE925	Gloster Meteor F8	Wales Aircraft Museum, Cardiff	
WE982	Slingsby Prefect TX1 (8781M)	RAF Museum, Hendon	
WF122	Sea Prince T1 (A2673) [575/CU]	Cornwall Aero Park, Helston	
WF125	Sea Prince T1 (A2674)	RN Predannack Fire School	
WF128	Sea Prince T1 (8611M) [CU]	Norfolk & Suffolk Aviation Museum, Flixton	
WF137	Sea Prince C1	Second World War Aircraft Preservation Society, Lasham	
WF219	Hawker Sea Hawk F1 (A2439)	FAA Museum, RNAS Yeovilton	
WF225	Hawker Sea Hawk F1 (A2645) [CU]	RNAS Culdrose, at main gate	
WF259	Hawker Sea Hawk F2 (A2483) [171/A]	Royal Scottish Museum of Flight, East Fortune	
WF369	Vickers Varsity T1 [F]	Newark Air Museum, Winthorpe	
WF372	Vickers Varsity T1 [T]	Nene Valley Aviation Society, Sibson	
WF376	Vickers Varsity T1	Bristol Airport Fire Section	
WF408	Vickers Varsity T1 (8395M)	RAF Cosford Aerospace Museum	
WF410	Vickers Varsity T1 [F]	Brunel Technical College, Bristol	
WF413	Vickers Varsity T1 [V]	CTE, RAF Manston	
WF425	Vickers Varsity T1	Imperial War Museum, Duxford	
WF643	Gloster Meteor F8 [X]	Norfolk & Suffolk Aviation Museum, Flixton	
WF714	Gloster Meteor F8 (Really WK914)	RAeS Medway Branch, Rochester	
WF784	Gloster Meteor T7 (7895M)	RAF Quedgeley, at main gate	
WF791	Gloster Meteor T7 (8354M)	RAF CFS, Scampton	
WF825	Gloster Meteor T7 (8359M) [Z]	No 2491 Sqn ATC, RAF Lyneham	
WF877	Gloster Meteor T7	Torbay Aircraft Museum, Paignton	
WF890	EE Canberra T17A [EJ]	RAF No 360 Sqn, Wyton	
WF911	EE Canberra B2 (nose only)	Privately owned, Preston	
WF916	EE Canberra T17 [EL]	RAF No 360 Sqn, Wyton	
WF922	EE Canberra PR3	Midland Air Museum, Coventry	
WG300	DH Chipmunk T10 PAX	RAFGSA, Bicester	
WG303	DH Chipmunk T10 (8208M)	RAFGSA, Bicester	
WG307	DH Chipmunk T10 (G-BCYJ)	Privately owned, Lossiemouth	
WG308	DH Chipmunk T10	RAF No 7 AEF, Newton	
WG316	DH Chipmunk T10 (G-BCAH)	Privately owned, Wyberton	
WG321	DH Chipmunk T10 [G]	AAC BFWF, Middle Wallop	
WG323	DH Chipmunk T10 [F]	AAC BFWF, Middle Wallop	
WG348	DH Chipmunk T10 (G-BBMV)	Privately owned, Moulton St Mary	
WG350	DH Chipmunk T10 (G-BPAL)	Privately owned, Denham	
WG362	DH Chipmunk T10 PAX (8437M/8630M)	RAF EFTS, Swinderby	
WG403	DH Chipmunk T10 [O]	AAC BFWF, Middle Wallop	
WG407	DH Chipmunk T10 [67]	RAF No 9 AEF, Finningley	
WG418	DH Chipmunk T10 PAX (8209M/G-ATDY)	RAF No 10 AEF, Woodvale	
WG419	DH Chipmunk T10 PAX (8206M)	No 1053 Sqn ATC, Armthorpe	
WG422	DH Chipmunk T10 (G-BFAX/8394M) [16]	Privately owned, Biggin Hill	
WG430	DH Chipmunk T10 [1]	RAF No 1 AEF, Manston	
WG432	DH Chipmunk T10 [L]	AAC BFWF, Middle Wallop	
WG458	DH Chipmunk T10	RAF, stored Shawbury	
WG463	DH Chipmunk T10 PAX (8363M/G-ATDX)	No 188 Sqn ATC, Ipswich	
WG464	DH Chipmunk T10 PAX (8364M/G-ATEA)	No 131 Sqn ATC, Newcastle	
WG465	DH Chipmunk T10 (G-BCEY)	Privately owned, Southend	
WG466	DH Chipmunk T10	RAF Gatow Station Flight, Berlin	
WG469	DH Chipmunk T10	RAF No 7 AEF, Newton	
WG471	DH Chipmunk T10 PAX (8210M)	No 1331 Sqn ATC, Stowmarket	

Notes	Serial	Type (alternative identity)	Owner, Operator or Location
	WG477	DH Chipmunk T10 PAX (8362M/G-ATDI/G-ATDP)	No 281 Sqn ATC, Birkdale
	WG478	DH Chipmunk T10 [J]	RAF No 6AEF, Abingdon
	WG479	DH Chipmunk T10 [K]	RAF EFTS, Swinderby
	WG480	DH Chipmunk T10 [D]	RAF EFTS, Swinderby
	WG486	DH Chipmunk T10	RAF Gatow Station Flight, Berlin
	WG511	Avro Shackleton T4 (nose only)	Cornwall Aero Park, Helston
	WG655	Hawker Sea Fury T20 [910/GN]	RN Historic Flight, RNAS Yeovilton
	WG677	EE Canberra B2 (nose only)	*see WJ677*
	WG718	WS51 Dragonfly HR5 (A2531) [934/-]	Wales Aircraft Museum, Cardiff
	WG719	WS51 Dragonfly HR5 (G-BRMA) [902]	British Rotorcraft Museum, Weston-super-Mare
	WG724	WS51 Dragonfly HR5 [932]	North East Aircraft Museum, Usworth
	WG751	WS51 Dragonfly HR5	Privately owned, Ramsgreave, Lancs
	WG752	WS51 Dragonfly HR3	Imperial War Museum, Duxford
	WG754	WS51 Dragonfly HR3 (really WG725) (7703M) [912-CU]	Cornwall Aero Park, Helston
	WG760	English Electric P1A (7755M)	RAF Cosford Aerospace Museum
	WG763	English Electric P1A (7816M)	Greater Manchester Museum of Science and Industry
	WG768	Short SB5 (8005M)	RAF Cosford Aerospace Museum
	WG774	BAC 221	Science Museum, RNAS Yeovilton
	WG777	Fairey FD2 (7986M)	RAF Cosford Aerospace Museum
	WG789	EE Canberra B2/6	Privately owned, Burgess Hill
	WH132	Gloster Meteor T7 (7906M) [J]	No 276 Sqn ATC, Chelmsford
	WH166	Gloster Meteor T7 (8052M)	RAF Digby, at main gate
	WH291	Gloster Meteor F8	Second World War Aircraft Preservation Society, Lasham
	WH301	Gloster Meteor F8 (7930M) [T]	RAF Museum, Hendon
	WH364	Gloster Meteor F8 (8169M)	RAF Kemble, at main gate
	WH453	Gloster Meteor D16 [L]	MoD(PE) RAE Llanbedr
	WH646	EE Canberra T17A [EG]	RAF No 360 Sqn, Wyton
	WH657	EE Canberra B2	Brenzett Aeronautical Collection
	WH664	EE Canberra T17 [EH]	RAF No 360 Sqn, Wyton
	WH665	EE Canberra T17 (8763M) [J]	BAe Samlesbury
	WH670	EE Canberra B2 [CB]	RAF No 100 Sqn, Wyton
	WH699	EE Canberra B2T (8755M) (really WJ637)	RAFC Cranwell, Trenchard Hall on display
	WH703	EE Canberra B2 (8490M) [S]	RAF Abingdon, BDRF
	WH718	EE Canberra TT18 [CW]	RAF No 100 Sqn, Wyton
	WH724	EE Canberra T19 (nose only)	RAF Shawbury Fire Section
	WH725	EE Canberra B2	Imperial War Museum, Duxford
	WH734	EE Canberra B(TT)2	Flight Refuelling Ltd, Llanbedr
	WH740	EE Canberra T17 (8762M) [X]	RAF No 2 SoTT, Cosford
	WH773	EE Canberra PR7 (8696M)	No 2331 Sqn ATC, RAF Wyton
	WH774	EE Canberra PR7	MoD(PE) RAE Bedford
	WH775	EE Canberra PR7 [O] (8128M/8868M)	RAF No 2 SoTT, Cosford
	WH779	EE Canberra PR7 [CK]	RAF No 100 Sqn, Wyton
	WH780	EE Canberra T22 [853]	RN, stored St Athan
	WH791	EE Canberra PR7 (8165M/8176M/8187M)	RAF Cottesmore, at main gate
	WH794	EE Canberra PR7 (8652M)	RAF FF&SS, Catterick
	WH796	EE Canberra PR7 (nose only)	Bomber County Aviation Museum, Cleethorpes
	WH797	EE Canberra T22 [851]	RN, stored St Athan
	WH798	EE Canberra PR7 (8130M)	Wales Aircraft Museum, Cardiff
	WH801	EE Canberra T22 [850]	RN, stored St Athan
	WH803	EE Canberra T22 [856]	RN, stored St Athan
	WH840	EE Canberra T4 (8350M)	RAF Locking, at main gate
	WH844	EE Canberra T4	MoD(PE) RAE Farnborough, stored
	WH846	EE Canberra T4	BAe, stored Samlesbury
	WH848	EE Canberra T4 [BD]	RAF No 231 OCU, Wyton
	WH849	EE Canberra T4 [BE]	RAF No 231 OCU, Wyton
	WH850	EE Canberra T4	BAe, stored Samlesbury
	WH854	EE Canberra T4 (nose only)	Martin Baker Aircraft, Chalgrove
	WH863	EE Canberra T17 (8693M)	RAF Marham, BDRT
	WH869	EE Canberra B2 (8515M)	RAF Abingdon, BDRF
	WH876	EE Canberra D14	MoD(PE) Boscombe Down, stored
	WH887	EE Canberra TT18 [847]	RN, stored St Athan
	WH902	EE Canberra T17 [EK]	RAF No 360 Sqn, Wyton

Serial	Type (alternative identity)	Owner, Operator or Location	Notes
WH903	EE Canberra B2 (8584M) (nose only)	RAF Exhibition Flight, Abingdon	
WH904	EE Canberra T19 [04]	Newark Air Museum, Winthorpe	
WH911	EE Canberra B2	Scrapped	
WH914	EE Canberra B2 (G-27-373) [U]	BAe, stored Samlesbury	
WH919	EE Canberra B2	RAF, stored St Athan	
WH946	EE Canberra B6 (Mod) (8185M) (nose only)	Privately owned, Tetney, Grimsby	
WH952	EE Canberra B6	Royal Artillery Museum, Woolwich	
WH953	EE Canberra B6	MoD(PE) RAE Bedford	
WH957	EE Canberra E15 (8869M) [N]	RAF No 2 SoTT, Cosford	
WH960	EE Canberra B15 (8344M) [A]	RAF No 2 SoTT, Cosford	
WH964	EE Canberra E15 (8870M) [CX]	RAF No 2 SoTT, Cosford	
WH972	EE Canberra E15 [CM]	RAF No 100 Sqn, Wyton	
WH981	EE Canberra E15 [CN]	RAF No 100 Sqn, Wyton	
WH983	EE Canberra E15 [CP]	RAF No 100 Sqn, Wyton	
WH984	EE Canberra B15 (8101M) [E]	RAF No 2 SoTT, Cosford	
WH991	WS51 Dragonfly HR5	Privately owned, Tattershall Thorpe	
WJ231	Hawker Sea Fury FB11 [115/O]	FAA Museum, RNAS Yeovilton	
WJ237	WAR Sea Fury Replica (G-BLTG) [113/O]	Privately owned, Little Gransden	
WJ288	Hawker Sea Fury FB11 (G-SALY) [029]	Privately owned, Duxford	
WJ329	HP Hastings C2	RAF Leeming Fire Section	
WJ350	Percival Sea Prince C2	Guernsey Airport Fire Section	
WJ358	Auster AOP6 (G-ARYD)	Museum of Army Flying, Middle Wallop	
WJ565	EE Canberra T17 (8871M) [C]	RAF No 2 SoTT, Cosford	
WJ567	EE Canberra B2 [CC]	RAF No 100 Sqn, Wyton	
WJ573	EE Canberra B2 (7656M)	RAF Museum Store, Henlow	
WJ574	EE Canberra TT18 [844]	RN, stored St Athan	
WJ576	EE Canberra T17	Wales Aircraft Museum, Cardiff	
WJ581	EE Canberra T17	Wales Aircraft Museum, Cardiff	
WJ603	EE Canberra B2 (8664M) [G]	RAF Wattisham Fire Section	
WJ607	EE Canberra T17A [EB]	RAF No 360 Sqn, Wyton	
WJ614	EE Canberra TT18 [846]	RN, stored St Athan	
WJ629	EE Canberra TT18 (8747M) [845]	RAF Chivenor, BDRT	
WJ630	EE Canberra T17 [ED]	RAF No 360 Sqn, Wyton	
WJ633	EE Canberra T17 [EF]	RAF No 360 Sqn, Wyton	
WJ635	EE Canberra B2	Scrapped February 1987 at RAF St Mawgan	
WJ636	EE Canberra TT18 [CX]	RAF No 100 Sqn, Wyton	
WJ639	EE Canberra TT18 [39]	BAe, stored Samlesbury	
WJ640	EE Canberra B2 (8722M) [L]	RAF No 2 SoTT, Cosford	
WJ676	EE Canberra B2 (7796M)	Princess Alexandra RAF Hospital, Wroughton	
WJ677	EE Canberra B2 (nose only)	RNAS Yeovilton Fire Section	
WJ678	EE Canberra B2 (8864M) [CF]	RAF Abingdon, BDRF	
WJ680	EE Canberra TT18 [CT]	RAF No 100 Sqn, Wyton	
WJ681	EE Canberra B2T (8735M)	RAF Brawdy Fire Section	
WJ682	EE Canberra TT18 [CU]	RAF No 100 Sqn, Wyton	
WJ715	EE Canberra TT18 [CV]	RAF No 100 Sqn, Wyton	
WJ717	EE Canberra TT18 [841]	RN, stored St Athan	
WJ721	EE Canberra TT18 [21]	BAe, stored Samlesbury	
WJ722	EE Canberra B2	Privately owned, Macclesfield	
WJ728	EE Canberra B2	RAE Farnborough, derelict	
WJ731	EE Canberra B2T [BK]	RAF No 231 OCU, Wyton	
WJ756	EE Canberra E15 [CL]	RAF No 100 Sqn, Wyton	
WJ775	EE Canberra B6 (8581M) [Z]	CSDE, RAF Swanton Morley	
WJ815	EE Canberra PR7 (8729M)	RAF Coningsby Fire Section	
WJ817	EE Canberra PR7 (8695M) [FO]	RAF Wyton, BDRT	
WJ821	EE Canberra PR7 (8668M)	Bassingbourn, on display	
WJ825	EE Canberra PR7 (8697M)	RAF FF&SS, Catterick	
WJ857	EE Canberra (nose only)	BAe Warton Fire Section	
WJ861	EE Canberra T4 [BF]	RAF No 231 OCU, Wyton	
WJ863	EE Canberra T4 (nose only)	Cambridge Airport Fire Section	
WJ865	EE Canberra T4	RAE Apprentice School, Farnborough	
WJ866	EE Canberra T4 [BL]	RAF No 231 OCU, Wyton	
WJ867	EE Canberra T4 (8643M)	RAF Abingdon, BDRF	
WJ870	EE Canberra T4 (8683M)	RAF St Mawgan, BDRT	

Notes	Serial	Type (alternative identity)	Owner, Operator or Location
	WJ872	EE Canberra T4 (8492M) (nose only)	No 327 Sqn ATC, Kilmarnock
	WJ874	EE Canberra T4 [BM]	RAF No 231 OCU, Wyton
	WJ876	EE Canberra T4 (nose only)	RAF Exhibition Flight, Abingdon
	WJ877	EE Canberra T4 [BG]	RAF No 231 OCU, Wyton
	WJ879	EE Canberra T4 [BH]	RAF No 231 OCU, Wyton
	WJ880	EE Canberra T4 (8491M) [39] (nose only)	No 2263 Sqn ATC, North Weald
	WJ893	Vickers Varsity T1	RAE Aberporth Fire Section
	WJ902	Vickers Varsity T1 [C]	RAF Wittering Fire Section
	WJ903	Vickers Varsity T1 [C]	Dumfries & Galloway Aviation Museum, Tinwald Downs
	WJ907	Vickers Varsity T1 [G]	Norwich Airport Fire Section
	WJ944	Vickers Varsity T1	Wales Aircraft Museum, Cardiff
	WJ945	Vickers Varsity T1 (G-BEDV) [21]	Duxford Aviation Society
	WJ975	EE Canberra T19 [S]	Bomber County Aviation Museum, Hemswell
	WJ977	EE Canberra T17 (8761M) [R]	RAF Wyton Fire Section
	WJ981	EE Canberra T17A [EN]	RAF No 360 Sqn, Wyton
	WJ986	EE Canberra T17 [EP]	RAF No 360 Sqn, Wyton
	WJ992	EE Canberra T4	MoD(PE) RAE Bedford
	WK102	EE Canberra T17 [EQ] (8780M)	RAF No 2 SoTT, Cosford
	WK111	EE Canberra T17 [EA]	RAF No 360 Sqn, Wyton
	WK118	EE Canberra TT18 [CQ]	RAF No 100 Sqn, Wyton
	WK122	EE Canberra TT18 [22]	BAe, stored Samlesbury
	WK123	EE Canberra TT18 [CY]	RAF No 100 Sqn, Wyton
	WK124	EE Canberra TT18 [CR]	RAF No 100 Sqn, Wyton
	WK126	EE Canberra TT18 [843]	RN FRADU, Yeovilton
	WK127	EE Canberra TT18 [CS]	RAF No 100 Sqn, Wyton
	WK128	EE Canberra B2	Flight Refuelling Ltd, Llanbedr
	WK142	EE Canberra TT18 [848]	RN FRADU, Yeovilton
	WK143	EE Canberra B2	MoD(PE) RAE Llanbedr Fire Section
	WK144	EE Canberra B2 (8689M)	RAF St Athan BDRT
	WK145	EE Canberra B2	MoD(PE) RAE Llanbedr Fire Section
	WK146	EE Canberra B2 (nose only)	RAF Exhibition Flight, Abingdon
	WK162	EE Canberra B2 [CA] (8887M)	RAF Wyton Fire Section
	WK163	EE Canberra B6	MoD(PE) RAE Bedford
	WK198	VS Swift F4 (7428M)	North East Aircraft Museum, Usworth
	WK275	VS Swift F4	Privately owned, Upper Hill, nr Leominster
	WK277	VS Swift FR5 (7719M) [N]	Newark Air Museum, Winthorpe
	WK281	VS Swift FR5 (7712M) [S]	RAF St Athan Historic Aircraft Collection
	WK511	DH Chipmunk T10	RN, stored Shawbury
	WK512	DH Chipmunk T10 [A]	AAC BFWF, Middle Wallop
	WK517	DH Chipmunk T10 [84]	RAF No 11 AEF, Teesside
	WK518	DH Chipmunk T10	RAF Battle of Britain Flight, Coningsby
	WK522	DH Chipmunk T10 (G-BCOU)	Privately owned, Audley End
	WK549	DH Chipmunk T10 [Y]	Privately owned, Currock Hill
	WK550	DH Chipmunk T10 [J]	RAF EFTS, Swinderby
	WK554	DH Chipmunk T10	RAF No 1 AEF, Manston
	WK559	DH Chipmunk T10 [M]	AAC BFWF, Middle Wallop
	WK562	DH Chipmunk T10 [T]	RAF No 3 AEF, Filton
	WK570	DH Chipmunk T10 PAX (8211M)	RAF No 2 AEF, Hurn
	WK572	DH Chipmunk T10 [X]	RAF No 3 AEF, Filton
	WK574	DH Chipmunk T10 [738/VL]	RNAS Yeovilton Station Flight
	WK575	DH Chipmunk T10 PAX [F]	No 301 Sqn ATC, Bury St Edmunds
	WK576	DH Chipmunk T10 PAX (8357M)	No 1206 Sqn ATC, Lichfield
	WK585	DH Chipmunk T10	RAF No 12 AEF, Turnhouse
	WK586	DH Chipmunk T10	RAF, stored Shawbury
	WK587	DH Chipmunk T10 PAX (8212M)	St Ignatius Coll, Enfield
	WK589	DH Chipmunk T10 [C]	RAF No 6 AEF, Abingdon
	WK590	DH Chipmunk T10 [69]	RAF No 9 AEF, Finningley
	WK608	DH Chipmunk T10 [906]	RN Flying Grading Flt, Plymouth
	WK609	DH Chipmunk T10 [L]	RAF No 3 AEF, Filton
	WK611	DH Chipmunk T10 (G-ARWB)	Privately owned, Shoreham

Serial	Type (alternative identity)	Owner, Operator or Location	Notes
WK613	DH Chipmunk T10 [P]	Pennine Aviation Museum, Bacup	
WK620	DH Chipmunk T10 [T]	AAC BFWF, Middle Wallop	
WK622	DH Chipmunk T10 (G-BCZH)	Privately owned, Norwich	
WK624	DH Chipmunk T10 [12]	RAF No 10 AEF, Woodvale	
WK626	DH Chipmunk T10 PAX (8213M)	Privately owned, Tilehurst, Berks	
WK628	DH Chipmunk T10 (G-BBMW)	Privately owned, Shoreham	
WK630	DH Chipmunk T10 [11]	RAF No 2 AEF, Hurn	
WK633	DH Chipmunk T10 [B]	RAF EFTS, Swinderby	
WK634	DH Chipmunk T10 [902]	RN Flying Grading Flt, Plymouth	
WK635	DH Chipmunk T10 [739]	RNAS Yeovilton Station Flight	
WK638	DH Chipmunk T10 [83]	RAF No 11 AEF, Teesside	
WK639	DH Chipmunk T10 [10]	RAF No 10 AEF, Woodvale	
WK640	DH Chipmunk T10 [C]	RAF EFTS, Swinderby	
WK642	DH Chipmunk T10	RAF No 4 AEF, Exeter	
WK643	DH Chipmunk T10 [G]	RAF EFTS, Swinderby	
WK654	Gloster Meteor F8 (8092M) [X]	RAF Neatishead, at main gate	
WK800	Gloster Meteor D16 [Z]	MoD(PE) RAE Llanbedr	
WK935	Gloster Meteor Prone Pilot (7869M)	RAF Cosford Aerospace Museum	
WK968	Gloster Meteor F8 (8053M) [A]	RAF Odiham Fire Section, scrapped	
WK991	Gloster Meteor F8 (7825M)	Imperial War Museum, Duxford	
WL131	Gloster Meteor F8 (nose only) (7751M)	Privately owned, Guernsey	
WL168	Gloster Meteor F8 (7750M) [A]	RAF St Athan Historic Aircraft Collection	
WL181	Gloster Meteor F8 [X]	North East Aircraft Museum, Usworth	
WL332	Gloster Meteor T7	Wales Aircraft Museum, Cardiff	
WL345	Gloster Meteor T7	Privately owned, Hollington, East Sussex	
WL349	Gloster Meteor T7 [Z]	Staverton Airport, on display	
WL360	Gloster Meteor T7 (7920M) [G]	RAF Locking, at main gate	
WL375	Gloster Meteor T7	Dumfries & Galloway Aviation Museum, Tinwald Downs	
WL405	Gloster Meteor T7	North East Aircraft Museum, Usworth	
WL419	Gloster Meteor T7	Martin Baker Aircraft, Chalgrove	
WL505	DH Vampire FB9 (7705M)	RAF St Athan Historic Aircraft Collection	
WL626	Vickers Varsity T1 (G-BHDD) [P]	East Midlands Aeropark	
WL627	Vickers Varsity T1 (8488M) [D]	RAF Police Dog Training School, Newton	
WL635	Vickers Varsity T1	RAF Machrihanish Police School	
WL679	Vickers Varsity T1	MoD(PE) RAE Farnborough	
WL732	BP Sea Balliol T21	RAF Cosford Aerospace Museum, store	
WL738	Avro Shackleton MR2C (8567M)	RAF Lossiemouth, at main gate	
WL741	Avro Shackleton AEW2 (8692M)	Burned at RAF Manston	
WL747	Avro Shackleton AEW2	RAF No 8 Sqn, Lossiemouth	
WL754	Avro Shackleton AEW2 (8665M) [54]	Scrapped July 1987 at RAF Valley	
WL756	Avro Shackleton AEW2	RAF No 8 Sqn, Lossiemouth	
WL757	Avro Shackleton AEW2	RAF No 8 Sqn, Lossiemouth	
WL790	Avro Shackleton AEW2	RAF No 8 Sqn, Lossiemouth	
WL795	Avro Shackleton AEW2 (8753M)	RAF St Mawgan, on display	
WL798	Avro Shackleton MR2C (8114M) [Z]	RAF Lossiemouth (wfu)	
WL925	Slingsby Cadet TX3 (really WV925)	Air Cadet Recruiting Team, Cosford	
WM145	AW Meteor NF11 (nose only)	N. Yorks Recovery Group, Chop Gate	
WM167	AW Meteor TT20 (G-LOSM) [M]	Brencham Historic Collection, Biggin Hill	
WM223	AW Meteor TT20	Second World War Aircraft Preservation Society, Lasham	
WM224	AW Meteor TT20 (8177M)	Privately owned, North Weald	
WM292	AW Meteor TT20 [841]	Wales Aircraft Museum, Cardiff	
WM366	AW Meteor NF13 (4X-FNA)	Second World War Aircraft Preservation Society, store	

Notes	Serial	Type (alternative identity)	Owner, Operator or Location
	WM367	AW Meteor NF13	Privately owned, Powick, Hereford & Worcs
	WM571	DH Sea Venom FAW 21 [742/VL]	Wessex Aviation Society, Wimborne
	WM729	DH Vampire NF10 (pod only) [A]	Booker Air Museum
	WM913	Hawker Sea Hawk FB5 (A2510/8162M) [616]	Newark Air Museum, Winthorpe
	WM961	Hawker Sea Hawk FB5 [J] (A2517)	Torbay Aircraft Museum, Paignton
	WM969	Hawker Sea Hawk FB5 (A2530)	Imperial War Museum, Duxford
	WM983	Hawker Sea Hawk FGA6 (really XE489)	Chilton Cantelo House School, Somerset
	WM993	Hawker Sea Hawk FB5 (A2522) [034]	Privately owned, Peasedown St John, Avon
	WM994	Hawker Sea Hawk FB5 (A2503/G-SEAH)	Privately owned,
	WN105	Hawker Sea Hawk FB3 (A2662/A2509/8164M) (really WF299)	Cornwall Aero Park, Helston
	WN108	Hawker Sea Hawk FB5 [033]	Shorts Apprentice School, Belfast
	WN149	BP Balliol T2 (nose only)	Privately owned, Preston
	WN464	Fairey Gannet AS6 (A2540)	Cornwall Aero Park, Helston
	WN493	WS51 Dragonfly HR5	FAA Museum, RNAS Yeovilton
	WN499	WS51 Dragonfly HR5 [Y]	Torbay Aircraft Museum, Paignton
	WN516	BP Balliol T2	North East Aircraft Museum, Usworth
	WN534	BP Balliol T2 (nose only)	Privately owned, Preston
	WN901	Hawker Hunter F2 (7543M)	RAF Newton Fire Section
	WN904	Hawker Hunter F2 (7544M) [3]	Imperial War Museum, Duxford
	WN907	Hawker Hunter F2 (7416M)	Staravia, Ascot
	WP180	Hawker Hunter F5 (7582M/8473M) [K] (really WP190)	RAF Stanbridge, at main gate
	WP185	Hawker Hunter F5 (7583M)	RAF Museum, Hendon
	WP232	DH Vampire NF10 (nose only) [T]	Privately owned, Ecclesfield, S. Yorks
	WP250	DH Vampire NF10 (nose only)	Friends of Biggin Hill, Sevenoaks
	WP270	EoN Eton TX1 (8598M)	Greater Manchester Museum of Science and Industry
	WP271	EoN Eton TX1	Stored Keevil
	WP309	Percival Sea Prince T1 [570/CU]	RNAS Yeovilton Fire Section
	WP313	Percival Sea Prince T1 [568/CU]	FAA Museum, stored Wroughton
	WP314	Percival Sea Prince T1 (8634M) [573/CU]	RAF Police Dog School, Syerston
	WP320	Percival Sea Prince T1 [573/CU]	RAF Leuchars Fire Section
	WP321	Percival Sea Prince T1 (G-BRFC) [750/CU]	Privately owned, Bourn
	WP503	WS51 Dragonfly HR3 [901]	Privately owned, Storwood, South Yorks
	WP515	EE Canberra B2 [CD]	RAF No 100 Sqn, Wyton
	WP772	DH Chipmunk T10 [Q]	AAC BFWF, Middle Wallop
	WP776	DH Chipmunk T10 [817]	RN No 771 Sqn, Culdrose
	WP778	DH Chipmunk T10 (G-BBNF)	Scrapped at Little Bursted, Essex
	WP784	DH Chipmunk T10	Privately owned, Tilehurst, Berks
	WP786	DH Chipmunk T10 [D]	RAF, stored Shawbury
	WP788	DH Chipmunk T10 (G-BCHL)	Privately owned, Sleap
	WP790	DH Chipmunk T10 (G-BBNC) [T]	Mosquito Aircraft Museum, London Colney
	WP795	DH Chipmunk T10 [901]	RN Flying Grading Flt, Plymouth
	WP801	DH Chipmunk T10 [911]	RN Flying Grading Flt, Plymouth
	WP803	DH Chipmunk T10	RN, stored Shawbury
	WP805	DH Chipmunk T10 [D]	RAF No 6 AEF, Abingdon
	WP808	DH Chipmunk T10 (G-BDEU)	Privately owned, Binham
	WP809	DH Chipmunk T10 [78]	RN, stored Shawbury
	WP833	DH Chipmunk T10	RAF No 4 AEF, Exeter
	WP837	DH Chipmunk T10 [L]	RAF No 5 AEF, Cambridge
	WP839	DH Chipmunk T10 [A]	RAF, stored Shawbury
	WP840	DH Chipmunk T10 [9]	RAF No 2 AEF, Hurn
	WP843	DH Chipmunk T10 (G-BDBP)	Privately owned, Tollerton

Serial	Type (alternative identity)	Owner, Operator or Location	Notes
WP844	DH Chipmunk T10	RAF No 10 AEF, Woodvale	
WP845	DH Chipmunk T10 PAX	No 1329 Sqn ATC, Stroud	
WP855	DH Chipmunk T10 [3]	RAF No 1 AEF, Manston	
WP856	DH Chipmunk T10 [904]	RN Flying Grading Flt, Plymouth	
WP857	DH Chipmunk T10 (G-BDRJ) [24]	Privately owned, Elstree	
WP859	DH Chipmunk T10 [E]	RAF No 8 AEF, Shawbury	
WP860	DH Chipmunk T10	RAF No 12 AEF, Turnhouse	
WP863	DH Chipmunk T10 PAX (8360M/G-ATJI)	No 1304 Sqn ATC, Chippenham	
WP869	DH Chipmunk T10 PAX (8215M)	RAF	
WP871	DH Chipmunk T10	RAF, stored Shawbury	
WP872	DH Chipmunk T10	RAF, stored Shawbury	
WP896	DH Chipmunk T10 [11]	RAF No 10 AEF, Woodvale	
WP900	DH Chipmunk T10 [13]	RAF No 10 AEF, Woodvale	
WP901	DH Chipmunk T10 [B]	RAF No 6 AEF, Abingdon	
WP903	DH Chipmunk T10 (G-BCGC)	RN Gliding Club, Culdrose	
WP904	DH Chipmunk T10 [909]	RN Flying Grading Flt, Plymouth	
WP906	DH Chipmunk T10 [816]	RN No 771 Sqn, Culdrose	
WP907	DH Chipmunk T10 PAX (7970M)	Privately owned	
WP912	DH Chipmunk T10 (8467M)	RAF Cosford Aerospace Museum	
WP914	DH Chipmunk T10 [E]	RAF No 6 AEF, Abingdon	
WP920	DH Chipmunk T10 [10]	RAF No 2 AEF, Hurn	
WP925	DH Chipmunk T10 [C]	AAC BFWF, Middle Wallop	
WP927	DH Chipmunk T10 PAX (8216M/G-ATJK)	No 247 Sqn ATC, Ashton-under-Lyne, Greater Manchester	
WP928	DH Chipmunk T10 [D]	AAC BFWF, Middle Wallop	
WP929	DH Chipmunk T10 [F]	RAF No 8 AEF, Shawbury	
WP930	DH Chipmunk T10 [J]	AAC BFWF, Middle Wallop	
WP962	DH Chipmunk T10 [V]	RAF No 3 AEF, Filton	
WP964	DH Chipmunk T10	AAC BFWF, Middle Wallop	
WP967	DH Chipmunk T10	RAF No 12 AEF, Turnhouse	
WP970	DH Chipmunk T10 [T]	RAF No 5 AEF, Cambridge	
WP972	DH Chipmunk T10 PAX (8667M)	CSDE, RAF Swanton Morley	
WP974	DH Chipmunk T10 [N]	RAF No 3 AEF, Filton	
WP977	DH Chipmunk T10 (G-BHRD)	Privately owned, Leicester	
WP978	DH Chipmunk T10 PAX (7467M)	RAF No 2 AEF, Hurn	
WP979	DH Chipmunk T10 [J]	CSDE, RAF Swanton Morley	
WP980	DH Chipmunk T10 [E]	RAF EFTS, Swinderby	
WP981	DH Chipmunk T10	AAC, stored Shawbury	
WP983	DH Chipmunk T10 [B]	AAC BFWF, Middle Wallop	
WP984	DH Chipmunk T10 [Y]	RAF No 7 AEF, Newton	
WR410	DH Venom FB54 (J1790/G-BLKA)	Privately owned, Cranfield	
WR539	DH Venom FB4 (8399M) [F]	Wales Aircraft Museum, Cardiff	
WR960	Avro Shackleton AEW2 (8772M)	Greater Manchester Museum of Science and Industry	
WR963	Avro Shackleton AEW2	RAF No 8 Sqn, Lossiemouth	
WR965	Avro Shackleton AEW2	RAF No 8 Sqn, Lossiemouth	
WR967	Avro Shackleton MR2C (8398M)	RAF Lossiemouth, as a simulator	
WR971	Avro Shackleton MR3 (8119M) [Q]	RAF No 2 SoTT, Cosford	
WR974	Avro Shackleton MR3 (8117M) [K]	RAF No 2 SoTT, Cosford	
WR977	Avro Shackleton MR3 (8186M) [B]	Newark Air Museum, Winthorpe	
WR982	Avro Shackleton MR3 (8106M) [J]	RAF No 2 SoTT, Cosford	
WR985	Avro Shackleton MR3 (8103M) [H]	RAF No 2 SoTT, Cosford	
WS103	Gloster Meteor T7 [709/VL]	FAA Museum, stored Wroughton	
WS692	Gloster Meteor NF12 (7605M) [C]	Newark Air Museum, Winthorpe	
WS726	Gloster Meteor NF14 (7960M) [G]	No 1855 Sqn ATC, Royton	
WS739	Gloster Meteor NF14 (7961M)	Newark Air Museum, Winthorpe	
WS760	Gloster Meteor NF14 (7964M)	Privately owned, Cranfield	
WS774	Gloster Meteor NF14 (7959M)	RAF Hospital, Ely, at main gate	
WS776	Gloster Meteor NF14 (7716M) [K]	RAF North Luffenham, at main gate	

Notes	Serial	Type (alternative identity)	Owner, Operator or Location
	WS792	Gloster Meteor NF14 (7965M) [K]	RAF Carlisle, at main gate
	WS807	Gloster Meteor NF14 (7973M) [N]	RAF Watton, at main gate
	WS832	Gloster Meteor NF14 [W]	Solway Aviation Society, Carlisle Airport
	WS838	Gloster Meteor NF14	Midland Air Museum, Coventry
	WS840	Gloster Meteor NF14 (7969M)	Aldergrove Fire Section
	WS843	Gloster Meteor NF14 (7937M) [Y]	RAF St Athan Historic Aircraft Collection
	WS844	Gloster Meteor NF14 (7967M) [JCF] (really WS788)	RAF Leeming, at main gate
	WT121	Douglas Skyraider AEW1 [415/CU] (really WT983)	FAA Museum, RNAS Yeovilton
	WT212	EE Canberra B2	Lovaux Ltd, Macclesfield
	WT301	EE Canberra B6 (Mod)	Defence School, Chattenden
	WT305	EE Canberra B6 (8511M) [X]	RAF Wyton, at main gate
	WT308	EE Canberra B(I)6	MoD(PE), stored RAE Farnborough
	WT309	EE Canberra B(I)6	MoD(PE) A&AEE Boscombe Down
	WT327	EE Canberra B(I)8	MoD(PE) RAE Bedford
	WT333	EE Canberra B(I)8	RAE Farnborough
	WT339	EE Canberra B(I)8 (8198M)	Scrapped at RAF Cranwell May 1987
	WT346	EE Canberra B(I)8 (8197M)	RAF Cosford Aerospace Museum
	WT478	EE Canberra T4 [BA]	RAF No 231 OCU, Wyton
	WT480	EE Canberra T4 [BC]	RAF No 231 OCU, Wyton
	WT483	EE Canberra T4 [83]	BAe, stored Samlesbury
	WT486	EE Canberra T4 (8102M) [C]	Aldergrove Fire Section
	WT488	EE Canberra T4	BAe, stored Samlesbury
	WT507	EE Canberra PR7 (8131M/8548M) [44] (nose only)	No 384 Sqn ATC, Mansfield
	WT509	EE Canberra PR7 [CG]	RAF No 100 Sqn, Wyton
	WT510	EE Canberra T22 [854]	RN, stored St Athan
	WT518	EE Canberra PR7 (8133M/8691M)	Wales Aircraft Museum, Cardiff
	WT519	EE Canberra PR7 [CH]	RAF No 100 Sqn, Wyton
	WT520	EE Canberra PR7 (8094M/8184M) [20]	RAF Swinderby,
	WT525	EE Canberra T22 [855]	RN, stored St Athan
	WT532	EE Canberra PR7 (8728M/ 8890M)	RAF No 2 SoTT, Cosford
	WT534	EE Canberra PR7 (8549M) [43] (nose only)	No 489 Sqn ATC, Solihull
	WT535	EE Canberra T22 [852]	RN, stored St Athan
	WT536	EE Canberra PR7 (8063M) [F]	RAF No 2 SoTT, Cosford
	WT537	EE Canberra PR7	BAe Samlesbury, on display
	WT538	EE Canberra PR7 [CJ]	RAF No 100 Sqn, Wyton
	WT555	Hawker Hunter F1 (7499M)	RAF Cosford Aerospace Museum
	WT569	Hawker Hunter F1 (7491M)	No 2117 Sqn ATC, Kenfig Hill, Mid-Glamorgan
	WT612	Hawker Hunter F1 (7496M)	RAF Henlow on display
	WT619	Hawker Hunter F1 (7525M)	Greater Manchester Museum of Science and Industry
	WT648	Hawker Hunter F1 (7530M) (nose section)	RAF St Athan Fire Section
	WT651	Hawker Hunter F1 (7532M) [C]	ROC Lawford Heath, Warwicks, on display
	WT660	Hawker Hunter F1 (7421M) [C]	RAF Carlisle, at main gate
	WT680	Hawker Hunter F1 (7533M) [Z]	No 1429 Sqn ATC at RAE Aberporth
	WT684	Hawker Hunter F1 (7422M)	RAF Brize Norton Fire Section
	WT694	Hawker Hunter F1 (7510M)	RAF Newton, at main gate
	WT711	Hawker Hunter GA11 [833/DD]	RNAS Culdrose, SAH
	WT722	Hawker Hunter T8C [879/VL]	RN, stored Shawbury
	WT723	Hawker Hunter PR11 [866/VL]	RN FRADU, Yeovilton
	WT744	Hawker Hunter GA11 [868/VL]	RN FRADU, Yeovilton
	WT745	Hawker Hunter T8C (8893M) [745] (rear fuselage)	RAF Coltishall, BDRT
	WT746	Hawker Hunter F4 (7770M) [A]	RAF No 1 SoTT, Halton
	WT799	Hawker Hunter T8C [879/-]	RN, stored Shawbury
	WT804	Hawker Hunter GA11 [831/DD]	RNAS Culdrose, SAH
	WT806	Hawker Hunter GA11	RAF No 2 TWU, Chivenor, preserved
	WT809	Hawker Hunter GA11 [867/VL]	RN FRADU, Yeovilton
	WT933	Bristol Sycamore 3 (G-ALSW/7709M)	Newark Air Museum, Winthorpe

Serial	Type (alternative identity)	Owner, Operator or Location	Notes
WV106	Douglas Skyraider AEW1 [427/C]	Cornwall Aero Park, Helston	
WV198	S55 Sikorsky HAR21 (G-BJWY/A2576) [K]	Helicopter Museum of GB, Heysham, Lancs	
WV256	Hawker Hunter GA11 [862/VL]	RN FRADU, Yeovilton	
WV267	Hawker Hunter GA11 [836/DD]	RNAS Culdrose, SAH	
WV276	Hawker Hunter F4 (7847M) [D]	RAF No 1 SoTT, Halton	
WV318	Hawker Hunter T7B	RAF No 208 Sqn, Lossiemouth	
WV322	Hawker Hunter T8C [U]	RAF No 237 OCU, Lossiemouth	
WV332	Hawker Hunter F4 (7673M) (nose only)	No 1254 Sqn ATC, Godalming	
WV363	Hawker Hunter T8C [872/VL]	RN FRADU, Yeovilton	
WV372	Hawker Hunter T7 [877/VL]	RN, stored Shawbury	
WV381	Hawker Hunter GA11 [732]	UKAEA, Culham, Oxon	
WV382	Hawker Hunter GA11 [830/VL]	RN Lee-on-Solent, BDRT	
WV383	Hawker Hunter T7	MoD(PE) RAE Farnborough	
WV396	Hawker Hunter T8C [879/VL]	RN FRADU, Yeovilton	
WV483	Percival Provost T1 (7693M) [N-E]	Privately owned	
WV486	Percival Provost T1 (7694M) [N-D]	Privately owned, Grazeley, Berks	
WV493	Percival Provost T1 (G-BDYG/7696M) [29]	Royal Scottish Museum of Flight, East Fortune	
WV495	Percival Provost T1 (7697M) [P-C]	Booker Air Museum	
WV499	Percival Provost T1 (7698M) [P-G]	RAF St Athan Historic Aircraft Collection	
WV544	Percival Provost T1 (7700M)	AAC Netheravon Fire Section	
WV562	Percival Provost T1 (7606M) [P-C]	RAF Cosford Aerospace Museum	
WV605	Percival Provost T1 [T-B]	Norfolk & Suffolk Aviation Museum, Flixton	
WV606	Percival Provost T1 (7622M) [P-B]	Newark Air Museum, Winthorpe	
WV679	Percival Provost T1 (7615M) [O-J]	Torbay Aircraft Museum, Paignton	
WV686	Percival Provost T1 (7621M) (G-BLFT) [O-P]	Privately owned, Camberley	
WV701	Percival Pembroke C1 (8936M)	RAF Wildenrath as 8936M	
WV703	Percival Pembroke C1 (8108M)	Privately owned, Tattershall Thorpe	
WV705	Percival Pembroke C1 (nose only)	Marine Aircraft Preservation Group, Wimborne	
WV740	Percival Pembroke C1	To G-BNPH, Benson	
WV746	Percival Pembroke C1	RAF Cosford Aerospace Museum	
WV753	Percival Pembroke C1 (8113M)	Wales Aircraft Museum, Cardiff	
WV781	Bristol Sycamore HR12 (G-ALTD/7839M)	Snowdon Mountain Aviation Collection, Caernarfon	
WV783	Bristol Sycamore HR12 (G-ALSP/7841M)	RAF Museum Store, Henlow	
WV787	EE Canberra B2/8 (8799M)	Newark Air Museum, Winthorpe	
WV795	Hawker Sea Hawk FGA6 (A2661/8151M)	Privately owned, Peasedown St John, Avon	
WV797	Hawker Sea Hawk FGA6 (A2637/8155M)	Midland Air Museum, Coventry	
WV798	Hawker Sea Hawk FGA6 (A2557) [028/CU]	Second World War Aircraft Preservation Society, Lasham	
WV826	Hawker Sea Hawk FGA6 (A2532) [147/Z]	Wales Aircraft Museum, Cardiff	
WV843	Hawker Sea Hawk FGA4 (nose only)	Torbay Aircraft Museum, Paignton	
WV856	Hawker Sea Hawk FGA6 [163]	FAA Museum, RNAS Yeovilton	
WV903	Hawker Sea Hawk FGA6 (A2632/8153M) [128/C] [SAH-8]	RNAS Lee-on-Solent	
WV908	Hawker Sea Hawk FGA6 (A2660/8154M) [188/A]	RN Historic Flight, RNAS Yeovilton	
WV911	Hawker Sea Hawk FGA4 (A2526) [115/C]	RN AES, Lee-on-Solent	
WW138	DH Sea Venom FAW22 [229/O]	FAA Museum, RNAS Yeovilton	

Notes	Serial	Type (alternative identity)	Owner, Operator or Location
	WW145	DH Sea Venom FAW22 [680/LM]	Royal Scottish Museum of Flight, East Fortune
	WW217	DH Sea Venom FAW22 [736]	Newark Air Museum, Winthorpe
	WW388	Percival Provost T1 (7616M) [O-F]	Wales Aircraft Museum, Cardiff
	WW397	Percival Provost T1 (8060M/ G-BKHP) [N-E]	Privately owned, RAF Lyneham
	WW421	Percival Provost T1 (7688M) [O]	Lincolnshire Aviation Museum, East Kirkby
	WW442	Percival Provost T1 (7618M) [V-K]	Privately owned, Leverstock Green, Herts
	WW444	Percival Provost T1 [D]	Privately owned, Sibson
	WW447	Percival Provost T1	Privately owned, Grazeley, Berks
	WW453	Percival Provost T1 [W-S]	Air Service Training, Perth
	WW654	Hawker Hunter GA11 [834/DD]	RNAS Culdrose, SAH
	WX788	DH Venom NF3	Wales Aircraft Museum, Cardiff
	WX853	DH Venom NF3 (7443M)	De Havilland Heritage Collection, Hatfield
	WX905	DH Venom NF3 (7458M)	RAF Museum Store, Henlow
	WZ415	DH Vampire T11 [72]	No 2 Sqn ATC, Leavesden
	WZ425	DH Vampire T11	Wales Aircraft Museum, Cardiff
	WZ450	DH Vampire T11 (pod only) [23]	No 2371 Sqn ATC, Tile Cross, W. Mids
	WZ464	DH Vampire T11 (N62430) [40]	Vintage Aircraft Team, Cranfield
	WZ476	DH Vampire T11 (really XE985)	Mosquito Aircraft Museum, stored Hatfield
	WZ507	DH Vampire T11 (G-VTII)	Privately owned, Cranfield
	WZ514	DH Vampire T11	Privately owned, Meols, Merseyside
	WZ515	DH Vampire T11 [60]	Skyfame Collection, stored
	WZ518	DH Vampire T11	North East Aircraft Museum, Usworth
	WZ549	DH Vampire T11 [F] (8118M)	Lincolnshire Aviation Museum, RAF Coningsby
	WZ550	DH Vampire T11 (7902M) [R]	Booker Aircraft Museum
	WZ553	DH Vampire T11 [40]	Wigston ATC, Leics
	WZ557	DH Vampire T11	N Yorks Recovery Group, Chop Gate
	WZ559	DH Vampire T11 (7736M) [45]	RAF Halton Fire Section
	WZ576	DH Vampire T11 (8174M)	No 2192 Sqn ATC, Appleby
	WZ581	DH Vampire T11 [77]	Privately owned, Ruislip
	WZ584	DH Vampire T11 [U]	St Albans College of FE
	WZ589	DH Vampire T11 [19]	Lashenden Air Warfare Museum, Headcorn
	WZ590	DH Vampire T11 [19]	Imperial War Museum, Duxford
	WZ608	DH Vampire T11 [56] (nose only)	Kibworth Aviation Group, Market Harborough
	WZ616	DH Vampire T11 [60]	Vintage Aircraft Team, Cranfield
	WZ662	Auster AOP9 (G-BKVK)	Privately owned, Swanton Morley
	WZ706	Auster AOP9 (7851M)	Royal Military College of Science, Shrivenham
	WZ711	Auster 9/Beagle E3 (G-AVHT)	Privately owned, Middle Wallop
	WZ721	Auster AOP9	Museum of Army Flying, Middle Wallop
	WZ724	Auster AOP9 (7432M)	AAC Middle Wallop, at main gate
	WZ736	Avro 707A (7868M)	Greater Manchester Museum of Science and Industry
	WZ744	Avro 707C (7932M)	RAF Cosford Aerospace Museum
	WZ753	Slingsby Grasshopper TX1	RAF No 1 MGSP, Halton
	WZ754	Slingsby Grasshopper TX1	RAF No 4 MGSP, Dishforth
	WZ755	Slingsby Grasshopper TX1	RAF No 625 VGS, South Cerney
	WZ756	Slingsby Grasshopper TX1	RAF No 2 MGSP, Locking
	WZ757	Slingsby Grasshopper TX1	RAF No 2 MGSP, Locking
	WZ758	Slingsby Grasshopper TX1	Sold 26 June 1987
	WZ760	Slingsby Grasshopper TX1	RAF No 2 MGSP, Locking
	WZ762	Slingsby Grasshopper TX1	RAF No 3 MGSP, Cosford
	WZ766	Slingsby Grasshopper TX1	Radley College CCF, Abingdon
	WZ767	Slingsby Grasshopper TX1	North East Aircraft Museum, Usworth
	WZ768	Slingsby Grasshopper TX1	RAF No 3 MGSP, Cosford
	WZ769	Slingsby Grasshopper TX1	RAF No 2 MGSP, Locking
	WZ772	Slingsby Grasshopper TX1	RAF No 1 MGSP, Halton
	WZ773	Slingsby Grasshopper TX1	Edinburgh Academy CCF, Lothian
	WZ778	Slingsby Grasshopper TX1	RAF No 3 MGSP, Cosford
	WZ779	Slingsby Grasshopper TX1	RAF No 3 MGSP, Cosford

Serial	Type (alternative identity)	Owner, Operator or Location	Notes
WZ780	Slingsby Grasshopper TX1	Clifton College CCF, Bristol	
WZ781	Slingsby Grasshopper TX1	RAF No 4 MGSP, Dishforth	
WZ782	Slingsby Grasshopper TX1	RAF No 1 MGSP, Halton	
WZ784	Slingsby Grasshopper TX1	RAF No 4 MGSP, Dishforth	
WZ785	Slingsby Grasshopper TX1	RAF No 3 MGSP, Cosford	
WZ787	Slingsby Grasshopper TX1	RAF No 4 MGSP, Dishforth	
WZ789	Slingsby Grasshopper TX1	RAF No 3 MGSP, Cosford	
WZ791	Slingsby Grasshopper TX1	RAF, stored Syerston	
WZ792	Slingsby Grasshopper TX1	RAF No 4 MGSP, Dishforth	
WZ793	Slingsby Grasshopper TX1	Lord Wandsworth College CCF, Basingstoke	
WZ794	Slingsby Grasshopper TX1	Sold 26 June 1987	
WZ795	Slingsby Grasshopper TX1	RAF No 1 MGSP, Halton	
WZ796	Slingsby Grasshopper TX1	RAF No 1 MGSP, Halton	
WZ797	Slingsby Grasshopper TX1	Canford School CCF, Dorset	
WZ798	Slingsby Grasshopper TX1	Stratford Aircraft Collection, Long Marston	
WZ816	Slingsby Grasshopper TX1	RAF No 2 MGSP, Locking	
WZ817	Slingsby Grasshopper TX1	RAF No 4 MGSP, Dishforth	
WZ818	Slingsby Grasshopper TX1	RAF No 3 MGSP, Cosford	
WZ819	Slingsby Grasshopper TX1	RAF No 618 VGS, West Malling	
WZ820	Slingsby Grasshopper TX1	Whitgift School CCF, Croydon	
WZ822	Slingsby Grasshopper TX1	Robertsbridge Aviation Society, E. Sussex	
WZ824	Slingsby Grasshopper TX1	RAF No 4 MGSP, Dishforth	
WZ825	Slingsby Grasshopper TX1	Bradfield College CCF, Reading, Berks	
WZ826	Slingsby Grasshopper TX1	RAF No 1 MGSP, Halton	
WZ827	Slingsby Grasshopper TX1	RAF, stored Syerston	
WZ828	Slingsby Grasshopper TX1	Heles School CCF, Exeter, Devon	
WZ829	Slingsby Grasshopper TX1	Launceston College CCF, Cornwall	
WZ831	Slingsby Grasshopper TX1	RAF No 1 MGSP, Halton	
WZ845	DH Chipmunk T10	RAF No 1 AEF, Manston	
WZ846	DH Chipmunk T10 PAX (G-BCSC/8439M)	No 1404 Sqn ATC, Chatham	
WZ847	DH Chipmunk T10 [F]	RAF No 6 AEF, Abingdon	
WZ856	DH Chipmunk T10 [Z]	RAF No 7 AEF, Newton	
WZ862	DH Chipmunk T10 [M]	RAF EFTS, Swinderby	
WZ866	DH Chipmunk T10 PAX (8217M) (G-ATEB)	No 2296 Sqn ATC, Dunoon, Strathclyde	
WZ868	DH Chipmunk T10 (G-BCIW) [H]	Privately owned, Duxford	
WZ869	DH Chipmunk T10 PAX (8019M) [R]	No 391 Sqn ATC, Handforth	
WZ872	DH Chipmunk T10 [E]	RAF No 5 AEF, Cambridge	
WZ877	DH Chipmunk T10 [G]	RAF ACCGS, Syerston	
WZ878	DH Chipmunk T10 [85]	RAF No 11 AEF, Teesside	
WZ879	DH Chipmunk T10 [L]	RAF EFTS, Swinderby	
WZ882	DH Chipmunk T10 [K]	AAC BFWF, Middle Wallop	
WZ884	DH Chipmunk T10 [P]	AAC BFWF, Middle Wallop	
XA109	DH Sea Vampire T22	Royal Scottish Museum of Flight, East Fortune	
XA127	DH Sea Vampire T22 (nose only)	FAA Museum, RNAS Yeovilton	
XA129	DH Sea Vampire T22	FAA Museum, stored Wroughton	
XA225	Slingsby Grasshopper TX1	Churchers College CCF, Petersfield	
XA228	Slingsby Grasshopper TX1	Glenalmond Trinity College CCF, Tayside	
XA229	Slingsby Grasshopper TX1	RAF No 3 MGSP, Cosford	
XA230	Slingsby Grasshopper TX1	Uppingham School CCF, Leics	
XA231	Slingsby Grasshopper TX1 (8888M)	E. Cheshire & S. Manchester Wing ATC HQ, RAF Sealand	
XA233	Slingsby Grasshopper TX1	RAF No 1 MGSP, Halton	
XA237	Slingsby Grasshopper TX1	Queen Victoria School CCF, Dunblane	
XA239	Slingsby Grasshopper TX1	Perse School CCF, Cambridge	
XA240	Slingsby Grasshopper TX1	Radley College CCF, Abingdon	
XA241	Slingsby Grasshopper TX1	Trinity School CCF, Croydon	
XA243	Slingsby Grasshopper TX1 (8886M)	RAF St Athan, ground instruction	
XA244	Slingsby Grasshopper TX1	RAF No 3 MGSP, Cosford	
XA282	Slingsby Cadet TX3	Snowdon Mountain Aviation Collection, Caernarfon	
XA293	Slingsby Cadet TX3	Stratford Aircraft Collection, Long Marston	
XA454	Fairey Gannet COD4	RNAS Yeovilton Fire Section	
XA459	Fairey Gannet ECM6 (A2608) [E/-]	Wales Aircraft Museum, Cardiff	

Notes	Serial	Type (alternative identity)	Owner, Operator or Location
	XA460	Fairey Gannet ECM6 [768/BY]	Kelsterton College of Technology, Connah's Quay
	XA466	Fairey Gannet COD4 [777/LM]	FAA Museum, stored Wroughton
	XA508	Fairey Gannet T2 (A2472) [627/GN]	Midland Air Museum, Coventry
	XA549	Gloster Javelin FAW1 (7717M) [E]	RAF Museum Store, Swinderby
	XA553	Gloster Javelin FAW1 (7470M)	RAF Stanmore Park, on display
	XA564	Gloster Javelin FAW1 (7464M)	RAF Cosford Aerospace Museum
	XA571	Gloster Javelin FAW1 (nose only) (7663M/7722M)	Booker Air Museum
	XA634	Gloster Javelin FAW4 (7641M) [L]	RAF Leeming, at main gate
	XA699	Gloster Javelin FAW5 (7809M)	Midland Air Museum, Coventry
	XA801	Gloster Javelin FAW2 (7739M)	RAF Stafford, at main gate
	XA847	English Electric P1B (8371M)	RAF Museum, Hendon
	XA862	WS55 Whirlwind HAR1 (A2542/G-AMJT) [9]	Midland Air Museum, Coventry
	XA864	WS55 Whirlwind HAR1	FAA Museum, RNAS Yeovilton
	XA870	WS55 Whirlwind HAR1 (A2543)	Cornwall Aero Park, Helston
	XA879	DH Devon C2	RAE, stored Llanbedr
	XA880	DH Devon C2	MoD(PE) RAE Llanbedr
	XA893	Avro Vulcan B1 (8591M) (nose only)	RAF Cosford Aerospace Museum
	XA900	Avro Vulcan B1 (7896M) (cockpit section)	RAF Cosford Aerospace Museum
	XA903	Avro Vulcan B1 (nose only)	Wales Aircraft Museum, Cardiff
	XA917	HP Victor B1 (7827M) (nose only)	RAF Marham, ground instruction
	XA932	HP Victor K1 (8517M)	Scrapped at Marham 11 December 1987
	XB259	Blackburn Beverley C1 (G-AOAI)	Museum of Army Transport, Beverley
	XB261	Blackburn Beverley C1	Southend Airport Hotel
	XB285	Blackburn Beverley C1	Privately owned, Worminghall, Bucks
	XB288	Blackburn Beverley C1	Privately owned, Worminghall, Bucks
	XB446	Grumman Avenger ECM6B [992/C]	FAA Museum, RNAS Yeovilton
	XB480	Hiller HT1 (A2577) [537]	FAA Museum, RNAS Yeovilton
	XB733	Canadair Sabre 4 (*G-ATBF*)	Privately owned, Much Hoole, Lancs
	XD145	SARO SR53	RAF Cosford Aerospace Museum
	XD163	WS55 Whirlwind HAR10 (8645M) [X]	British Rotorcraft Museum, Wroughton
	XD165	WS55 Whirlwind HAR10 (8673M) [B]	RAF No 1 SoTT, Halton
	XD182	WS55 Whirlwind HAR10 (8612M)	RAF FF&SS, Catterick
	XD186	WS55 Whirlwind HAR10 (8730M)	RAF Chivenor, on display
	XD234	VS Scimitar F1 [834]	RAE, derelict Farnborough
	XD317	VS Scimitar F1 [112/R]	FAA Museum, RNAS Yeovilton
	XD332	VS Scimitar F1 (A2574) [612]	Cornwall Aero Park, Helston
	XD375	DH Vampire T11 (7887M)	City of Norwich Aviation Museum
	XD377	DH Vampire T11 (8203M) [A]	RAF Cosford
	XD382	DH Vampire T11 (8033M)	RAF Shawbury, at main gate
	XD425	DH Vampire T11 [16]	Dumfries & Galloway Aviation Museum, Tinwald Downs
	XD429	DH Vampire T11 (7604M) [28] (really XD542)	RAF Cranwell, at main gate
	XD434	DH Vampire T11 [25]	Manchester University, Barton
	XD435	DH Vampire T11 [26]	No 480 Sqn ATC, Kenilworth, Warwicks
	XD445	DH Vampire T11 [51]	Bomber County Aviation Museum, Hemswell
	XD447	DH Vampire T11 [50]	Lincolnshire Aviation Museum, East Kirkby
	XD452	DH Vampire T11 (7990M) [66]	De Havilland Heritage Collection, Hatfield
	XD453	DH Vampire T11 (7890M)	No 58 Sqn ATC, Yorkshire Air Museum, Elvington
	XD459	DH Vampire T11 [63]	Vintage Aircraft Team, Cranfield

Serial	Type (alternative identity)	Owner, Operator or Location	Notes
XD463	DH Vampire T11 (8023M)	No 1360 Sqn ATC, Stapleford, Notts	
XD506	DH Vampire T11 (7983M) [E]	RAF Swinderby, on display	
XD515	DH Vampire T11 (7998M)	Newark Air Museum, Winthorpe	
XD525	DH Vampire T11 (7882M) (pod only)	Campbell College CCF, Belfast	
XD527	DH Vampire T11	CTE, RAF Manston	
XD528	DH Vampire T11 (8159M)	No 2415 Sqn ATC, Penkridge, Staffs	
XD534	DH Vampire T11 [41]	Military Aircraft Preservation Group, Hadfield, Derbys	
XD535	DH Vampire T11	Friends of Biggin Hill, Sevenoaks store	
XD536	DH Vampire T11 (7734M)	Southall Technical College	
XD547	DH Vampire T11 [Z] (pod only)	Scotland West Aircraft Investigation Group, Strathallan	
XD593	DH Vampire T11 [50]	Newark Air Museum, Winthorpe	
XD595	DH Vampire T11 (pod only)	Privately owned, Altrincham	
XD596	DH Vampire T11 (7939M) [V2]	Ocean Village, Southampton Docks	
XD599	DH Vampire T11 [A]	Snowdon Mountain Aviation Collection, Caernarfon	
XD602	DH Vampire T11 (7737M)	No 495 Sqn ATC, Wylde Green, W Midlands	
XD613	DH Vampire T11 (8122M) [M]	RAF Cosford, on parade ground	
XD616	DH Vampire T11 [56]	No 1239 Sqn ATC, Hoddesdon, Herts	
XD622	DH Vampire T11 (8160M)	No 2214 Sqn ATC, Usworth	
XD624	DH Vampire T11 [O]	Macclesfield Technical College	
XD626	DH Vampire T11 [Q]	Midland Air Museum, Coventry	
XD674	Hunting Jet Provost T1 (7570M) [T]	RAF Cosford Aerospace Museum	
XD816	Vickers Valiant B(K)1 (nose only)	RAF Museum Store, Henlow	
XD818	Vickers Valiant B(K)1 (7894M)	Bomber Command Museum, Hendon	
XD826	Vickers Valiant B(K)1 (7872M) (nose only)	Wales Aircraft Museum, Cardiff	
XD875	Vickers Valiant B(K)1 (nose only)	No 163 Sqn ATC, Coventry	
XE317	Bristol Sycamore HR14 (G-AMWO) [S-N]	Newark Air Museum, Winthorpe	
XE327	Hawker Sea Hawk FGA6 (A2556) [644/LH]	RN Llangennech, Dyfed, on display	
XE339	Hawker Sea Hawk FGA6 (8156M/A2635) [149/E] [SAH-7]	RNAS, stored Lee-on-Solent	
XE340	Hawker Sea Hawk FGA6 [131/Z]	Strathallan Aircraft Collection	
XE364	Hawker Sea Hawk FB5 (really WM983/A2511) (G-JETH)	Privately owned, Surrey	
XE368	Hawker Sea Hawk FGA6 (A2534) [200/J]	Cornwall Aero Park, Helston	
XE369	Hawker Sea Hawk FGA6 [5] (A2580/8158M/A2633)	RNAS Yeovilton Fire Section	
XE521	Fairey Rotodyne Y	British Rotorcraft Museum, Weston-super-Mare	
XE531	Hawker Hunter T12	RAE Farnborough Fire Section	
XE587	Hawker Hunter F6 [7]	MoD(PE), stored RAE Farnborough	
XE597	Hawker Hunter FGA9 (8874M) [F]	RAF No 1 SoTT, Halton	
XE601	Hawker Hunter FGA9	MoD(PE) A&AEE Boscombe Down	
XE624	Hawker Hunter FGA9 (8875M) [G]	RAF Brawdy, on display	
XE627	Hawker Hunter F6A	Imperial War Museum, Duxford	
XE643	Hawker Hunter FGA9 (8586M) (nose only)	RAF Exhibition Flight, Abingdon	
XE650	Hawker Hunter FGA9 (G-9-449)	Lovaux Ltd, Macclesfield	
XE653	Hawker Hunter F6A (8829M) [D]	RAF TMTS, Scampton	
XE656	Hawker Hunter F6 (8678M)	RAF No 1 SoTT, Halton	
XE665	Hawker Hunter T8C [876/VL]	RN FRADU, Yeovilton	
XE668	Hawker Hunter GA11 [832/DD]	RNAS Culdrose, SAH	
XE670	Hawker Hunter F4 (7762M/8585M) (nose only)	RAF Exhibition Flight, Abingdon	
XE673	Hawker Hunter GA11 (8846M) (tail from XE689) [680/VL]	RAF Bawdsey, BDRT	

Notes	Serial	Type (alternative identity)	Owner, Operator or Location
	XE677	Hawker Hunter F4	Lincolnshire Aviation Museum, East Kirkby
	XE682	Hawker Hunter GA11 [835]	RNAS Culdrose Fire Section
	XE685	Hawker Hunter GA11 [861/VL]	RN FRADU, Yeovilton
	XE689	Hawker Hunter GA11 [864/VL]	RN FRADU, Yeovilton
	XE707	Hawker Hunter GA11 [865/VL]	RN FRADU, Yeovilton
	XE712	Hawker Hunter GA11 [708]	RN Lee-on-Solent, BDRT
	XE793	Slingsby Cadet TX3	RAF St Athan, instructional use
	XE799	Slingsby Cadet TX3 [R]	RAF Syerston
	XE849	DH Vampire T11 (7928M) [V3]	No 936 Sqn ATC, Ware, Herts
	XE852	DH Vampire T11 [60]	BAe Apprentice School, Hawarden
	XE855	DH Vampire T11	Midland Air Museum, Coventry
	XE856	DH Vampire T11	Second World War Aircraft Preservation Society, Lasham
	XE864	DH Vampire T11	No 480 Sqn ATC, Studley, Warwicks
	XE872	DH Vampire T11 [62]	Midland Air Museum, Coventry
	XE874	DH Vampire T11 (8582M) [61]	RAF Valley on display
	XE897	DH Vampire T11 (really XD403)	Strathallan Aircraft Collection
	XE920	DH Vampire T11 (8196M) [D]	RAF Museum Store, Henlow
	XE921	DH Vampire T11 [64]	Privately owned, Keevil
	XE928	DH Vampire T11 [76]	Privately owned, Keevil
	XE935	DH Vampire T11 [30]	S Yorks Air Museum, Firbeck
	XE946	DH Vampire T11 (7473M) (nose only)	RAF Museum Store, Cardington
	XE956	DH Vampire T11 [N]	St Albans College of FE
	XE979	DH Vampire T11 [54]	Privately owned, Stonehouse, Glos
	XE982	DH Vampire T11 (7564M)	No 124 Sqn ATC, RAF Credenhill, Hereford
	XE993	DH Vampire T11 (8161M)	RAF Cosford Fire Section
	XE995	DH Vampire T11 [53]	Torbay Aircraft Museum, Paignton
	XE998	DH Vampire T11 [36]	Privately owned, Biggin Hill
	XF113	VS Swift F7 (nose only) [19]	Privately owned, Peasedown St John, Avon
	XF114	VS Swift F7	Kelsterton College of Technology, Connah's Quay
	XF274	Gloster Meteor T7	RAE/AIU on display, Farnborough
	XF289	Hawker Hunter T8C [875/VL]	RN FRADU, Yeovilton
	XF300	Hawker Hunter GA11 [860/VL]	RN FRADU, Yeovilton
	XF301	Hawker Hunter GA11 [834/VL]	RN FRADU, Yeovilton
	XF310	Hawker Hunter T7 [869/VL]	RN FRADU, Yeovilton
	XF314	Hawker Hunter F51 [N] (really E-412)	Tangmere Military Aviation Museum
	XF319	Hawker Hunter F4 (7849M) [B]	RAF No 1 SoTT, Halton
	XF321	Hawker Hunter T7	RNEC Manadon
	XF357	Hawker Hunter T8C [871/VL]	RN FRADU, Yeovilton
	XF358	Hawker Hunter T8C [870/VL]	RN FRADU, Yeovilton
	XF368	Hawker Hunter GA11 [863/VL]	RN FRADU, Yeovilton
	XF375	Hawker Hunter F6 (8736M) [05]	RAFC Cranwell, Engineering Wing
	XF382	Hawker Hunter F6A [15]	Midland Air Museum, Coventry
	XF383	Hawker Hunter F6 (8706M) [V]	RAF Wittering, BDRT
	XF383	Hawker Hunter F51 [71] (really E-409)	Wales Aircraft Museum, Cardiff
	XF386	Hawker Hunter F6 (8707M)	To RAF bombing ranges, Otterburn
	XF419	Hawker Hunter FGA9 [C]	To Zimbabwe AF, September 87
	XF431	Hawker Hunter FGA9 [O]	To Zimbabwe AF, September 87
	XF435	Hawker Hunter FGA9 (8880M) [52]	RAF Brawdy, BDRT
	XF445	Hawker Hunter FGA9 (8715M) [T] (really XG264)	RAF Brawdy Fire Section
	XF509	Hawker Hunter F6 (8708M) [73]	RAF Chivenor, at main gate
	XF515	Hawker Hunter F6A (8830M) [C]	RAF TMTS, Scampton
	XF516	Hawker Hunter F6A (8685M) [66]	RAFC Cranwell, Engineering Wing
	XF519	Hawker Hunter FGA9 [J] (8677M/ 8738M) (composite with XJ695)	CTE, RAF Manston
	XF526	Hawker Hunter F6 (8679M) [78/E]	Privately owned, RAF St Athan
	XF527	Hawker Hunter F6 (8680M)	RAF Halton, on display

Serial	Type (alternative identity)	Owner, Operator or Location	Notes
XF545	Percival Provost T1 (7957M) [O-K]	RAF Linton-on-Ouse, at main gate	
XF597	Percival Provost T1 (G-BKFW) [G]	Privately owned, Oakington	
XF603	Percival Provost T1 [H]	Rolls-Royce Tech Coll, Filton	
XF690	Percival Provost T1 (G-BGKA/ 8041M)	Privately owned, Bottesford	
XF708	Avro Shackleton MR3 [203/C]	Imperial War Museum, Duxford	
XF785	Bristol 173 (G-ALBN/7648M)	RAF Museum Store, Henlow	
XF799	Percival Pembroke C1PR	RAF No 60 Sqn, Wildenrath	
XF836	Percival Provost T1 (8043M/ G-AWRY) [JG]	Privately owned, Popham	
XF844	Percival Provost T1 [30]	RAE Farnborough Apprentice School	
XF877	Percival Provost T1 (G-AWVF) [JX]	Privately owned, Compton Abbas	
XF898	Percival Provost T1 [Z]	Booker Fire Section	
XF914	Percival Provost T1	Vintage Aircraft Team, Cranfield	
XF926	Bristol 188 (8368M)	RAF Cosford Aerospace Museum	
XF967	Hawker Hunter T8C [V]	RAF No 237 OCU, Lossiemouth	
XF974	Hawker Hunter F4 (7949M) [C]	RAF No 1 SoTT, Halton	
XF979	Hawker Hunter F51 (really E-408 RDanAF) (8565M) [A]	RAFC Cranwell, on display	
XF985	Hawker Hunter T8C [873/VL]	RN, stored Shawbury	
XF990	Hawker Hunter F6 (8007M) (nose only)	RAF FF&SS, Catterick	
XF994	Hawker Hunter T8C [873/VL]	RN FRADU, Yeovilton	
XF995	Hawker Hunter T8B [W]	RAF No 12 Sqn, Lossiemouth	
XG151	Hawker Hunter FGA9 (8798M) (nose only) [H]	RAF Lossiemouth Fire Section	
XG154	Hawker Hunter FGA9 (8863M) [54]	RAF Museum, Hendon	
XG158	Hawker Hunter F6A (8686M) [21]	RAE Farnborough Apprentice School	
XG160	Hawker Hunter F6A [B] (8831M)	RAF TMTS, Scampton	
XG164	Hawker Hunter F6 [31] (8681M)	RAF No 1 SoTT, Halton	
XG172	Hawker Hunter F6A [A] (8832M)	RAF TMTS, Scampton	
XG194	Hawker Hunter FGA9 [55] (8839M)	RAF No 2 SoTT, Cosford	
XG195	Hawker Hunter FGA9 (composite with XG297)	Bomber County Aviation Museum, Hemswell	
XG196	Hawker Hunter F6A (8702M)	RAF Bracknell, on gate	
XG209	Hawker Hunter F6 [69] (8709M)	RAF No 1 SoTT, Halton	
XG210	Hawker Hunter F6	RAE Apprentice School, Bedford	
XG225	Hawker Hunter F6A (8713M) [S]	RAF No 2 SoTT, Cosford	
XG226	Hawker Hunter F6A (8800M) (fuselage, etc)	RAF Abingdon BDRF	
XG226	Hawker Hunter F6A (8800M) [28] (nose only)	RAF FF&SS, Catterick	
XG228	Hawker Hunter FGA9 [56]	To Zimbabwe AF, September 1987	
XG252	Hawker Hunter FGA9 (8840M) [U]	RAF No 2 SoTT, Cosford	
XG254	Hawker Hunter FGA9 (8881M) [57]	RAF Coltishall, BDRT	
XG274	Hawker Hunter F6 [71] (8710M)	RAF No 1 SoTT, Halton	
XG290	Hawker Hunter F6 [74] (8711M)	RAF Bentley Priory, on display	
XG297	Hawker Hunter FGA9 (nose only)	Privately owned, Preston	
XG325	EE Lightning F1 (nose only)	No 1476 Sqn ATC, Rayleigh, Essex	
XG327	EE Lightning F1 (8188M)	CTE, RAF Manston	
XG329	EE Lightning F1 (8050M)	RAF Swinderby	
XG331	EE Lightning F1 (nose only)	No 2342 Sqn ATC, CARG store, RAF Innsworth	
XG337	EE Lightning F1 (8056M) [M]	RAF Cosford Aerospace Museum	
XG452	Bristol Belvedere HC1 (G-BRMB/7997M)	British Rotorcraft Museum, Weston-super-Mare	
XG454	Bristol Belvedere HC1 (8366M)	Greater Manchester Museum of Science and Industry	

Notes	Serial	Type (alternative identity)	Owner, Operator or Location
	XG474	Bristol Belvedere HC1 (8367M) [O]	RAF Museum, Hendon
	XG502	Bristol Sycamore HR14	Museum of Army Flying, Middle Wallop
	XG504	Bristol Sycamore HR14	Scrapped February 1987
	XG506	Bristol Sycamore HR14 (7852M)	Bomber County Aviation Museum, Hemswell
	XG518	Bristol Sycamore HR14 (8009M) [S-E]	North East Aircraft Museum, Usworth
	XG540	Bristol Sycamore HR14 (7899M/8345M) [Y-S]	RAF Shawbury at main gate
	XG544	Bristol Sycamore HR14	Torbay Aircraft Museum, Paignton
	XG547	Bristol Sycamore HR14 (G-HAPR/8010M) [S-T]	British Rotorcraft Museum, Weston-super-Mare
	XG573	WS55 Whirlwind HAR3	CDE, Porton Down, Wilts
	XG574	WS55 Whirlwind HAR3 (A2575) [752/PO]	FAA Museum, stored Wroughton
	XG577	WS55 Whirlwind HAR3 (A2571)	RE 39 Regt, Waterbeach, on display
	XG592	WS55 Whirlwind HAS7 [54]	Wales Aircraft Museum, Cardiff
	XG594	WS55 Whirlwind HAS7 [517/PO]	Strathallan Aircraft Collection
	XG596	WS55 Whirlwind HAS7 (A2651) [66]	British Rotorcraft Museum, Weston-super-Mare
	XG613	DH Sea Venom FAW21	Imperial War Museum, Duxford
	XG629	DH Sea Venom FAW22	Torbay Aircraft Museum, Paignton
	XG680	DH Sea Venom FAW22 [735/VL]	North East Aircraft Museum, Usworth
	XG691	DH Sea Venom FAW22 [493/J]	Cornwall Aero Park, Helston
	XG692	DH Sea Venom FAW22 [668/LM]	Midland Warplane Museum, Long Marston
	XG730	DH Sea Venom FAW22 [499/A]	Mosquito Aircraft Museum, London Colney
	XG734	DH Sea Venom FAW22	Ulster Aviation Society, Newtownards
	XG736	DH Sea Venom FAW22	Ulster Aviation Society, Newtownards
	XG737	DH Sea Venom FAW22 [220/Z]	Wales Aircraft Museum, Cardiff
	XG743	DH Sea Vampire T22 [597/LM]	Imperial War Museum, Duxford
	XG797	Fairey Gannet ECM6 [766/BY]	Imperial War Museum, Duxford
	XG831	Fairey Gannet ECM6 (A2539) [396]	Cornwall Aero Park, Helston
	XG882	Fairey Gannet T5 (8754M) [771/LM]	RAF Lossiemouth on display
	XG883	Fairey Gannet T5 [773/BY]	Wales Aircraft Museum, Cardiff
	XG888	Fairey Gannet T5 [-/LM]	RNAS, stored Lee-on-Solent
	XG900	Short SC1	Science Museum, Wroughton
	XG905	Short SC1	Ulster Folk & Transport Museum, County Down
	XH124	Blackburn Beverley C1 (8025M)	RAF Museum, Hendon
	XH131	EE Canberra PR9 [AF]	RAF No 1 PRU, Wyton
	XH132	Short SC9 Canberra (8915M)	RAF St Mawgan BDRT
	XH133	EE Canberra PR9	RAF No 1 PRU, Wyton
	XH134	EE Canberra PR9	RAF No 1 PRU, Wyton
	XH135	EE Canberra PR9 [AG]	RAF No 1 PRU, Wyton
	XH136	EE Canberra PR9 (8782M) [W]	RAF No 2 SoTT, Cosford
	XH165	EE Canberra PR9 [AK]	RAF No 1 PRU, Wyton
	XH169	EE Canberra PR9 [AQ]	RAF No 1 PRU, Wyton
	XH170	EE Canberra PR9 (8739M)	RAF Wyton, on gate
	XH171	EE Canberra PR9 (8746M) [U]	RAF No 2 SoTT, Cosford
	XH174	EE Canberra PR9 [AN]	RAF No 1 PRU, Wyton
	XH175	EE Canberra PR9 [AP]	RAF No 1 PRU, Wyton
	XH274	DH Vampire T11	RAF Ternhill Fire Section
	XH278	DH Vampire T11 (8595M/7866M)	No 2482 Sqn ATC, RAF Henlow
	XH312	DH Vampire T11 [18]	Privately owned, Chester
	XH313	DH Vampire T11 [E]	St Albans College of FE
	XH318	DH Vampire T11 [64] (7761M)	No 424 Sqn ATC, Hants
	XH328	DH Vampire T11 [66]	Privately owned, Hemel Hempstead
	XH329	DH Vampire T11 [70]	Privately owned, Keevil
	XH330	DH Vampire T11 [73]	Privately owned, Bridgnorth
	XH537	Avro Vulcan B2 MRR (8749M)	RAF Abingdon, on display
	XH539	Avro Vulcan B2	RAF Waddington, rescue training

Serial	Type (alternative identity)	Owner, Operator or Location	Notes
XH558	Avro Vulcan B2	RAF Vulcan Memorial Flight, Waddington	
XH560	Avro Vulcan K2	RAF Marham Fire Section	
XH567	EE Canberra B6(mod)	MoD(PE) RAE Bedford	
XH568	EE Canberra B6(mod)	MoD(PE) RAE Bedford	
XH583	EE Canberra T4 (G-27-374)	BAe, stored Samlesbury	
XH590	HP Victor K1A	CTE, RAF Manston	
XH592	HP Victor K1A (8429M) [L]	RAF Cosford Aerospace Museum	
XH593	HP Victor K1A (8428M) [T]	RAF No 2 SoTT, Cosford	
XH616	HP Victor K1A	CTE, RAF Manston	
XH648	HP Victor K1A	Imperial War Museum, Duxford	
XH669	HP Victor K2	RAF No 55 Sqn, Marham	
XH670	HP Victor SR2 (nose only)	Lincolnshire Aviation Museum, East Kirkby	
XH671	HP Victor K2	RAF No 55 Sqn, Marham	
XH672	HP Victor K2	RAF No 55 Sqn, Marham	
XH673	HP Victor K2 (8911M)	RAF Marham, on display	
XH675	HP Victor K2	RAF No 55 Sqn, Marham	
XH764	Gloster Javelin FAW9 (7972M)	RAF Manston, on display	
XH767	Gloster Javelin FAW9 (7955M) [K]	Wessex Aviation Museum, Monkton Farleigh Mines, Bath	
XH837	Gloster Javelin FAW7 (8032M) (nose only)	Snowdon Mountain Aviation Collection, Caernarfon	
XH892	Gloster Javelin FAW9 (7982M) [B]	Norfolk & Suffolk Aviation Museum, Flixton	
XH897	Gloster Javelin FAW9	Imperial War Museum, Duxford	
XH903	Gloster Javelin FAW9 (7938M)	RAF Innsworth, at main gate	
XH980	Gloster Javelin FAW8 (7867M) [A]	RAF West Raynham, at main gate	
XH992	Gloster Javelin FAW8 (7829M) [P]	Newark Air Museum, Winthorpe	
XJ314	RR Thrust Measuring Rig	Museum of Flight, East Fortune	
XJ319	DH Sea Devon C20 (G-AMXP)	RN, Prestwick Station Flight	
XJ324	DH Sea Devon C20 (G-AMXZ)	RN, Prestwick Station Flight	
XJ348	DH Sea Devon C20 (G-AMXX/ G-NAVY)	Privately owned, Shoreham	
XJ380	Bristol Sycamore HR14 (8628M)	RAF Finningley, for display	
XJ389	Fairey Jet Gyrodyne (XD759/ G-AJJP)	RAF Cosford Aerospace Museum	
XJ393	WS55 Whirlwind HAR3 (A2538)	Torbay Aircraft Museum, Paignton	
XJ396	WS55 Whirlwind HAR10	RAE Farnborough Fire Section	
XJ402	WS55 Whirlwind HAR3 (A2572) [61]	FAA Museum Store, RNAS Yeovilton	
XJ407	WS55 Whirlwind HAR10 (G-BKHB)	Privately owned, Tattershall Thorpe	
XJ409	WS55 Whirlwind HAR10	Wales Aircraft Museum, Cardiff	
XJ411	WS55 Whirlwind HAR10 [Z]	RAE Farnborough Fire Section	
XJ430	WS55 Whirlwind HAR10	CTE, RAF Manston	
XJ435	WS55 Whirlwind HAR10 (8671M) [V]	RAF No 1 SoTT, Halton	
XJ445	WS55 Whirlwind HAR5	CDE, Porton Down, Wilts	
XJ476	DH Sea Vixen FAW1 (nose section)	No 424 Sqn ATC, Southampton Hall of Aviation	
XJ481	DH Sea Vixen FAW1 [VL]	On display Ocean Village, Southampton	
XJ482	DH Sea Vixen FAW1 (A2598) [713/VL]	Norfolk & Suffolk Aviation Museum, Flixton	
XJ494	DH Sea Vixen FAW2	Privately owned, Kings Langley, Herts	
XJ560	DH Sea Vixen FAW2 (8142M) [243]	Newark Air Museum, Winthorpe	
XJ565	DH Sea Vixen FAW2 [127/E]	Mosquito Aircraft Museum, London Colney	
XJ571	DH Sea Vixen FAW2 (8140M) [242/R]	Privately owned, Southampton Airport	
XJ575	DH Sea Vixen FAW2 (A2611) [-/VL] [SAH-13]	Cornwall Aero Park, Helston	
XJ580	DH Sea Vixen FAW2 [131/E]	Christchurch Memorial Group	
XJ582	DH Sea Vixen FAW2 (8139M) [702]	RAF Cottesmore Fire Section	

Notes	Serial	Type (alternative identity)	Owner, Operator or Location
	XJ584	DH Sea Vixen FAW2 (A2621) [SAH-16]	Cornwall Aero Park, Helston
	XJ604	DH Sea Vixen FAW2 (8222M)	Cranfield Institute of Technology
	XJ607	DH Sea Vixen FAW2 (8171M) [O] [VL]	Privately owned
	XJ608	DH Sea Vixen FAW2 (8802M)	RAF North Luffenham Fire Section
	XJ609	DH Sea Vixen FAW2 (8172M) painted 8171M [702/VL]	RAF Abingdon Fire Section
	XJ634	Hawker Hunter F6A (8684M) [29]	RAFC Cranwell, Engineering Wing
	XJ639	Hawker Hunter F6A (8687M) [31]	RAFC Cranwell, Engineering Wing
	XJ676	Hawker Hunter F6A [32] (8844M)	RAF Lyneham BDRF
	XJ683	Hawker Hunter FGA9 [X]	To Zimbabwe AF, September 87
	XJ690	Hawker Hunter FGA9 (composite with XG195)	Lovaux Ltd, Hurn
	XJ723	WS55 Whirlwind HAR10	OPITB, Montrose
	XJ726	WS55 Whirlwind HAR10 [F]	Snowdon Mountain Aviation Collection, Caernarfon
	XJ727	WS55 Whirlwind HAR10 (8661M) [L]	RAF No 1 SoTT, Halton
	XJ729	WS55 Whirlwind HAR10 (8732M)	RAF Finningley, for display
	XJ763	WS55 Whirlwind HAR10 (G-BKHA)	Privately owned, North Weald
	XJ772	DH Vampire T11 [H]	Brooklands Technical College
	XJ782	Avro Vulcan B2 MRR (8766M)	RAF Finningley Fire Section
	XJ823	Avro Vulcan B2A	Privately owned, Carlisle Airport
	XJ824	Avro Vulcan B2A	Imperial War Museum, Duxford
	XJ825	Avro Vulcan K2 (8810M)	RAF Waddington, BDRT
	XJ917	Bristol Sycamore HR14 [S-H]	Cornwall Aero Park, Helston
	XJ918	Bristol Sycamore HR14 (8190M)	RAF Cosford Aerospace Museum
	XK149	Hawker Hunter F6A [34] (8714M)	RAFC Cranwell, Engineering Wing
	XK412	Auster AOP9	Privately owned, Wootton Bassett
	XK416	Auster AOP9 (G-AYUA/ 7855M)	Vintage Aircraft Team, Cranfield
	XK417	Auster AOP9 (G-AVXY)	Privately owned, Leicester
	XK418	Auster AOP9 (7976M)	Second World War Aircraft Preservation Society, Lasham
	XK421	Auster AOP9 (8365M)	Cotswold Aircraft Restoration Group, RAF Innsworth
	XK482	Saro Skeeter AOP12 (7840M/ G-BJWC) [C]	Privately owned, Tattershall Thorpe
	XK488	Blackburn Buccaneer S1	FAA Museum, RNAS Yeovilton
	XK526	Blackburn Buccaneer S2 (8648M)	RAF Honington, at main gate
	XK530	Blackburn Buccaneer S1	RAE Bedford Fire Section
	XK531	Blackburn Buccaneer S1 (8403M)	Defence School, Winterbourne Gunner
	XK532	Blackburn Buccaneer S1 (8867M/A2581) [632/LM]	RAF Lossiemouth, on display
	XK533	Blackburn Buccaneer S1 (nose only)	Museum of Flight, East Fortune
	XK590	DH Vampire T11 [V]	Wellesbourne Aviation Group
	XK623	DH Vampire T11 [56]	Snowdon Mountain Aviation Collection, Caernarfon
	XK624	DH Vampire T11 [32]	Norfolk & Suffolk Aviation Museum, Flixton
	XK625	DH Vampire T11 [12]	Privately owned, North Weald
	XK627	DH Vampire T11	Pennine Aviation Museum, Bacup
	XK632	DH Vampire T11 [67]	Privately owned
	XK637	DH Vampire T11 [56]	No 1855 Sqn ATC, Royton, Greater Manchester
	XK655	DH Comet 2R (G-AMXA)	Strathallan Aircraft Collection
	XK659	DH Comet 2 (nose only)	Privately owned, Elland, W. Yorks
	XK695	DH Comet 2R (G-AMXH)	Imperial War Museum, Duxford
	XK697	DH Comet 2R (G-AMXJ) [D]	Scrapped at Wyton, September 1987
	XK699	DH Comet C2 (7971M)	RAF Lyneham on display
	XK724	Folland Gnat F1 (7715M)	RAF Cosford Aerospace Museum

Serial	Type (alternative identity)	Owner, Operator or Location	Notes
XK740	Folland Gnat F1 (8396M)	Southampton Hall of Aviation	
XK741	Folland Gnat F1	Midland Air Museum, Coventry	
XK776	ML Utility 1	Museum of Army Flying, Middle Wallop	
XK788	Slingsby Grasshopper TX1	RAF No 1 MGSP, Halton	
XK789	Slingsby Grasshopper TX1	RAF No 3 MGSP, Cosford	
XK819	Slingsby Grasshopper TX1	RAF No 3 MGSP, Cosford	
XK820	Slingsby Grasshopper TX1	RAF No 2 MGSP, Locking	
XK822	Slingsby Grasshopper TX1	Kings College School CCF, Wimbledon	
XK824	Slingsby Grasshopper TX1	Wycliffe School CCF, Stonehouse, Glos	
XK884	Percival Pembroke C1	To G-BNPG, Duxford	
XK895	DH Sea Devon C20	RN, Prestwick Station Flight	
XK906	WS55 Whirlwind HAS7	AAC Netheravon Fire Section	
XK907	WS55 Whirlwind HAS7 [U]	Midland Air Museum, Coventry	
XK911	WS55 Whirlwind HAS7 (A2603) [519/PO]	RN, stored Wroughton	
XK912	WS55 Whirlwind HAS7 [60/CU]	Privately owned, Crudwell, Wilts	
XK936	WS55 Whirlwind HAS7 [62]	Imperial War Museum, Duxford	
XK943	WS55 Whirlwind HAS7 (A2653/8796M) [57]	RAF Abingdon, Fire Section	
XK944	WS55 Whirlwind HAS7 (A2607)	No 617 Sqn ATC, Malpas School	
XK968	WS55 Whirlwind HAR10 (8445M) [E]	RAF Manston, on display	
XK969	WS55 Whirlwind HAR10 (8646M)	CTE, RAF Manston	
XK970	WS55 Whirlwind HAR10 (8789M)	RAF Odiham, BDRT	
XK986	WS55 Whirlwind HAR10 (8790M)	RAF Odiham, BDRT	
XK987	WS55 Whirlwind HAR10 (8393M)	MoD Swynnerton, Staffs	
XK988	WS55 Whirlwind HAR10 (A2646) [N]	Museum of Army Flying, Middle Wallop	
XL149	Blackburn Beverley C1 (nose only) (7988M)	Newark Air Museum, Winthorpe	
XL158	HP Victor K2	RAF No 55 Sqn, Marham	
XL160	HP Victor K2 (8910M)	RAF Marham Fire Section	
XL161	HP Victor K2	RAF No 55 Sqn, Marham	
XL162	HP Victor K2	RAF No 55 Sqn, Marham	
XL163	HP Victor K2 (8916M)	RAF St Athan, BDRT	
XL164	HP Victor K2	RAF No 55 Sqn, Marham	
XL188	HP Victor K2	RAF No 55 Sqn, Marham	
XL189	HP Victor K2 (8912M)	RAF Waddington on display	
XL190	HP Victor K2	RAF No 55 Sqn, Marham	
XL191	HP Victor K2	Written off 19 June 1986 Hamilton, Ontario	
XL192	HP Victor K2	RAF No 55 Sqn, Marham	
XL231	HP Victor K2	RAF No 55 Sqn, Marham	
XL233	HP Victor K2 (89..M)	RAF St Athan Fire Section	
XL318	Avro Vulcan B2 (8733M)	Bomber Command Museum, Hendon	
XL319	Avro Vulcan B2	North East Aircraft Museum, Usworth	
XL360	Avro Vulcan B2	Midland Air Museum, Coventry	
XL384	Avro Vulcan B2 (8505M/8670M)	RAF Scampton Fire Section	
XL386	Avro Vulcan B2A (8760M)	CTE, RAF Manston	
XL388	Avro Vulcan B2 (nose only)	Privately owned, Walpole, Suffolk	
XL391	Avro Vulcan B2	Privately owned, Blackpool	
XL392	Avro Vulcan B2 (8745M)	RAF Valley Fire Section	
XL426	Avro Vulcan B2 (G-VJET)	Privately owned, Southend	
XL427	Avro Vulcan B2 (8756M)	RAF Machrihanish Fire Section	
XL445	Avro Vulcan K2 (8811M)	RAF Lyneham Fire Section	
XL449	Fairey Gannet AEW3	Wales Aircraft Museum, Cardiff	
XL471	Fairey Gannet AEW3 [043/R]	Dumfries & Galloway Aviation Museum, Tinwald Downs	
XL472	Fairey Gannet AEW3 [044/R]	A&AEE Boscombe Down, derelict	
XL497	Fairey Gannet AEW3 [041/R]	HMS *Gannet*, Prestwick, at gate	
XL500	Fairey Gannet AEW3 (A2701)	RNAS, stored Lee-on-Solent	
XL502	Fairey Gannet AEW3 (8610M) (G-BMYP)	Privately owned, Carlisle	
XL503	Fairey Gannet AEW3 [070/E]	FAA Museum, RNAS Yeovilton	
XL511	HP Victor K2	CTE, RAF Manston	
XL512	HP Victor K2	RAF No 55 Sqn, Marham	
XL563	Hawker Hunter T7	MoD(PE) RAE/IAM Farnborough	
XL564	Hawker Hunter T7 [4]	MoD(PE) ETPS Boscombe Down	

Notes	Serial	Type (alternative identity)	Owner, Operator or Location
	XL565	Hawker Hunter T7	MoD(PE) IAM/RAE Farnborough
	XL567	Hawker Hunter T7 (8723M) [84]	RAF Chivenor Fire Section
	XL568	Hawker Hunter T7A [N]	RAF No 237 OCU, Lossiemouth
	XL569	Hawker Hunter T7 (8833M) [80]	RAF No 2 SoTT, Cosford
	XL572	Hawker Hunter T7 (8834M) [83]	RAF No 2 SoTT, Cosford
	XL573	Hawker Hunter T7	RAF No 12 Sqn, Lossiemouth
	XL576	Hawker Hunter T7 (8835M) [81]	RAF No 2 SoTT, Cosford
	XL577	Hawker Hunter T7 (8676M) [01]	RAFC Cranwell, Engineering Wing
	XL578	Hawker Hunter T7 [77]	RAF, stored St Athan
	XL580	Hawker Hunter T8M [719]	RN No 899 Sqn, Yeovilton
	XL586	Hawker Hunter T7 [85]	MoD(PE) BAe Warton
	XL587	Hawker Hunter T7 (8807M) [Z]	RAF TMTS, Scampton
	XL591	Hawker Hunter T7 [G]	RAF No 237 OCU, Lossiemouth
	XL592	Hawker Hunter T7 (8836M) [Y]	RAF TMTS, Scampton
	XL595	Hawker Hunter T7 [78]	RAF, stored St Athan
	XL598	Hawker Hunter T8C [880/VL]	RN FRADU, Yeovilton
	XL600	Hawker Hunter T7 [FL]	RNAY Fleetlands Apprentice School
	XL601	Hawker Hunter T7 [874/VL]	RN FRADU, Yeovilton
	XL602	Hawker Hunter T8M	MoD(PE) BAe Dunsfold
	XL603	Hawker Hunter T8M [720/VL]	RN No 899 Sqn, Yeovilton
	XL609	Hawker Hunter T7 (8866M) [YF]	RAF Lossiemouth, BDRT
	XL612	Hawker Hunter T7	MoD(PE) ETPS Boscombe Down
	XL613	Hawker Hunter T7A	RAF No 237 OCU, Lossiemouth
	XL614	Hawker Hunter T7 [O]	RAF No 237 OCU, Lossiemouth
	XL616	Hawker Hunter T7 [P]	RAF No 208 Sqn, Lossiemouth
	XL617	Hawker Hunter T7 [89] (8837M)	RAF No 2 SoTT, Cosford
	XL618	Hawker Hunter T7 (8892M) [05]	RAF Cottesmore BDRT
	XL621	Hawker Hunter T7 (G-BNCX)	Lovaux Ltd, Hurn
	XL623	Hawker Hunter T7 [90] (8770M)	RAF No 2 SoTT, Cosford
	XL629	EE Lightning T4	A&AEE Boscombe Down, at main gate
	XL703	SAL Pioneer CC1 (8034M)	Greater Manchester Museum of Science and Industry
	XL717	DH Tiger Moth (G-AOXG/T7291) [LM]	FAA Museum, RNAS Yeovilton
	XL728	WS58 Wessex HAS1	To Pendine Ranges
	XL738	Saro Skeeter AOP12 (7860M)	AAC Centre, Middle Wallop, on display
	XL762	Saro Skeeter AOP12 (8017M)	Royal Scottish Museum of Flight, East Fortune
	XL763	Saro Skeeter AOP12	Southall Technical College
	XL764	Saro Skeeter AOP12 (7940M)	Newark Air Museum, Winthorpe
	XL765	Saro Skeeter AOP12	Privately owned, Leamington Spa
	XL770	Saro Skeeter AOP12 (8046M)	Southampton Hall of Aviation
	XL809	Saro Skeeter AOP12 (G-BLIX/PH-HOF)	Privately owned, Clapham, Beds
	XL811	Saro Skeeter AOP12 [157]	The Aircraft Collection, Warmingham
	XL812	Saro Skeeter AOP12 (G-SARO)	Privately owned, Old Buckenham
	XL813	Saro Skeeter AOP12	Museum of Army Flying, Middle Wallop
	XL814	Saro Skeeter AOP12	AAC Historic Aircraft Flight, Middle Wallop
	XL824	Bristol Sycamore HR14 (8021M)	Greater Manchester Museum of Science and Industry
	XL829	Bristol Sycamore HR14	Bristol Industrial Museum
	XL836	WS55 Whirlwind HAS7 (A2642) [65/FL]	RN Predannack Fire School
	XL840	WS55 Whirlwind HAS7 [56]	City of Norwich Aviation Museum
	XL846	WS55 Whirlwind HAS7 (A2625) [85]	RN Predannack Fire School
	XL847	WS55 Whirlwind HAS7 (A2626) [83]	AAC Middle Wallop, Fire Section
	XL853	WS55 Whirlwind HAS7 (A2630)	Southampton Hall of Aviation
	XL875	WS55 Whirlwind HAR9	Air Service Training, Perth
	XL880	WS55 Whirlwind HAR9 (A2714) [433/ED]	RN Lee-on-Solent, BDRT
	XL898	WS55 Whirlwind HAR9 (8654M) [30/ED]	Boscombe Down Fire Section
	XL899	WS55 Whirlwind HAR9 [587/CU]	RN Predannack Fire School
	XL929	Percival Pembroke C1	To G-BNPU, Sandown
	XL954	Percival Pembroke C1PR	RAF No 60 Sqn, Wildenrath
	XL993	SAL Twin Pioneer CC1 (8388M)	RAF Cosford Aerospace Museum
	XM135	BAC Lightning F1 [135]	Imperial War Museum, Duxford

Serial	Type (alternative identity)	Owner, Operator or Location	Notes
XM139	BAC Lightning F1 (8411M)	To Pendine Ranges	
XM144	BAC Lightning F1 (8417M) [J]	RAF Leuchars, at main gate	
XM147	BAC Lightning F1 (8412M) (tail fin only)	RAF Wattisham Fire Section	
XM169	BAC Lightning F1A (8422M) [W]	RAF Leuchars Fire Section	
XM172	BAC Lightning F1A (8427M) [B]	RAF Coltishall, at main gate	
XM173	BAC Lightning F1A (8414M) [A]	RAF Bentley Priory, at main gate	
XM178	BAC Lightning F1A (8418M) [Y]	RAF Leuchars Fire Section	
XM181	BAC Lightning F1A (8415M) [8]	Scrapped 1987 at Binbrook	
XM183	BAC Lightning F1A (8416M) [7]	Scrapped 1987 at Binbrook	
XM191	BAC Lightning F1A (7854M/ 8590M) (nose only)	RAF Exhibition Flight, Abingdon	
XM192	BAC Lightning F1A (8413M) [K]	RAF Wattisham, at main gate	
XM223	DH Devon C2 [J]	MoD(PE) RAE West Freugh	
XM279	EE Canberra B(I)8 (nose only)	S Yorks Air Museum, Firbeck	
XM296	DH Heron C4	RN FONAC, RNAS Yeovilton	
XM300	WS58 Wessex HAS1	Wales Aircraft Museum, Cardiff	
XM326	WS58 Wessex HAS1 [515]	RNAS Portland Fire Section	
XM327	WS58 Wessex HAS3 [401/KE]	College of Nautical Studies, Warsash	
XM328	WS58 Wessex HAS3	RNAS Culdrose, SAH	
XM329	WS58 Wessex HAS1 [533/PO] (A2609)	RN Predannack Fire School	
XM330	WS58 Wessex HAS1	MoD(PE) RAE Farnborough	
XM331	WS58 Wessex HAS3	RN Predannack Fire School	
XM349	Hunting Jet Provost T3A [H]	RAF CFS, Scampton	
XM350	Hunting Jet Provost T3A [89]	RAF No 7 FTS, Church Fenton	
XM351	Hunting Jet Provost T3 [Y] (8078M)	RAF No 2 SoTT, Cosford	
XM352	Hunting Jet Provost T3A [21]	RAF No 1 FTS, Linton-on-Ouse	
XM355	Hunting Jet Provost T3 (8229M) [D]	RAF No 1 SoTT, Halton	
XM357	Hunting Jet Provost T3A [45]	RAF No 1 FTS, Linton-on-Ouse	
XM358	Hunting Jet Provost T3A [53]	RAF No 1 FTS, Linton-on-Ouse	
XM362	Hunting Jet Provost T3 (8230M)	RAF No 1 SoTT, Halton	
XM365	Hunting Jet Provost T3A [37]	RAF No 1 FTS, Linton-on-Ouse	
XM367	Hunting Jet Provost T3 [Z] (8083M)	RAF No 2 SoTT, Cosford	
XM369	Hunting Jet Provost T3 (8084M) [07]	RAF No 1 SoTT, Halton	
XM370	Hunting Jet Provost T3A [10]	RAF No 1 FTS, Linton-on-Ouse	
XM371	Hunting Jet Provost T3A [K]	RAF CFS, Scampton	
XM372	Hunting Jet Provost T3A [55] (8917M)	RAF Linton-on-Ouse Fire Section	
XM374	Hunting Jet Provost T3A [18]	RAF No 1 FTS, Linton-on-Ouse	
XM375	Hunting Jet Provost T3 (8231M) [B]	RAF No 1 SoTT, Halton	
XM376	Hunting Jet Provost T3A [27]	RAF No 1 FTS, Linton-on-Ouse	
XM378	Hunting Jet Provost T3A	RAF St Athan	
XM379	Hunting Jet Provost T3	Army Apprentice College, Arborfield	
XM381	Hunting Jet Provost T3 (8232M) [O]	RAF No 1 SoTT, Halton	
XM383	Hunting Jet Provost T3A [90]	RAF No 7 FTS, Church Fenton	
XM386	Hunting Jet Provost T3 (8076M) [08]	RAF No 1 SoTT, Halton	
XM387	Hunting Jet Provost T3A [I]	RAF CFS, Scampton	
XM401	Hunting Jet Provost T3A [17]	RAF No 1 FTS, Linton-on-Ouse	
XM402	Hunting Jet Provost T3 (8055AM) [J]	RAF No 1 SoTT, Halton	
XM403	Hunting Jet Provost T3A [A]	RAF CFS, Scampton	
XM404	Hunting Jet Provost T3 (8055BM) [24]	RAF No 1 SoTT, Halton	
XM405	Hunting Jet Provost T3A [42]	RAF No 1 FTS, Linton-on-Ouse	
XM408	Hunting Jet Provost T3 (8233M) [P]	RAF No 1 SoTT, Halton	
XM409	Hunting Jet Provost T3 (8082M) [A]	RAF No 1 SoTT, Halton	

Notes	Serial	Type (alternative identity)	Owner, Operator or Location
	XM410	Hunting Jet Provost T3 (8054AM) [C]	RAF No 1 SoTT, Halton
	XM411	Hunting Jet Provost T3 (8434M) [L]	RAF No 1 SoTT, Halton
	XM412	Hunting Jet Provost T3A [41]	RAF No 1 FTS, Linton-on-Ouse
	XM413	Hunting Jet Provost T3	Army Apprentice College, Arborfield
	XM414	Hunting Jet Provost T3A [101]	RAF No 7 FTS, Church Fenton
	XM415	Hunting Jet Provost T3 (nose only)	No 424 Sqn ATC, Southampton Hall of Aviation
	XM417	Hunting Jet Provost T3 (8054BM) [D]	RAF No 1 SoTT, Halton
	XM419	Hunting Jet Provost T3A [102]	RAF No 7 FTS, Church Fenton
	XM424	Hunting Jet Provost T3A [30]	RAF No 1 FTS, Linton-on-Ouse
	XM425	Hunting Jet Provost T3A [88]	RAF No 7 FTS, Church Fenton
	XM426	Hunting Jet Provost T3 (nose only)	No 1151 Sqn ATC, Wallsend-on-Tyne
	XM455	Hunting Jet Provost T3A [F]	RAF CFS, Scampton
	XM458	Hunting Jet Provost T3A [B]	RAF CFS, Scampton
	XM459	Hunting Jet Provost T3A [104]	RAF No 7 FTS, Church Fenton
	XM461	Hunting Jet Provost T3A [11]	RAF No 1 FTS, Linton-on-Ouse
	XM463	Hunting Jet Provost T3A [38]	RAF No 1 FTS, Linton-on-Ouse
	XM464	Hunting Jet Provost T3A [23]	RAF No 1 FTS, Linton-on-Ouse
	XM465	Hunting Jet Provost T3A [85]	RAF No 7 FTS, Church Fenton
	XM466	Hunting Jet Provost T3A [31]	RAF No 1 FTS, Linton-on-Ouse
	XM467	Hunting Jet Provost T3 (8085M) [06] [69]	RAF No 1 SoTT, Halton
	XM468	Hunting Jet Provost T3 (8081M) [B]	RAF No 1 SoTT, Halton
	XM470	Hunting Jet Provost T3A [M]	RAF CFS, Scampton
	XM471	Hunting Jet Provost T3A [93]	RAF No 7 FTS, Church Fenton
	XM472	Hunting Jet Provost T3A [22]	RAF No 1 FTS, Linton-on-Ouse
	XM473	Hunting Jet Provost T3A [81]	RAF No 7 FTS, Church Fenton
	XM475	Hunting Jet Provost T3A [96]	RAF No 7 FTS, Church Fenton
	XM478	Hunting Jet Provost T3A [33]	RAF No 1 FTS, Linton-on-Ouse
	XM479	Hunting Jet Provost T3A [54]	RAF No 1 FTS, Linton-on-Ouse
	XM480	Hunting Jet Provost T3 (8080M)	RAF No 1 SoTT, Halton
	XM529	Saro Skeeter AOP12 (7979M/ G-BDNS)	Privately owned, Handforth
	XM553	Saro Skeeter AOP12 (G-AWSV)	Privately owned, Middle Wallop
	XM555	Saro Skeeter AOP12 (8027M)	RAF Cosford Aerospace Museum
	XM556	Saro Skeeter AOP12 (G-HELI/7870M) [V]	British Rotorcraft Museum, Weston-super-Mare
	XM561	Saro Skeeter AOP12 (7980M)	Lincolnshire Aviation Museum, East Kirkby
	XM564	Saro Skeeter AOP12	Royal Armoured Corps, Bovington
	XM569	Avro Vulcan B2	Wales Aircraft Museum, Cardiff
	XM575	Avro Vulcan B2A (G-BLMC)	East Midlands Aeropark
	XM594	Avro Vulcan B2	Newark Air Museum, Winthorpe
	XM597	Avro Vulcan B2	Royal Scottish Museum of Flight, East Fortune
	XM598	Avro Vulcan B2 (8778M)	RAF Cosford Aerospace Museum
	XM602	Avro Vulcan B2 (8771M)	RAF St Athan Historic Aircraft Collection
	XM603	Avro Vulcan B2	BAe Woodford
	XM607	Avro Vulcan B2 (8779M)	RAF Waddington, on display
	XM612	Avro Vulcan B2	City of Norwich Aviation Museum
	XM652	Avro Vulcan B2 (nose only)	Privately owned, Burntwood, Staffs
	XM655	Avro Vulcan B2 (G-VULC/ N655AV)	Privately owned, Wellesbourne Mountford
	XM656	Avro Vulcan B2 (8757M) (nose only)	RAF Cottesmore Fire Section
	XM657	Avro Vulcan B2A (8734M)	CTE, RAF Manston
	XM660	WS55 Whirlwind HAS7 [78]	North East Aircraft Museum, Usworth
	XM665	WS55 Whirlwind HAS7	Booker Aircraft Museum
	XM667	WS55 Whirlwind HAS7 (A2629) [56/CU]	RN Predannack Fire School
	XM685	WS55 Whirlwind HAS7 (G-AYZJ) [518/PO]	Newark Air Museum, Winthorpe
	XM693	HS Gnat T1 (7891M)	BAe Hamble on display
	XM694	HS Gnat T1	RAE Bedford Apprentice School
	XM697	HS Gnat T1	No 1349 Sqn ATC, Woking

Serial	Type (alternative identity)	Owner, Operator or Location	Notes
XM698	HS Gnat T1 (8090M/8497M)	To USA as N698XM	
XM705	HS Gnat T1 (8574M)	To USA as N705XM	
XM706	HS Gnat T1 (8572M) [13]	RAF No 1 SoTT, Halton	
XM708	HS Gnat T1 (8573M)	RAF Locking, on display	
XM709	HS Gnat T1 (8617M) [67]	RAF No 1 SoTT, Halton	
XM715	HP Victor K2	RAF No 55 Sqn, Marham	
XM717	HP Victor K2	RAF No 55 Sqn, Marham	
XM832	WS58 Wessex HAS1	RN NASU, Yeovilton	
XM833	WS58 Wessex HAS3	Wessex Aviation Museum, Monkton Farleigh Mines, Bath	
XM836	WS58 Wessex HAS3 [651/PO]	RNAY Fleetlands, instructional use	
XM838	WS58 Wessex HAS3 [405/LN]	RN Predannack Fire School	
XM841	WS58 Wessex HAS1 [510]	RN Predannack Fire School	
XM843	WS58 Wessex HAS1 (A2693) [527/LS]	RNAS Lee-on-Solent Fire Section	
XM845	WS58 Wessex HAS1 (A2682) [530/PO]	RNAS Yeovilton Fire Section	
XM868	WS58 Wessex HAS1 (A2706) [517/PO]	RN AES, Lee-on-Solent	
XM870	WS58 Wessex HAS3 [652/PO]	RN AES, Lee-on-Solent	
XM874	WS58 Wessex HAS1 (A2689) [521/CU]	RNAS Culdrose, SAH	
XM916	WS58 Wessex HAS3 [666/PO]	Fire Section, Wroughton	
XM917	WS58 Wessex HAS1 (A2692) [528/CU]	RNAS Lee-on-Solent Fire Section	
XM919	WS58 Wessex HAS3 [55]	RNAY Fleetlands Apprentice School	
XM923	WS58 Wessex HAS3	RNAY Fleetlands Fire Section	
XM926	WS58 Wessex HAS1	MoD(PE) RAE Farnborough	
XM927	WS58 Wessex HAS3 (8814M) [660/PO]	RAF Shawbury, BDRT	
XM969	BAC Lightning T4 (8592M)	RAF Binbrook Fire Section	
XM987	BAC Lightning T4	RAF Coningsby, BDRT	
XM997	BAC Lightning T4	RAF FF&SS, Catterick	
XN126	WS55 Whirlwind HAR10 (8655M) [S]	RAF No 1 SoTT, Halton	
XN132	Sud Alouette AH2	AAC UNFICYP, Nicosia	
XN137	Hunting Jet Provost T3 [95] (nose only)	RAF Exhibition Flight, Abingdon	
XN185	Slingsby Sedbergh TX1	RAF Syerston, preserved	
XN239	Slingsby Cadet TX3 [G] (8889M)	Imperial War Museum, Duxford	
XN258	WS55 Whirlwind HAR9 [589/CU]	Cornwall Aero Park, Helston	
XN263	WS55 Whirlwind HAS7	Royal Military College of Science, stored, Shrivenham	
XN264	WS55 Whirlwind HAS7 [53]	Burned at Grovesend, Avon	
XN297	WS55 Whirlwind HAR9 (really XN311/A2643)	RNAS Lee-on-Solent Fire Section	
XN298	WS55 Whirlwind HAR9 [810/LS]	Privately owned, Stoke-on-Trent	
XN299	WS55 Whirlwind HAS7 [758]	Torbay Aircraft Museum, Paignton	
XN302	WS55 Whirlwind HAS7 (A2654) [LS]	RNAS Lee-on-Solent Fire Section	
XN304	WS55 Whirlwind HAS7 [64]	Norfolk & Suffolk Aviation Museum, Flixton	
XN306	WS55 Whirlwind HAR9 [434/ED]	RNAS Portland Fire Section	
XN308	WS55 Whirlwind HAS7 (A2605) [510/PO]	RNAS Yeovilton Fire Section	
XN309	WS55 Whirlwind HAR9 (A2663) [590/CU]	Second World War Aircraft Preservation Society, Lasham	
XN314	WS55 Whirlwind HAS7 (A2614)	RN Predannack Fire School	
XN332	Saro P531 (G-APNV/A2579) [759]	FAA Museum, on loan BRM, Weston-super-Mare	
XN334	Saro P531 (A2525)	British Rotorcraft Museum, under restoration, Crawley	
XN341	Saro Skeeter AOP12 (8022M)	RAF St Athan Historic Aircraft Collection	
XN344	Saro Skeeter AOP12 (8018M)	Science Museum, South Kensington	
XN351	Saro Skeeter AOP12 (G-BKSC)	Privately owned, Shempston	
XN359	WS55 Whirlwind HAR9 (A2712) [434/ED]	RNAS Lee-on-Solent, BDRT	

Notes	Serial	Type (alternative identity)	Owner, Operator or Location
	XN380	WS55 Whirlwind HAS7 [67]	Lashenden Air Warfare Museum, Headcorn
	XN382	WS55 Whirlwind HAS7 [17]	Privately owned
	XN385	WS55 Whirlwind HAS7	RN Historic Flight, stored Wroughton
	XN386	WS55 Whirlwind HAR9 [435/ED] (A2713)	Privately owned, Blackpool Airport
	XN387	WS55 Whirlwind HAR9 (8564M)	RAF Odiham, BDRT
	XN412	Auster AOP9	Cotswold Aircraft Restoration Group, RAF Innsworth
	XN435	Auster AOP9 (G-BGBU)	Privately owned, Egham
	XN437	Auster AOP9 (G-AXWA)	Privately owned, Welling, Kent
	XN441	Auster AOP9 (G-BGKT)	Privately owned, Reymerston Hall
	XN453	DH Comet 2e	RAE Farnborough Fire Section
	XN458	Hunting Jet Provost T3 [19] (8234M)	RAF CTTS, St Athan
	XN459	Hunting Jet Provost T3A [20]	RAF No 1 FTS, Linton-on-Ouse
	XN461	Hunting Jet Provost T3A [28]	RAF No 1 FTS, Linton-on-Ouse
	XN462	Hunting Jet Provost T3A [87]	RAF No 7 FTS, Church Fenton
	XN466	Hunting Jet Provost T3A [29]	RAF No 1 FTS, Linton-on-Ouse
	XN467	Hunting Jet Provost T4 (8559M) [F]	RAF No 1 SoTT, Halton
	XN470	Hunting Jet Provost T3A [84]	RAF No 7 FTS, Church Fenton
	XN471	Hunting Jet Provost T3A [24]	RAF No 1 FTS, Linton-on-Ouse
	XN472	Hunting Jet Provost T3A [86]	RAF No 7 FTS, Church Fenton
	XN473	Hunting Jet Provost T3A (8862M) [98]	RAF Church Fenton Fire Section
	XN492	Hunting Jet Provost T3 [X] (8079M)	RAF No 2 SoTT, Cosford
	XN493	Hunting Jet Provost T3 (nose only)	RAF Exhibition Flight, Abingdon
	XN494	Hunting Jet Provost T3A [43]	RAF No 1 FTS, Linton-on-Ouse
	XN495	Hunting Jet Provost T3A [102] (8786M)	RAF Abingdon, BDRF
	XN497	Hunting Jet Provost T3A [52]	RAF No 1 FTS, Linton-on-Ouse
	XN498	Hunting Jet Provost T3A [16]	RAF No 1 FTS, Linton-on-Ouse
	XN499	Hunting Jet Provost T3A [L]	RAF CFS, Scampton
	XN500	Hunting Jet Provost T3A [80]	RAF No 7 FTS, Church Fenton
	XN501	Hunting Jet Provost T3A [S]	RAF CFS, Scampton
	XN502	Hunting Jet Provost T3A [D]	RAF CFS, Scampton
	XN503	Hunting Jet Provost T3 (nose only)	RAF Exhibition Flight, Abingdon
	XN505	Hunting Jet Provost T3A [25]	RAF No 1 FTS, Linton-on-Ouse
	XN506	Hunting Jet Provost T3A [19]	RAF No 1 FTS, Linton-on-Ouse
	XN508	Hunting Jet Provost T3A [98]	RAF No 7 FTS, Church Fenton
	XN509	Hunting Jet Provost T3A [50]	RAF No 1 FTS, Linton-on-Ouse
	XN510	Hunting Jet Provost T3A [40]	RAF No 1 FTS, Linton-on-Ouse
	XN511	Hunting Jet Provost T3 [21] (nose only)	No 177 Sqn ATC, Blackpool Airport
	XN512	Hunting Jet Provost T3 (8435M)	RAF No 1 SoTT, Halton
	XN547	Hunting Jet Provost T3A [48]	RAF No 1 FTS, Linton-on-Ouse
	XN548	Hunting Jet Provost T3A [103]	RAF No 7 FTS, Church Fenton
	XN549	Hunting Jet Provost T3 (8235M) [R]	RAF No 1 SoTT, Halton
	XN551	Hunting Jet Provost T3A [100]	RAF No 7 FTS, Church Fenton
	XN552	Hunting Jet Provost T3A [32]	RAF No 1 FTS, Linton-on-Ouse
	XN553	Hunting Jet Provost T3A	RAF St Athan Station Flight
	XN554	Hunting Jet Provost T3 (8436M) [K]	RAF No 1 SoTT, Halton
	XN574	Hunting Jet Provost T3A [92]	RAF No 7 FTS, Church Fenton
	XN577	Hunting Jet Provost T3A [83]	RAF No 7 FTS, Church Fenton
	XN579	Hunting Jet Provost T3A [14]	RAF No 1 FTS, Linton-on-Ouse
	XN581	Hunting Jet Provost T3A [C]	RAF CFS, Scampton
	XN582	Hunting Jet Provost T3A [95]	RAF No 7 FTS, Church Fenton
	XN584	Hunting Jet Provost T3A [E]	RAF CFS, Scampton
	XN585	Hunting Jet Provost T3A [12]	RAF Linton-on-Ouse Fire Section
	XN586	Hunting Jet Provost T3A [91]	RAF No 7 FTS, Church Fenton
	XN589	Hunting Jet Provost T3A [46]	RAF No 1 FTS, Linton-on-Ouse
	XN592	Hunting Jet Provost T3 (nose only)	No 1105 Sqn ATC, Winchester
	XN593	Hunting Jet Provost T3A [97]	RAF No 7 FTS, Church Fenton
	XN594	Hunting Jet Provost T3 [W] (8077M)	RAF No 2 SoTT, Cosford

Serial	Type (alternative identity)	Owner, Operator or Location	Notes
XN595	Hunting Jet Provost T3A [82]	RAF No 7 FTS, Church Fenton	
XN597	Hunting Jet Provost T3 (7984M) [11] (nose only)	Scrapped 1987	
XN602	Hunting Jet Provost T3 (8088M)	CTE, RAF Manston	
XN605	Hunting Jet Provost T3A [J]	RAF CFS, Scampton	
XN606	Hunting Jet Provost T3A [36]	RAF No 1 FTS, Linton-on-Ouse	
XN629	Hunting Jet Provost T3A [39]	RAF No 1 FTS, Linton-on-Ouse	
XN632	Hunting Jet Provost T3 (8352M)	RAF St Athan, CTTS	
XN634	Hunting Jet Provost T3A [94]	RAF No 7 FTS, Church Fenton	
XN635	Hunting Jet Provost T3 (nose only)	RN Predannack Fire School	
XN636	Hunting Jet Provost T3A [15]	RAF No 1 FTS, Linton-on-Ouse	
XN637	Hunting Jet Provost T3 (G-BKOU)	Vintage Aircraft Team, Cranfield	
XN640	Hunting Jet Provost T3A [99]	RAF No 7 FTS, Church Fenton	
XN641	Hunting Jet Provost T3A (8865M) [47]	RAF Newton Fire Section	
XN643	Hunting Jet Provost T3A (8704M) [26]	RAF Abingdon, BDRF	
XN647	DH Sea Vixen FAW2 (A2610)	Cornwall Aero Park, Helston	
XN649	DH Sea Vixen FAW2 [126]	MoD(PE), stored RAE Farnborough	
XN650	DH Sea Vixen FAW2 (A2612/A2620/A2639) [VL]	Wales Aircraft Museum, Cardiff	
XN651	DH Sea Vixen FAW2 (A2616) (nose only)	Privately owned, Pucklechurch, Avon	
XN657	DH Sea Vixen D3 [TR-1]	MoD(PE) RAE Llanbedr Fire Section	
XN685	DH Sea Vixen FAW2 (8173M) [P] [-/VL]	BAe Hawarden Apprentice School	
XN688	DH Sea Vixen FAW2 (8141M)	RAE Farnborough Fire Section	
XN691	DH Sea Vixen FAW2 [N] [H] (8143M)	RAF No 2 SoTT, Cosford	
XN692	DH Sea Vixen FAW2 (A2624) [SAH-17] [254/H]	RNAS Yeovilton for display	
XN694	DH Sea Vixen FAW2	Flight Refuelling Ltd, Hurn	
XN696	DH Sea Vixen FAW2 [751]	Privately owned, Suffolk	
XN699	DH Sea Vixen FAW2 [752] (8224M)	RAF North Luffenham	
XN714	Hunting H126	RAF Cosford Aerospace Museum	
XN724	BAC Lightning F2A [F] (8513M)	Privately owned, Newcastle-on-Tyne	
XN728	BAC Lightning F2A (8546M) [V]	Privately owned, Balderton, Notts	
XN734	BAC Lightning F2/3A (8346M/G-27-239/G-BNCA)	Privately owned, North Weald	
XN769	BAC Lightning F2 (8402M) [Z]	London ATCC, West Drayton	
XN774	BAC Lightning F2A (8551M) [F]	RAF Coningsby, BDRT	
XN776	BAC Lightning F2A [B] (8535M)	Royal Scottish Museum of Flight, East Fortune	
XN781	BAC Lightning F2A (8538M) [B]	RAF Leuchars Fire Section	
XN816	AW Argosy E1 (8489M) [G]	RAF No 2 SoTT, Cosford	
XN817	AW Argosy C1	MoD(PE) RAE West Freugh Fire Section	
XN819	AW Argosy C1 (8205M) (nose only)	Newark Air Museum, Winthorpe	
XN855	AW Argosy E1 (8556M)	CTE, RAF Manston	
XN923	HS Buccaneer S1	MoD(PE) A&AEE Boscombe Down	
XN925	HS Buccaneer S1 (8087M/A2602)	RAF FF&SS, Catterick	
XN928	HS Buccaneer S1 (8179M)	Wales Aircraft Museum, Cardiff	
XN929	HS Buccaneer S1 (8051M) (nose only)	RAF Lossiemouth procedures trainer	
XN930	HS Buccaneer S1 (8180M) [632/LM]	RAF Honington, BDRT	
XN934	HS Buccaneer S1 (A2600) [631/LS]	RN Predannack Fire School	
XN953	HS Buccaneer S1 (A2655/8182M)	RNAS Culdrose Fire Section	
XN957	HS Buccaneer S1 [630/LM]	FAA Museum, RNAS Yeovilton	
XN964	HS Buccaneer S1 [613/LM]	Phoenix Aviation Museum, Bruntingthorpe	
XN967	HS Buccaneer S1 (A2627) [103/E]	Cornwall Aero Park, Helston	

Notes	Serial	Type (alternative identity)	Owner, Operator or Location
	XN972	HS Buccaneer S1 (8183M) (nose only) (really XN962)	RAF Exhibition Flight, Abingdon
	XN973	HS Buccaneer S1 (nose only) [633]	BAe Warton Fire Section
	XN974	HS Buccaneer S2A	MoD(PE) BAe Warton
	XN976	HS Buccaneer S2B	RAF No 12 Sqn, Lossiemouth
	XN977	HS Buccaneer S2B [G]	RAF, stored Shawbury
	XN979	HS Buccaneer S2 (nose only)	Cranfield Institute of Technology
	XN981	HS Buccaneer S2B [981]	RAF No 12 Sqn, Lossiemouth
	XN982	HS Buccaneer S2A	MoD(PE) BAe Brough
	XN983	HS Buccaneer S2B	RAF No 237 OCU, Lossiemouth
	XP107	WS58 Wessex HAS1 (A2527)	RN Predannack Fire School
	XP110	WS58 Wessex HAS3 [55/FL]	RNAY Fleetlands Apprentice School
	XP116	WS58 Wessex HAS3 (A2618) [520]	RN AES, Lee-on-Solent
	XP117	WS58 Wessex HAS1 (A2681)	Scrapped at Culdrose
	XP137	WS58 Wessex HAS3 [665/PO]	RN AES, Lee-on-Solent
	XP139	WS58 Wessex HAS3	Burned at RN Predannack
	XP140	WS58 Wessex HAS3 (8806M) [653/PO]	RAF Chilmark, BDRT
	XP142	WS58 Wessex HAS3	FAA Museum, RNAS Yeovilton
	XP149	WS58 Wessex HAS1 (A2669) [574/CU]	RN Predannack Fire School
	XP150	WS58 Wessex HAS3 [406/AN]	RN AES, Lee-on-Solent
	XP151	WS58 Wessex HAS1 (A2684) [047/R]	RN AES, Lee-on-Solent
	XP155	WS58 Wessex HAS1 (A2640)	RNAS Culdrose Fire Section
	XP157	WS58 Wessex HAS1 (A2680)	RN AES, Lee-on-Solent
	XP158	WS58 Wessex HAS1 (A2688) [522/CU]	RN NACDS, Culdrose
	XP159	WS58 Wessex HAS1 (8877M) [047/R]	RAF Odiham, BDRT
	XP160	WS58 Wessex HAS1 (A2650) [521/CU]	RN NACDS, Culdrose
	XP165	WS Scout AH1	British Rotorcraft Museum, Weston-super-Mare
	XP166	WS Scout AH1 (G-APVL)	MoD(PE) RAE Farnborough, in store
	XP167	WS Scout AH1	RAE Farnborough Fire Section
	XP190	WS Scout AH1	AAC, stored Wroughton
	XP191	WS Scout AH1	AAC Middle Wallop, BDRT
	XP226	Fairey Gannet AEW3 (A2667) [073/E]	Newark Air Museum, Winthorpe
	XP241	Auster AOP9	Tagmore Nurseries, Rabley Heath, Herts
	XP242	Auster AOP9	Museum of Army Flying, stored Middle Wallop
	XP244	Auster AOP9 (7864M) [M7922]	Army Apprentice College, Arborfield
	XP248	Auster AOP9 (7822M)	Vintage Aircraft Team, Cranfield
	XP279	Auster AOP9 (G-BWKK)	Privately owned, Shoreham
	XP280	Auster AOP9	Leicester Museum of Technology store
	XP281	Auster AOP9	Imperial War Museum, Duxford
	XP282	Auster AOP9 (G-BGTC)	Privately owned, Swanton Morley
	XP283	Auster AOP9 (7859M)	Vintage Aircraft Team, Cranfield
	XP299	WS55 Whirlwind HAR10 (8726M)	RAF Cosford Aerospace Museum
	XP328	WS55 Whirlwind HAR10 (G-BKHC)	Privately owned, Whatfield
	XP329	WS55 Whirlwind HAR10 [V] (8791M) [UN]	Privately owned, Tattershall Thorpe
	XP330	WS55 Whirlwind HAR10	CAA Fire School, Teesside Airport
	XP333	WS55 Whirlwind HAR10 (8650M) [G]	CTE, RAF Manston
	XP338	WS55 Whirlwind HAR10 (8647M) [N]	RAF No 2 SoTT, Cosford
	XP339	WS55 Whirlwind HAR10	To West German AF Museum
	XP344	WS55 Whirlwind HAR10 (8764M) [X]	RAFC Cranwell, Engineering Wing
	XP345	WS55 Whirlwind HAR10 [N] (8792M)	Privately owned, Tattershall Thorpe

Serial	Type (alternative identity)	Owner, Operator or Location	Notes
XP346	WS55 Whirlwind HAR10 (8793M)	Privately owned, Tattershall Thorpe	
XP350	WS55 Whirlwind HAR10	Cornwall Aero Park, Helston	
XP351	WS55 Whirlwind HAR10 (8672M) [Z]	RAF Shawbury, BDRT	
XP352	WS55 Whirlwind HAR10 (8701M)	RAF Abingdon, BDRF	
XP354	WS55 Whirlwind HAR10 (8721M)	RAF No 1 SoTT, Halton	
XP355	WS55 Whirlwind HAR10 (8463M/G-BEBC) [A]	City of Norwich Aviation Museum	
XP356	WS55 Whirlwind HAR10	RAE Farnborough Fire Section	
XP357	WS55 Whirlwind HAR10 (8499M)	CTE, RAF Manston	
XP359	WS55 Whirlwind HAR10 (8447M)	RAF Exhibition Flight, Abingdon	
XP360	WS55 Whirlwind HAR10 [V]	Second World War Aircraft Preservation Society, Lasham	
XP361	WS55 Whirlwind HAR10 (8731M)	RAF Valley, preserved at gate	
XP393	WS55 Whirlwind HAR10 [U]	RAE Farnborough Fire Section	
XP394	WS55 Whirlwind HAR10 [C]	CTE, RAF Manston	
XP395	WS55 Whirlwind HAR10 (8674M) [A]	Privately owned, Tattershall Thorpe	
XP398	WS55 Whirlwind HAR10 (8794M)	Privately owned, Bitteswell	
XP399	WS55 Whirlwind HAR10	Privately owned, Tor View Garage, Glastonbury, Som	
XP400	WS55 Whirlwind HAR10 (8444M) [N]	CTE, RAF Manston	
XP404	WS55 Whirlwind HAR10 (8682M)	RAF SAREW, Finningley	
XP405	WS55 Whirlwind HAR10 (8656M) [Y]	RAF No 1 SoTT, Halton	
XP411	AW Argosy C1 (8442M) [C]	RAF Cosford Aerospace Museum	
XP439	AW Argosy E1 (8558M)	RAF Lossiemouth Fire Section	
XP442	AW Argosy T2 (8454M) [442]	RAF No 1 SoTT, Halton	
XP444	AW Argosy C1 (8455M) [D]	RAF No 2 SoTT, Cosford	
XP454	Slingsby Grasshopper TX1	Kimbolton School CCF, Cambs	
XP459	Slingsby Grasshopper TX1	RAF No 1 MGSP, Halton	
XP462	Slingsby Grasshopper TX1	RAF No 1 MGSP, Halton	
XP463	Slingsby Grasshopper TX1	RAF No 1 MGSP, Halton	
XP464	Slingsby Grasshopper TX1	Sherborne School CCF, Dorset	
XP487	Slingsby Grasshopper TX1	Sold 26 June 1987	
XP490	Slingsby Grasshopper TX1	RAF ACCGS, Syerston	
XP492	Slingsby Grasshopper TX1	King's College CCF, Taunton	
XP493	Slingsby Grasshopper TX1	Sold 26 June 1987	
XP494	Slingsby Grasshopper TX1	Stamford School, Lincs	
XP502	HS Gnat T1 (8576M) [02]	RAF St Athan, CTTS	
XP503	HS Gnat T1 (8568M) [73]	RAF No 1 SoTT, Halton	
XP504	HS Gnat T1 (8618M) [68] [04]	RAF No 1 SoTT, Halton	
XP505	HS Gnat T1 [05]	Science Museum, South Kensington	
XP511	HS Gnat T1 (8619M) [65]	RAF No 1 SoTT, Halton	
XP514	HS Gnat T1 (8635M)	RAF No 2 SoTT, Cosford	
XP515	HS Gnat T1 (8614M) [59]	To Otterburn ranges	
XP516	HS Gnat T1 (8580M) [16]	MoD(PE) RAE Farnborough	
XP530	HS Gnat T1 (8606M) [60]	RAF No 1 SoTT, Halton	
XP532	HS Gnat T1 (8577M/8615M) [32]	MoD(PE) RAE Farnborough	
XP533	HS Gnat T1 (8632M)	RAF No 2 SoTT, Cosford	
XP534	HS Gnat T1 (8620M) [64]	RAF No 1 SoTT, Halton	
XP535	HS Gnat T1 (A2679) [SAH-1]		
XP538	HS Gnat T1 (8607M) [61]	RAF No 2 SoTT, Cosford	
XP540	HS Gnat T1 (8608M) [62]	RAF No 1 SoTT, Halton	
XP541	HS Gnat T1 (8616M) [41]	RAF	
XP542	HS Gnat T1 (8575M) [42]	RAF St Athan, CTTS	
XP547	Hunting Jet Provost T4	RAF No 1 TWU, Brawdy	
XP556	Hunting Jet Provost T4 [B]	RAF CATCS, Shawbury	
XP557	Hunting Jet Provost T4 (8494M)	RAF No 1 SoTT, Halton	
XP558	Hunting Jet Provost T4 (8627M/A2628) [20]	RAF St Athan, CTTS	
XP563	Hunting Jet Provost T4 [C]	RAF CATCS, Shawbury	
XP567	Hunting Jet Provost T4 (8510M) [23]	RAF No 1 SoTT, Halton	

Notes	Serial	Type (alternative identity)	Owner, Operator or Location
	XP573	Hunting Jet Provost T4 (8236M) [19]	RAF No 1 SoTT, Halton
	XP585	Hunting Jet Provost T4 (8407M) [24]	RAF No 1 SoTT, Halton
	XP627	Hunting Jet Provost T4	North East Aircraft Museum, Usworth
	XP629	Hunting Jet Provost T4 [P]	RAF CATCS, Shawbury
	XP638	Hunting Jet Provost T4 [A]	RAF CATCS, Shawbury
	XP640	Hunting Jet Provost T4 (8501M) [E]	RAF No 1 SoTT, Halton
	XP672	Hunting Jet Provost T4 (8458M) [27]	RAF No 1 SoTT, Halton
	XP677	Hunting Jet Provost T4 (8587M) (nose only)	No 2530 Sqn ATC, Headley Court, Uckfield, East Sussex
	XP680	Hunting Jet Provost T4 (8460M)	RAF St Athan, CTTS
	XP686	Hunting Jet Provost T4 (8401M/8502M) [G]	RAF No 1 SoTT, Halton
	XP688	Hunting Jet Provost T4 [E]	RAF CATCS, Shawbury
	XP693	BAC Lightning F6	MoD(PE) BAe Warton
	XP694	BAC Lightning F3	RAF, stored Binbrook
	XP695	BAC Lightning F3 (8808M) [6]	Scrapped at RAF Binbrook
	XP701	BAC Lightning F3 (8924M)	RAF Binbrook decoy
	XP702	BAC Lightning F3	RAF, stored Binbrook
	XP706	BAC Lightning F3 (8925M)	RAF Binbrook decoy
	XP707	BAC Lightning F3 [DB]	RAF Binbrook
	XP741	BAC Lightning F3 [AR]	CTE, RAF Manston
	XP745	BAC Lightning F3 (8453M) [H]	RAF Boulmer, at main gate
	XP748	BAC Lightning F3 (8446M)	RAF Binbrook, at main gate
	XP749	BAC Lightning F3 [DA] (8926M)	RAF Binbrook decoy
	XP750	BAC Lightning F3 (8927M)	RAF Binbrook decoy
	XP751	BAC Lightning F3 (8928M)	RAF Binbrook decoy
	XP761	BAC Lightning F3 (8438M) [N]	RAF Binbrook Fire Section
	XP764	BAC Lightning F3 [DC] (8929M)	RAF Binbrook decoy
	XP769	DHC Beaver AL1	AAC, Aldergrove
	XP771	DHC Beaver AL1	AAC, Aldergrove
	XP772	DHC Beaver AL1	Museum of Army Transport, Beverley
	XP774	DHC Beaver AL1	To USA as N9067F
	XP775	DHC Beaver AL1	AAC, stored Shawbury
	XP778	DHC Beaver AL1	AAC Beaver Training Flt, Middle Wallop
	XP779	DHC Beaver AL1	AAC, stored Shawbury
	XP780	DHC Beaver AL1	To USA as N9063G
	XP804	DHC Beaver AL1	
	XP806	DHC Beaver AL1	AAC, stored Shawbury
	XP808	DHC Beaver AL1	To USA as N9066P
	XP810	DHC Beaver AL1	AAC, stored Shawbury
	XP814	DHC Beaver AL1	AAC, stored Shawbury
	XP816	DHC Beaver AL1	To USA as N9063V
	XP817	DHC Beaver AL1	To USA as N9063Q
	XP818	DHC Beaver AL1	To USA as N1215
	XP820	DHC Beaver AL1	AAC Beaver Training Flt, Middle Wallop
	XP821	DHC Beaver AL1 [MCO]	Museum of Army Flying, Middle Wallop
	XP822	DHC Beaver AL1	Museum of Army Flying, Middle Wallop
	XP823	DHC Beaver AL1	
	XP825	DHC Beaver AL1	AAC, Aldergrove
	XP827	DHC Beaver AL1	AAC, stored Shawbury
	XP831	Hawker P1127 (8406M)	RAF Museum, Hendon
	XP841	Handley Page HP115	FAA Museum, RNAS Yeovilton
	XP846	WS Scout AH1 [B]	AAC, stored Wroughton
	XP847	WS Scout AH1	Museum of Army Flying, Middle Wallop
	XP848	WS Scout AH1	AAC AETW, Middle Wallop
	XP849	WS Scout AH1	MoD(PE) ETPS Boscombe Down
	XP850	WS Scout AH1	AAC, stored Wroughton
	XP852	WS Scout AH1	AAC, stored Wroughton
	XP853	WS Scout AH1	AAC AETW, Middle Wallop
	XP854	WS Scout AH1 (7898M/ TAD043)	AAC AETW, Middle Wallop
	XP855	WS Scout AH1	AAC, stored Wroughton
	XP856	WS Scout AH1	AAC AETW, Middle Wallop
	XP857	WS Scout AH1	Museum of Army Flying store, Middle Wallop
	XP883	WS Scout AH1	AAC, stored Wroughton
	XP884	WS Scout AH1	AAC AETW, Middle Wallop

Serial	Type (alternative identity)	Owner, Operator or Location	Notes
XP885	WS Scout AH1 [Y]	AAC No 666 (TA) Sqn, Netheravon	
XP886	WS Scout AH1	Army Apprentice College, Arborfield	
XP887	WS Scout AH1 [C]	AAC No 660 Sqn, Sek Kong	
XP888	WS Scout AH1	AAC AETW, Middle Wallop	
XP890	WS Scout AH1 [G]	AAC, stored Wroughton	
XP891	WS Scout AH1 [S]	AAC No 666 (TA) Sqn, Netheravon	
XP893	WS Scout AH1	AAC Garrison Air Sqn, Falklands	
XP894	WS Scout AH1 [D]	AAC No 660 Sqn, Sek Kong	
XP897	WS Scout AH1	AAC, stored Wroughton	
XP898	WS Scout AH1	AAC, stored Wroughton	
XP899	WS Scout AH1 [D]	Army Apprentice College, Arborfield	
XP900	WS Scout AH1 [Z]	AAC, stored Wroughton	
XP901	WS Scout AH1 [E]	AAC No 660 Sqn, Sek Kong	
XP902	WS Scout AH1	AAC Garrison Air Sqn, Falklands	
XP903	WS Scout AH1	AAC, stored Wroughton	
XP905	WS Scout AH1	AAC AETW, Middle Wallop	
XP907	WS Scout AH1	Composite with XR630	
XP909	WS Scout AH1	AAC AETW, Middle Wallop	
XP910	WS Scout AH1	AAC, stored Wroughton	
XP915	DH Comet 3B (G-ANLO)	BAe Woodford Fire Section	
XP919	DH Sea Vixen FAW2 (8163M) [706/VL]	City of Norwich Aviation Museum	
XP921	DH Sea Vixen FAW2 (8226M)	RAF Credenhill on display	
XP924	DH Sea Vixen D3	MoD(PE) RAE Llanbedr	
XP967	Sud Alouette AH2	AAC No 16 Flt, Dhekelia	
XP976	Hawker Kestrel FGA1	Scrapped, remains at Faygate	
XP980	Hawker Kestrel FGA1 (A2700)	RNAS Culdrose, SAH	
XP984	Hawker Kestrel FGA1 (A2658)	RNEC Manadon, for instruction	
XR107	AW Argosy T2 (8441M)	RAF No 2 SoTT, Cosford	
XR137	AW Argosy E1	Snowdon Mountain Aviation Collection, Caernarfon	
XR140	AW Argosy E1 (8579M) [56]	RAF No 1 SoTT, Halton	
XR220	BAC TSR2 (7933M)	RAF Cosford Aerospace Museum	
XR222	BAC TSR2	Imperial War Museum, Duxford	
XR232	Sud Alouette AH2 (F-WEIP)	AAC UNFICYP, Nicosia	
XR240	Auster AOP9 (G-BDFH)	Privately owned, Booker	
XR241	Auster AOP9 (G-AXRR)	Privately owned, Duxford	
XR243	Auster AOP9 (8057M)	RAF St Athan Historic Aircraft Collection	
XR244	Auster AOP9	AAC Historic Aircraft Flight, Middle Wallop	
XR246	Auster AOP9 (7862M/ G-AZBU)	Privately owned, Reymerston Hall	
XR267	Auster AOP9 (G-BJXR)	Cotswold Aircraft Restoration Group, RAF Innsworth	
XR269	Auster AOP9 (G-BDXY)	Privately owned, Eaglescott, Devon	
XR271	Auster AOP9	Museum of Artillery, Woolwich	
XR363	SC5 Belfast C1 (G-OHCA)	Privately owned, Southend	
XR371	SC5 Belfast C1	RAF Cosford Aerospace Museum	
XR376	Sud Alouette AH2	AAC UNFICYP, Nicosia	
XR378	Sud Alouette AH2	AAC No 16 Flt, Dhekelia	
XR379	Sud Alouette AH2	AAC No 16 Flt, Dhekelia	
XR382	Sud Alouette AH2	AAC UNFICYP, Nicosia	
XR385	Sud Alouette AH2	AAC No 16 Flt, Dhekelia	
XR386	Sud Alouette AH2	AAC UNFICYP, Nicosia	
XR396	DH Comet 4C (8882M) (G-BDIU)	RAF Kinloss BDRT	
XR436	Saro Scout AH1	AAC Middle Wallop, BDRT	
XR441	DH Sea Heron C1 (G-AORG)	RNAS Yeovilton, Station Flight	
XR442	DH Sea Heron C1 (G-AORH)	RN NATIU, Lee-on-Solent	
XR443	DH Sea Heron C1 (G-ARKU)	RN FONAC, Yeovilton	
XR445	DH Sea Heron C1 (G-ARKW)	RNAS Yeovilton, Station Flight	
XR453	WS55 Whirlwind HAR10 (8873M) [A]	RAF Odiham, on display	
XR458	WS55 Whirlwind HAR10 (8662M) [H]	RAF No 1 SoTT, Halton	
XR478	WS55 Whirlwind HAR10 [P]	Defence School, Winterbourne Gunner	
XR479	WS55 Whirlwind HAR10 [A]	RAE Farnborough Fire Section	
XR481	WS55 Whirlwind HAR10	RAF, stored Wroughton	
XR482	WS55 Whirlwind HAR10 [G]	Defence School, Winterbourne Gunner	
XR483	WS55 Whirlwind HAR10	RAF, stored Wroughton	
XR485	WS55 Whirlwind HAR10 [Q]	Norfolk & Suffolk Aviation Museum, Flixton	
XR486	WS55 Whirlwind HCC12 (8727M)	RAF St Athan Historic Aircraft Collection	

Notes	Serial	Type (alternative identity)	Owner, Operator or Location
	XR493	Saro Scout AH1 (G-APVM/8040M)	MoD(PE) RAE Farnborough
	XR497	WS58 Wessex HC2	RAF No 22 Sqn SAR*
	XR498	WS58 Wessex HC2 [X]	RAF No 72 Sqn, Aldergrove
	XR499	WS58 Wessex HC2 [W]	RAF No 72 Sqn, Aldergrove
	XR501	WS58 Wessex HC2	RAF No 22 Sqn SAR*
	XR502	WS58 Wessex HC2 [Z]	RAF No 72 Sqn, Aldergrove
	XR503	WS58 Wessex HC2	MoD(PE) RAE Bedford
	XR504	WS58 Wessex HC2	RAF No 22 Sqn SAR*
	XR505	WS58 Wessex HC2 [WA]	RAF No 2 FTS, Shawbury
	XR506	WS58 Wessex HC2 [V]	RAF No 72 Sqn, Aldergrove
	XR507	WS58 Wessex HC2	RAF No 22 Sqn SAR*
	XR508	WS58 Wessex HC2 [D]	RAF No 28 Sqn, Sek Kong
	XR509	WS58 Wessex HC2 (8752M)	RAF WSF, Benson
	XR511	WS58 Wessex HC2 [L]	RAF No 72 Sqn, Aldergrove
	XR515	WS58 Wessex HC2 [B]	RAF No 28 Sqn, Sek Kong
	XR516	WS58 Wessex HC2 [WB]	RAF No 2 FTS, Shawbury
	XR517	WS58 Wessex HC2 [N]	RAF No 72 Sqn, Aldergrove
	XR518	WS58 Wessex HC2	RAF No 22 Sqn SAR*
	XR519	WS58 Wessex HC2 [WC]	RAF No 2 FTS, Shawbury
	XR520	WS58 Wessex HC2	RAF No 22 Sqn SAR*
	XR521	WS58 Wessex HC2 [WD]	RAF No 2 FTS, Shawbury
	XR522	WS58 Wessex HC2 [I]	RAF No 28 Sqn, Sek Kong
	XR523	WS58 Wessex HC2 [M]	RAF No 72 Sqn, Aldergrove
	XR524	WS58 Wessex HC2	RAF No 22 Sqn SAR*
	XR525	WS58 Wessex HC2 [G]	RAF No 72 Sqn, Aldergrove
	XR526	WS58 Wessex HC2 (8147M)	Westlands, Sherborne
	XR527	WS58 Wessex HC2	RAF Benson
	XR528	WS58 Wessex HC2	RAF Benson
	XR529	WS58 Wessex HC2 [E]	RAF No 72 Sqn, Aldergrove
	XR534	HS Gnat T1 (8578M) [65]	RAF Valley on display
	XR535	HS Gnat T1 (8569M) [05]	Privately owned, Bitteswell
	XR537	HS Gnat T1 (8642M) [T]	RAF No 2 SoTT, Cosford
	XR538	HS Gnat T1 (8621M) [69]	RAF No 1 SoTT, Halton
	XR540	HS Gnat T1 (8636M/A2708)	To Canada February 1987
	XR541	HS Gnat T1 (8602M)	RAF St Athan, CTTS
	XR544	HS Gnat T1	RAE Farnborough Fire Section
	XR569	HS Gnat T1 (8560M) [08]	RAF No 1 SoTT, Halton
	XR571	HS Gnat T1 (8493M) [23]	RAF *Red Arrows* Scampton on display
	XR572	HS Gnat T1 (A2676) [SAH-3]	Privately owned, Leavesden
	XR574	HS Gnat T1 (8631M) [72]	RAF No 1 SoTT, Halton
	XR588	WS58 Wessex HC2	RAF No 22 Sqn SAR*
	XR595	WS Scout AH1 [M]	AAC No 666 (TA) Sqn, Netheravon
	XR597	WS Scout AH1	AAC AETW, Middle Wallop
	XR600	WS Scout AH1 [B]	AAC, stored Wroughton
	XR601	WS Scout AH1	Army Apprentice College, Arborfield
	XR602	WS Scout AH1	AAC, stored Wroughton
	XR603	WS Scout AH1 [A]	AAC, stored Wroughton
	XR604	WS Scout AH1	AAC Middle Wallop, BDRT
	XR627	WS Scout AH1	AAC Garrison Air Sqn, Falklands
	XR629	WS Scout AH1	AAC, stored Wroughton
	XR630	WS Scout AH1 [U] (really XP907)	AAC Middle Wallop, BDRT
	XR632	WS Scout AH1 [Q]	AAC No 666 (TA) Sqn, Netheravon
	XR635	WS Scout AH1	AAC AETW, Middle Wallop
	XR637	WS Scout AH1	AAC, stored Wroughton
	XR639	WS Scout AH1 [X]	AAC, stored Wroughton
	XR643	Hunting Jet Provost T4 (8516M) [26]	RAF No 1 SoTT, Halton
	XR650	Hunting Jet Provost T4 (8459M) [28]	RAF No 1 SoTT, Halton
	XR651	Hunting Jet Provost T4 (8431M) [A]	RAF No 1 SoTT, Halton
	XR653	Hunting Jet Provost T4 [H]	RAF CATCS, Shawbury
	XR654	Hunting Jet Provost T4	Lovaux Ltd, Macclesfield
	XR658	Hunting Jet Provost T4 (8192M)	RAF Exhibition Flight, Abingdon
	XR662	Hunting Jet Provost T4 (8410M) [25]	RAF No 1 SoTT, Halton

Note: *The SAR Wing and SAREW are based at RAF Finningley. No 22 Sqn SAR has detached flights: A Flt—RAF Chivenor; B Flt—RAF Leuchars; C Flt and SAFTF—RAF Valley; D Flt—RAF Leconfield; E Flt—RAF Manston.

Serial	Type (alternative identity)	Owner, Operator or Location	Notes
XR669	Hunting Jet Provost T4 (8062M) [02] (nose only)	RAF No 1 SoTT, Halton	
XR670	Hunting Jet Provost T4 (8498M)	RAF No 1 SoTT, Halton	
XR672	Hunting Jet Provost T4 (8495M) [C] [73]	RAF No 1 SoTT, Halton	
XR673	Hunting Jet Provost T4 [L]	RAF CATCS, Shawbury	
XR674	Hunting Jet Provost T4 [D]	RAF CATCS, Shawbury	
XR679	Hunting Jet Provost T4 [04]	RAF No 1 TWU/79 Sqn Brawdy	
XR681	Hunting Jet Provost T4 (8588M) (nose only)	No 1349 Sqn ATC, Odiham	
XR700	Hunting Jet Provost T4 (8589M) (nose only)	RAF Exhibition Flight, Aldergrove	
XR701	Hunting Jet Provost T4 [K]	RAF CATCS, Shawbury	
XR704	Hunting Jet Provost T4 (8506M) [30]	RAF No 1 SoTT, Halton	
XR713	EE Lightning F3 [DC] (8935M)	RAF Leuchars, BDRT	
XR716	EE Lightning F3 [AQ]	RAF Cottesmore Fire Section	
XR717	EE Lightning F3	A&AEE Boscombe Down Fire Section	
XR718	EE Lightning F3 [DA] (8932M)	RAF Wattisham BDRT	
XR720	EE Lightning F3 (8930M)	RAF Binbrook decoy	
XR724	EE Lightning F6 [AE]	RAF No 5 Sqn, Binbrook	
XR725	EE Lightning F6 [BA]	RAF No 11 Sqn, Binbrook	
XR726	EE Lightning F6 [BM]	RAF No 11 Sqn, Binbrook	
XR727	EE Lightning F6 [BH]	RAF No 11 Sqn, Binbrook	
XR728	EE Lightning F6 [JS]	RAF No 11 Sqn, Binbrook	
XR747	EE Lightning F6 [AL]	RAF No 5 Sqn, Binbrook	
XR749	EE Lightning F3 [Q] (8934M)	RAF Leuchars, BDRT	
XR751	EE Lightning F3	RAF, stored Binbrook	
XR752	EE Lightning F6	Scrapped at RAF Binbrook	
XR753	EE Lightning F6 [BP]	RAF No 11 Sqn, Binbrook	
XR754	EE Lightning F6 [BC]	RAF No 11 Sqn, Binbrook	
XR755	EE Lightning F6 [BN]	RAF No 11 Sqn, Binbrook	
XR756	EE Lightning F6	RAF, stored Binbrook	
XR757	EE Lightning F6	RAF No 11 Sqn, Binbrook	
XR758	EE Lightning F6 [AM]	RAF No 5 Sqn, Binbrook	
XR759	EE Lightning F6 [BJ]	RAF No 15 Sqn, Binbrook	
XR763	EE Lightning F6	Crashed Akrotiri 1 July 1987	
XR769	EE Lightning F6 [AM]	RAF No 5 Sqn, Binbrook	
XR770	EE Lightning F6 [AA]	RAF No 5 Sqn, Binbrook	
XR771	EE Lightning F6 [AN]	RAF No 5 Sqn, Binbrook	
XR772	EE Lightning F6	Crashed 6 March 1985	
XR773	EE Lightning F6 [BR]	RAF No 11 Sqn, Binbrook	
XR777	WS Scout AH1 (really XT625)	St George's Barracks, Sutton Coldfield	
XR806	BAC VC10 C1	RAF No 10 Sqn, Brize Norton	
XR807	BAC VC10 C1	RAF No 10 Sqn, Brize Norton	
XR808	BAC VC10 C1	RAF No 10 Sqn, Brize Norton	
XR810	BAC VC10 C1	RAF No 10 Sqn, Brize Norton	
XR944	Wallis WA116 (G-ATTB)	Privately owned, Reymerston Hall	
XR951	HS Gnat T1 (8603M) [26]	RAF	
XR953	HS Gnat T1 (8609M) [63]	RAF No 1 SoTT, Halton	
XR954	HS Gnat T1 (8570M) [30]	Privately owned, Bitteswell	
XR955	HS Gnat T1 (A2678) [SAH-2]		
XR977	HS Gnat T1 (8640M)	RAF Cosford Aerospace Museum	
XR980	HS Gnat T1 (8622M) [70]	RAF No 1 SoTT, Halton	
XR984	HS Gnat T1 (8571M)	RAF No 1 SoTT, Halton	
XR987	HS Gnat T1 (8641M) [10] [S]	RAF No 2 SoTT, Cosford	
XR991	HS Gnat T1 (8637M/ A2709) [SAH-6]		
XR993	HS Gnat T1 (A2677/8878M) [SAH-4]	To Canada February 1987	
XR998	HS Gnat T1 (8623M) [71]	RAF No 1 SoTT, Halton	
XS100	HS Gnat T1 (8561M) [57]	Privately owned, Bitteswell	
XS101	HS Gnat T1 (8638M) (G-GNAT)	Privately owned, Cranfield	
XS102	HS Gnat T1 (8624M) [66]	RAF No 2 SoTT, Cosford	
XS104	HS Gnat T1 (8604M) [44]	RAF No 2 SoTT, Cosford	
XS105	HS Gnat T1 (8625M) [35] [V]	RAF No 2 SoTT, Cosford	
XS107	HS Gnat T1 (8639M) [U]	RAF No 2 SoTT, Cosford	
XS109	HS Gnat T1 (8626M) [75]	RAF No 1 SoTT, Halton	
XS110	HS Gnat T1 (8562M) [20]	RAF No 1 SoTT, Halton	
XS119	WS58 Wessex HAS3 [655]	RN Predannack Fire School	

Notes	Serial	Type (alternative identity)	Owner, Operator or Location
	XS120	WS58 Wessex HAS1 (8653M) [520/CU]	RAF Wroughton Fire Section
	XS122	WS58 Wessex HAS3 (A2707) [655/PO]	RNEC Manadon, for instruction
	XS125	WS58 Wessex HAS1 (A2648) [517/PO]	RN Predannack Fire School
	XS127	WS58 Wessex HAS3	Burned at Predannack
	XS128	WS58 Wessex HAS1 (A2670)	RNAS Yeovilton BDRT
	XS149	WS58 Wessex HAS3 [661/GL]	Plessey Naval Systems, Templecombe
	XS153	WS58 Wessex HAS3 [662/PO]	RNEC Manadon, for instruction
	XS176	Hunting Jet Provost T4 (8514M) [N]	RAF No 1 SoTT, Halton
	XS177	Hunting Jet Provost T4 [N]	RAF CATCS, Shawbury
	XS178	Hunting Jet Provost T4 [05]	RAF No 1 TWU/79 Sqn, Brawdy
	XS179	Hunting Jet Provost T4 (8237M) [20]	RAF No 1 SoTT, Halton
	XS180	Hunting Jet Provost T4 (8238M) [21]	RAF No 1 SoTT, Halton
	XS181	Hunting Jet Provost T4 [F]	RAF CATCS, Shawbury
	XS186	Hunting Jet Provost T4 (8408M) [M]	RAF No 1 SoTT, Halton
	XS209	Hunting Jet Provost T4 (8409M) [29]	RAF No 1 SoTT, Halton
	XS210	Hunting Jet Provost T4 (8239M) [22]	RAF No 1 SoTT, Halton
	XS215	Hunting Jet Provost T4 (8507M) [17]	RAF No 1 SoTT, Halton
	XS216	Hunting Jet Provost T4 [Q]	RAF Finningley, for rescue training
	XS217	Hunting Jet Provost T4 [O]	RAF CATCS, Shawbury
	XS218	Hunting Jet Provost T4 (8508M) [18]	RAF No 1 SoTT, Halton
	XS219	Hunting Jet Provost T4 [06]	RAF No 1 TWU/79 Sqn, Brawdy
	XS230	BAC Jet Provost T5P	MoD(PE) ETPS Boscombe Down
	XS231	BAC Jet Provost T5 (G-ATAJ)	RAF, stored Shawbury
	XS235	HS Comet 4C	MoD(PE) A&AEE Boscombe Down
	XS241	WS58 Wessex HU5	MoD(PE) RAE Farnborough
	XS416	EE Lightning T5 [AZ]	RAF No 5 Sqn, Binbrook
	XS417	EE Lightning T5 [DZ]	RAF, stored Binbrook
	XS418	EE Lightning T5 (8531M) [2]	Scrapped at RAF Binbrook
	XS419	EE Lightning T5 [DV]	RAF Binbrook
	XS420	EE Lightning T5	RAF Binbrook decoy
	XS422	EE Lightning T5	MoD(PE) ETPS Boscombe Down
	XS423	EE Lightning T5 (8532M) [4]	Scrapped at RAF Binbrook
	XS449	EE Lightning T5 (8533M) [5]	Scrapped at RAF Binbrook
	XS450	EE Lightning T5 (8534M) [1]	Scrapped at RAF Binbrook
	XS451	EE Lightning T5 (8503M)	Privately owned, Cranfield
	XS452	EE Lightning T5 [BT]	RAF, stored Binbrook
	XS454	EE Lightning T5 (8535M) [3]	Scrapped at RAF Binbrook
	XS456	EE Lightning T5 [DX]	RAF Binbrook
	XS457	EE Lightning T5 [AT]	RAF, decoy Binbrook
	XS458	EE Lightning T5 [DY]	RAF No 5 Sqn, Binbrook
	XS459	EE Lightning T5 [AW]	RAF, stored Binbrook
	XS463	WS Wasp HAS1 (A2647)	RN Predannack Fire School
	XS463	WS Wasp HAS1 (really XT431)	British Rotorcraft Museum, Weston-super-Mare
	XS479	WS58 Wessex HU5 [XF] (8819M)	RAF Brize Norton Fire Section
	XS481	WS58 Wessex HU5	RN, stored Wroughton
	XS482	WS58 Wessex HU5 [A-D]	RAE Farnborough Apprentice School
	XS483	WS58 Wessex HU5 [T]	RN AES, Lee-on-Solent
	XS484	WS58 Wessex HU5 [821/CU]	RN No 771 Sqn, Culdrose
	XS485	WS58 Wessex HC5C (*Hearts*)	RAF No 84 Sqn, Akrotiri
	XS486	WS58 Wessex HU5 [825/CU]	RN, stored Wroughton
	XS488	WS58 Wessex HU5 [XK]	RN, stored Wroughton
	XS489	WS58 Wessex HU5 [R]	RN, stored Wroughton
	XS491	WS58 Wessex HU5 [XM]	RN, stored Wroughton
	XS492	WS58 Wessex HU5 [623/PO]	RN No 772 Sqn, Portland
	XS493	WS58 Wessex HU5 (*Clubs*)	Department of Naval Recruitment, (846 Sqn), Fleetlands

Serial	Type (alternative identity)	Owner, Operator or Location	Notes
XS496	WS58 Wessex HU5 [625/PO]	RN No 772 Sqn, Portland	
XS498	WS58 Wessex HC5C (*Diamonds*)	RAF No 84 Sqn, Akrotiri	
XS506	WS58 Wessex HU5 [XE]	RN, stored Wroughton	
XS507	WS58 Wessex HU5 [627/PO]	RN No 772 Sqn, Portland	
XS508	WS58 Wessex HU5	RN No 707 Sqn, Yeovilton	
XS509	WS58 Wessex HU5 (A2597)	MoD(PE) ETPS Boscombe Down	
XS510	WS58 Wessex HU5 [626/PO]	RN No 772 Sqn, Portland	
XS511	WS58 Wessex HU5 [M]	RN AES, Lee-on-Solent	
XS513	WS58 Wessex HU5 [419/PO]	RN AES, Lee-on-Solent	
XS514	WS58 Wessex HU5 [L]	RN AES, Lee-on-Solent	
XS515	WS58 Wessex HU5 [N]	RN AES, Lee-on-Solent	
XS516	WS58 Wessex HU5 [Q]	RN AES, Lee-on-Solent	
XS517	WS58 Wessex HC5C (*Spades*)	RAF No 84 Sqn, Akrotiri	
XS518	WS58 Wessex HC5C (*Joker*)	Crashed 4 November 1986 into Mediterranean	
XS520	WS58 Wessex HU5 [F]	RN AES, Lee-on-Solent	
XS521	WS58 Wessex HU5 [YB]	REME Hospital, Kings Heath, Birmingham	
XS522	WS58 Wessex HU5 [ZL]	RN AES, Lee-on-Solent	
XS523	WS58 Wessex HU5 [824/CU]	RN No 771 Sqn, Culdrose	
XS527	WS Wasp HAS1	FAA Museum, RNAS Yeovilton	
XS529	WS Wasp HAS1 [461]	RN AES, Lee-on-Solent	
XS535	WS Wasp HAS1 [500]	RAOC, West Moors, Dorset	
XS537	WS Wasp HAS1 (A2672) [582]	RNAS Portland Fire Section	
XS538	WS Wasp HAS1 [451]	RN Lee-on-Solent, BDRT	
XS539	WS Wasp HAS1 [435/E]	RN AES, Lee-on-Solent	
XS541	WS Wasp HAS1 [602]	RN, stored Wroughton	
XS545	WS Wasp HAS1 (A2702) [635]	RN AES, Lee-on-Solent	
XS562	WS Wasp HAS1 [605]	RN, stored Wroughton	
XS565	WS Wasp HAS1 [445]	MoD(PE) RAE Farnborough	
XS566	WS Wasp HAS1 [607]	RN No 829 Sqn, Portland	
XS567	WS Wasp HAS1 [434/E]	RN AES, Lee-on-Solent	
XS568	WS Wasp HAS1 [441]	RNAY Fleetlands Apprentice School	
XS569	WS Wasp HAS1	RNAY Fleetlands Apprentice School	
XS570	WS Wasp HAS1 (A2699) [P]	RN AES, Lee-on-Solent	
XS572	WS Wasp HAS1 (8845M) [414]	RAF Stafford Fire Section (No 16 MU)	
XS576	DH Sea Vixen FAW2 [125/E]	Imperial War Museum, Duxford	
XS577	DH Sea Vixen D3	MoD(PE) RAE Llanbedr	
XS587	DH Sea Vixen FAW(TT)2 (G-VIXN/8828M)	Privately owned, Hurn	
XS590	DH Sea Vixen FAW2 [131/E]	FAA Museum, RNAS Yeovilton	
XS595	HS Andover C1 [A]	Burned at Brize Norton	
XS596	HS Andover C1	RAF No 115 Sqn, Benson	
XS597	HS Andover C1	RAF No 60 Sqn, Wildenrath	
XS598	HS Andover C1 [E]	RAF AMS, Brize Norton	
XS603	HS Andover E3	RAF No 115 Sqn, Benson	
XS605	HS Andover E3	RAF No 115 Sqn, Benson	
XS606	HS Andover C1	MoD(PE) ETPS Boscombe Down	
XS607	HS Andover C1	MoD(PE) RAE Bedford	
XS610	HS Andover E3	RAF No 115 Sqn, Benson	
XS637	HS Andover C1	RAF No 60 Sqn, Wildenrath	
XS639	HS Andover E3A	RAF No 115 Sqn, Benson	
XS640	HS Andover E3	RAF No 115 Sqn, Benson	
XS641	HS Andover E3A	RAF No 115 Sqn, Benson	
XS642	HS Andover C1 [C] (8785M)	RAF Benson Fire Section	
XS643	HS Andover E3A	RAF No 115 Sqn, Benson	
XS644	HS Andover C1	RAF No 115 Sqn, Benson	
XS646	HS Andover C1	MoD(PE) RAE Farnborough	
XS647	HS Andover C1	BAe Hatfield (ATP mock-up)	
XS650	Slingsby Swallow TX1 (8801M)	RAF St Athan Historic Aircraft Collection	
XS674	WS58 Wessex HC2 [R]	RAF No 72 Sqn, Aldergrove	
XS675	WS58 Wessex HC2	RAF No 22 Sqn SAR*	
XS676	WS58 Wessex HC2 [WJ]	RAF No 2 FTS, Shawbury	
XS677	WS58 Wessex HC2 [WK]	RAF No 2 FTS, Shawbury	
XS679	WS58 Wessex HC2 [WG]	RAF No 2 FTS, Shawbury	

Notes	Serial	Type (alternative identity)	Owner, Operator or Location
	XS695	HS Kestrel FGA1 (A2619) [SAH-6]	RNAS Culdrose, SAH
	XS709	HS Dominie T1 [M]	RAF No 6 FTS, Finningley
	XS710	HS Dominie T1 [O]	RAF No 6 FTS, Finningley
	XS711	HS Dominie T1 [L]	RAF No 6 FTS, Finningley
	XS712	HS Dominie T1 [A]	RAF No 6 FTS, Finningley
	XS713	HS Dominie T1 [C]	RAF No 6 FTS, Finningley
	XS714	HS Dominie T1 [P]	RAF No 6 FTS, Finningley
	XS726	HS Dominie T1 [T]	RAF No 6 FTS, Finningley
	XS727	HS Dominie T1 [D]	RAF No 6 FTS, Finningley
	XS728	HS Dominie T1 [E]	RAF No 6 FTS, Finningley
	XS729	HS Dominie T1 [G]	RAF No 6 FTS, Finningley
	XS730	HS Dominie T1 [H]	RAF No 6 FTS, Finningley
	XS731	HS Dominie T1 [J]	RAF No 6 FTS, Finningley
	XS732	HS Dominie T1 [B]	RAF No 6 FTS, Finningley
	XS733	HS Dominie T1 [Q]	RAF No 6 FTS, Finningley
	XS734	HS Dominie T1 [N]	RAF No 6 FTS, Finningley
	XS735	HS Dominie T1 [R]	RAF No 6 FTS, Finningley
	XS736	HS Dominie T1 [S]	RAF No 6 FTS, Finningley
	XS737	HS Dominie T1 [K]	RAF No 6 FTS, Finningley
	XS738	HS Dominie T1 [U]	RAF No 6 FTS, Finningley
	XS739	HS Dominie T1 [F]	RAF No 6 FTS, Finningley
	XS743	Beagle Basset CC1	MoD(PE) ETPS Boscombe Down
	XS765	Beagle Basset CC1 (G-BSET)	Privately owned, Shoreham
	XS770	Beagle Basset CC1	RAF Cosford Aerospace Museum
	XS789	HS Andover CC2	RAF No 32 Sqn, Northolt
	XS790	HS Andover CC2	RAF Queen's Flight, Benson
	XS791	HS Andover CC2	RAF No 32 Sqn, Northolt
	XS792	HS Andover CC2	RAF No 32 Sqn, Northolt
	XS793	HS Andover CC2	RAF No 60 Sqn, Wildenrath
	XS794	HS Andover CC2	RAF No 32 Sqn, Northolt
	XS862	WS58 Wessex HAS3 [650]	RNAS Lee-on-Solent, at gate
	XS863	WS58 Wessex HAS1	Imperial War Museum, Duxford
	XS865	WS58 Wessex HAS1 (A2694) [529/CU]	RNAS Lee-on-Solent Fire Section
	XS866	WS58 Wessex HAS1 (A2705) [520/CU]	RN AES, Lee-on-Solent
	XS867	WS58 Wessex HAS1 (A2671)	RNAS Lee-on-Solent Fire Section
	XS868	WS58 Wessex HAS1 (A2691)	RNAY Fleetlands, on gate
	XS869	WS58 Wessex HAS1 (A2649) [508/PO]	FAA Air Medical School, Seafield Park, rescue training
	XS870	WS58 Wessex HAS1 (A2697) [-/PO]	RN AES, Lee-on-Solent
	XS871	WS58 Wessex HAS1 (8457M) [AI]	RAF Odiham Fire Section
	XS872	WS58 Wessex HAS1 (A2666) [572/CU]	RNAY Fleetlands Apprentice School
	XS873	WS58 Wessex HAS1 (A2686) [525/CU]	RN Predannack Fire School
	XS876	WS58 Wessex HAS1 (A2695) [523]	RN AES, Lee-on-Solent
	XS877	WS58 Wessex HAS1 (A2687) [516/PO]	RNAS Culdrose, SAH
	XS878	WS58 Wessex HAS1 (A2683)	RN AES, Lee-on-Solent
	XS881	WS58 Wessex HAS1 (A2675) [046/CU]	FAA Museum, stored Yeovilton
	XS882	WS58 Wessex HAS1 (A2696) [524]	RN HMS *Phoenix* Fire School, Portsmouth
	XS885	WS58 Wessex HAS1 (A2668) [512/PO]	RNAS Culdrose, SAH
	XS886	WS58 Wessex HAS1 (A2685) [527/CU]	RN HMS *Gamecock*, Shirley, W. Mids
	XS887	WS58 Wessex HAS1 (A2690) [514/PO]	Cornwall Aero Park, Helston
	XS888	WS58 Wessex HAS1 [521]	RN Exhibition Unit, Fleetlands
	XS895	EE Lightning F6 [AO]	RAF No 5 Sqn, Binbrook
	XS897	EE Lightning F6 [AC]	RAF No 5 Sqn, Binbrook
	XS898	EE Lightning F6 [BD]	RAF No 11 Sqn, Binbrook
	XS899	EE Lightning F6 [AF]	RAF No 5 Sqn, Binbrook

Serial	Type (alternative identity)	Owner, Operator or Location	Notes
XS901	EE Lightning F6 [AH]	RAF No 5 Sqn, Binbrook	
XS903	EE Lightning F6	RAF No 11 Sqn, Binbrook	
XS904	EE Lightning F6 [BQ]	RAF No 11 Sqn, Binbrook	
XS919	EE Lightning F6 [BB]	RAF No 11 Sqn, Binbrook	
XS922	EE Lightning F6 [BJ]	RAF No 11 Sqn, Binbrook	
XS923	EE Lightning F6 [BE]	RAF No 11 Sqn, Binbrook	
XS925	EE Lightning F6 [BD]	RAF, stored Binbrook	
XS927	EE Lightning F6 [BB]	RAF No 11 Sqn, Binbrook	
XS928	EE Lightning F6 [AD]	RAF No 5 Sqn, Binbrook	
XS929	EE Lightning F6 [BG]	RAF No 11 Sqn, Binbrook	
XS932	EE Lightning F6 [AG]	RAF No 5 Sqn, Binbrook	
XS933	EE Lightning F6 [AJ]	RAF No 5 Sqn, Binbrook	
XS935	EE Lightning F6 [AK]	RAF No 5 Sqn, Binbrook	
XS936	EE Lightning F6 [AB]	RAF No 5 Sqn, Binbrook	
XT108	Agusta-Bell Sioux AH1 [U]	Museum of Army Flying, Middle Wallop	
XT131	Agusta-Bell Sioux AH1 [B]	AAC Historic Aircraft Flight, Middle Wallop	
XT133	Agusta-Bell Sioux AH1 (7923M)	Royal Engineers' Museum, Chatham	
XT140	Agusta-Bell Sioux AH1	Air Service Training, Perth	
XT141	Agusta-Bell Sioux AH1 (8509M)	RAF AMS, Brize Norton	
XT148	Agusta-Bell Sioux AH1	Privately owned, Panshanger	
XT150	Agusta-Bell Sioux AH1 (7883M) [R]	Museum of Army Flying, Middle Wallop	
XT151	WS Sioux AH1	Museum of Army Flying store, Middle Wallop	
XT175	WS Sioux AH1 (TAD175)	CSE Oxford for ground instruction	
XT176	WS Sioux AH1 [U]	FAA Museum, RNAS Yeovilton	
XT190	WS Sioux AH1	Museum of Army Flying, Middle Wallop	
XT200	WS Sioux AH1 [F]	Newark Air Museum, Winthorpe	
XT236	WS Sioux AH1 (frame only)	Museum of Army Flying, Middle Wallop	
XT255	WS58 Wessex HAS3 (8751M)	RAF No 14 MU, Carlisle, BDRT	
XT256	WS58 Wessex HAS3 (A2615)	RNAS Lee-on-Solent Fire Section	
XT257	WS58 Wessex HAS3 (8719M)	RAF No 1 SoTT, Halton	
XT270	HS Buccaneer S2B	RAF, stored Shawbury	
XT271	HS Buccaneer S2A	RAF No 237 OCU, Lossiemouth	
XT272	HS Buccaneer S2	MoD(PE) RAE Farnborough	
XT273	HS Buccaneer S2A	RAF No 208 Sqn, Lossiemouth	
XT274	HS Buccaneer S2A (8856M) [E]	RAF Abingdon, BDRF	
XT275	HS Buccaneer S2B [A]	RAF, stored Shawbury	
XT276	HS Buccaneer S2B [S]	RAF, stored Shawbury	
XT277	HS Buccaneer S2A (8853M) [F] [M]	RAF No 2 SoTT, Cosford	
XT279	HS Buccaneer S2B	RAF, BAe Woodford	
XT280	HS Buccaneer S2B [NS]	RAF No 208 Sqn, Lossiemouth	
XT281	HS Buccaneer S2B (8705M) [ET]	RAF Lossiemouth, ground instruction	
XT283	HS Buccaneer S2A [283]	RAF No 237 OCU, Lossiemouth	
XT284	HS Buccaneer S2A (8855M) [H]	RAF Abingdon, BDRF	
XT286	HS Buccaneer S2B	RAF No 208 Sqn, Lossiemouth	
XT287	HS Buccaneer S2B	RAF No 208 Sqn, Lossiemouth	
XT288	HS Buccaneer S2B	RAF No 12 Sqn, Lossiemouth	
XT415	WS Wasp HAS1 [FIR3]	Privately owned, Hurn	
XT416	WS Wasp HAS1	RNAY Fleetlands	
XT420	WS Wasp HAS1 [606]	RN No 829 Sqn, Portland	
XT421	WS Wasp HAS1 [FIR4]	RN, stored Wroughton	
XT422	WS Wasp HAS1 [326]	Privately owned, Burgess Hill	
XT423	WS Wasp HAS1 [434/E]	RN Falklands, ground instruction	
XT426	WS Wasp HAS1 [FIR2]	RN, stored Wroughton	
XT427	WS Wasp HAS1 [606]	Cornwall Aero Park, Helston	
XT429	WS Wasp HAS1 [445/PLY]	RN No 829 Sqn, Portland	
XT430	WS Wasp HAS1 [444]	Defence School, Winterbourne Gunner	
XT432	WS Wasp HAS1 [609]	RN No 829 Sqn, Portland	
XT434	WS Wasp HAS1 [455/AE]	RN No 829 Sqn, Portland	
XT437	WS Wasp HAS1 [FIR1]	RN	
XT439	WS Wasp HAS1 [605]	Cranfield Institute of Technology	
XT441	WS Wasp HAS1 (A2703) [337]	RN Predannack Fire School	

Notes	Serial	Type (alternative identity)	Owner, Operator or Location
	XT443	WS Wasp HAS1 [422/AU]	RN, stored Wroughton
	XT449	WS58 Wessex HU5 [C]	RN AES, Lee-on-Solent
	XT450	WS58 Wessex HU5 [V]	RN Predannack Fire School
	XT451	WS58 Wessex HU5 [XN]	RN, stored Wroughton
	XT453	WS58 Wessex HU5 [A]	RN AES, Lee-on-Solent
	XT455	WS58 Wessex HU5 [U]	RN AES, Lee-on-Solent
	XT456	WS58 Wessex HU5 [XZ]	RN, stored Wroughton
	XT458	WS58 Wessex HU5 [622/PO]	RN No 772 Sqn, Portland
	XT459	WS58 Wessex HU5 [D]	RNAS Lee-on-Solent Fire Section
	XT460	WS58 Wessex HU5 [K]	RN, stored Wroughton
	XT461	WS58 Wessex HU5 [825/CU]	Written off 16 October 1987
	XT463	WS58 Wessex HC5C (*Clubs*)	RAF No 84 Sqn, Akrotiri
	XT466	WS58 Wessex HU5 [XV] (8921M)	RAF No 2 SoTT, Cosford
	XT467	WS58 Wessex HU5	To RAF Gutersloh as 8922M for BDRT
	XT468	WS58 Wessex HU5 [628/PO]	RN No 772 Sqn, Portland
	XT469	WS58 Wessex HU5 (8920M)	RAF Stafford ground instruction
	XT470	WS58 Wessex HU5 [A]	AAC Netheravon Fire Section
	XT471	WS58 Wessex HU5	RN, stored Wroughton
	XT472	WS58 Wessex HU5 [XC]	RAF Hullavington for instruction
	XT474	WS58 Wessex HU5 [820/CU]	RN, stored Wroughton
	XT475	WS58 Wessex HU5 [624/PO]	RN No 772 Sqn, Portland
	XT479	WS58 Wessex HC5C	RAF No 84 Sqn, Akrotiri
	XT480	WS58 Wessex HU5 [XQ]	RN, stored Wroughton
	XT481	WS58 Wessex HU5 [XF]	RN, stored Wroughton
	XT482	WS58 Wessex HU5 [ZM]	RN AES, Lee-on-Solent
	XT484	WS58 Wessex HU5 [H]	RN AES, Lee-on-Solent
	XT485	WS58 Wessex HU5 [621/PO]	RN No 772 Sqn, Portland
	XT486	WS58 Wessex HU5 [XR] (8919M)	RAF JATE, Brize Norton
	XT487	WS58 Wessex HU5 (A2723) [815/LS]	RNAS Lee-on-Solent Fire Section
	XT548	WS Sioux AH1 [D]	Army Apprentice College, Arborfield
	XT550	WS Sioux AH1 [D]	Museum of Army Flying, Middle Wallop
	XT567	WS Sioux AH1	Privately owned, Fairoaks
	XT575	Vickers Viscount (OE-LAG)	MoD(PE) RS&RE Bedford
	XT595	McD Phantom FG1 (fuselage etc) (8851M)	Scrapped at Coningsby 1981
	XT595	McD Phantom FG1 (nose only) (8550M/8851M)	RAF St Athan, BDRT
	XT596	McD Phantom FG1	MoD(PE) BAe Scampton
	XT597	McD Phantom FG1	MoD(PE) A&AEE Boscombe Down
	XT601	WS58 Wessex HC2	RAF No 22 Sqn SAR*
	XT602	WS58 Wessex HC2	RAF No 22 Sqn SAR*
	XT603	WS58 Wessex HC2 [WF]	RAF No 2 FTS, Shawbury
	XT604	WS58 Wessex HC2	RAF No 22 Sqn SAR*
	XT605	WS58 Wessex HC2 [E]	RAF No 28 Sqn, Sek Kong
	XT606	WS58 Wessex HC2	RAF No 22 Sqn SAR*
	XT607	WS58 Wessex HC2 [P]	RAF No 72 Sqn, Aldergrove
	XT614	WS Scout AH1 [G]	AAC No 660 Sqn, Sek Kong
	XT616	WS Scout AH1	AAC, stored Wroughton
	XT617	WS Scout AH1	AAC, stored Wroughton
	XT618	WS Scout AH1 [K]	AAC No 660 Sqn, Brunei
	XT620	WS Scout AH1 [B]	AAC, stored Wroughton
	XT621	WS Scout AH1	Royal Military College of Science, Shrivenham
	XT623	WS Scout AH1	AAC, stored Wroughton
	XT624	WS Scout AH1 [W]	AAC, stored Wroughton
	XT626	WS Scout AH1	AAC, stored Wroughton
	XT627	WS Scout AH1 [H]	AAC No 660 Sqn, Sek Kong
	XT628	WS Scout AH1 [J]	AAC No 660 Sqn, Sek Kong
	XT630	WS Scout AH1 [F]	AAC, stored Wroughton
	XT631	WS Scout AH1	MoD(PE) A&AEE Boscombe Down
	XT632	WS Scout AH1 [U]	AAC No 666 (TA) Sqn, Netheravon
	XT633	WS Scout AH1	AAC, stored Wroughton
	XT634	WS Scout AH1 [T]	AAC No 666 (TA) Sqn, Netheravon
	XT636	WS Scout AH1 [X]	AAC, stored Wroughton
	XT637	WS Scout AH1	AAC, stored Wroughton
	XT638	WS Scout AH1 [N]	AAC No 666 (TA) Sqn, Netheravon
	XT639	WS Scout AH1 [Y]	AAC, stored Wroughton
	XT640	WS Scout AH1	AAC AETW, Middle Wallop
	XT642	WS Scout AH1	AAC, stored Wroughton
	XT643	WS Scout AH1 [B]	AAC No 660 Sqn, Sek Kong
	XT644	WS Scout AH1 [W]	AAC No 666 (TA) Sqn, Netheravon

Serial	Type (alternative identity)	Owner, Operator or Location	Notes
XT645	WS Scout AH1	AAC, stored Wroughton	
XT646	WS Scout AH1 [Z]	AAC No 666 (TA) Sqn, Netheravon	
XT648	WS Scout AH1	AAC, stored Wroughton	
XT649	WS Scout AH1	AAC No 658 Sqn, Netheravon	
XT657	BHC SR.N6 Winchester 5	British Hovercraft Corpn	
XT661	Vickers Viscount (9G-AAV)	MoD(PE) RS&RE Bedford	
XT667	WS58 Wessex HC2 [F]	RAF No 28 Sqn, Sek Kong	
XT668	WS58 Wessex HC2 [S]	RAF No 72 Sqn, Aldergrove	
XT669	WS58 Wessex HC2 (8894M) [T]	RAF Aldergrove Fire Section	
XT670	WS58 Wessex HC2	RAF No 22 Sqn SAR*	
XT671	WS58 Wessex HC2 [D]	RAF No 72 Sqn, Aldergrove	
XT672	WS58 Wessex HC2 [WE]	RAF No 2 FTS, Shawbury	
XT673	WS58 Wessex HC2 [G]	RAF No 28 Sqn, Sek Kong	
XT674	WS58 Wessex HC2	Crashed 1 Feb 87. Remains stored at Leuchars	
XT675	WS58 Wessex HC2 [J]	RAF No 28 Sqn, Sek Kong	
XT676	WS58 Wessex HC2 [I]	RAF No 72 Sqn, Aldergrove	
XT678	WS58 Wessex HC2 [H]	RAF No 28 Sqn, Sek Kong	
XT680	WS58 Wessex HC2	RAF No 22 Sqn SAR*	
XT681	WS58 Wessex HC2 [U]	RAF No 72 Sqn, Aldergrove	
XT752	Fairey Gannet T5 [-/LM] (G-APYO/WN365)	RNAS, stored Lee-on-Solent	
XT755	WS58 Wessex HU5 [V]	RN, stored Wroughton	
XT756	WS58 Wessex HU5 [ZJ]	RN, stored Wroughton	
XT757	WS58 Wessex HU5 (A2722)	RN Predannack Fire School	
XT759	WS58 Wessex HU5 [XY]	RN, stored Wroughton	
XT760	WS58 Wessex HU5 [418/PO]	RN No 772 Sqn, Portland	
XT761	WS58 Wessex HU5	RN, stored Wroughton	
XT762	WS58 Wessex HU5	RNAS Culdrose, SAH	
XT764	WS58 Wessex HU5 [G]	RN, stored Wroughton	
XT765	WS58 Wessex HU5 [J]	RN AES, Lee-on-Solent	
XT766	WS58 Wessex HU5 [822/CU]	RN No 771 Sqn, Culdrose	
XT768	WS58 Wessex HU5	RN, stored Wroughton	
XT769	WS58 Wessex HU5 [823/CU]	RN No 771 Sqn, Culdrose	
XT770	WS58 Wessex HU5 [P]	RN, stored Wroughton	
XT771	WS58 Wessex HU5 [620/PO]	RN No 772 Sqn, Portland	
XT772	WS58 Wessex HU5 (8805M)	RAF SARTU, Valley	
XT773	WS58 Wessex HU5 [826/CU]	RN, stored Wroughton	
XT778	WS Wasp HAS1 [430]	RN No 829 Sqn, Portland	
XT779	WS Wasp HAS1 [456]	RN, stored Wroughton	
XT780	WS Wasp HAS1 [636]	RNAY Fleetlands Apprentice School	
XT782	WS Wasp HAS1 [324]	RN, stored Wroughton	
XT783	WS Wasp HAS1 [470]	RN No 829 Sqn, Portland	
XT784	WS Wasp HAS1 [FIR3]	RN, stored Wroughton	
XT785	WS Wasp HAS1 [462]	RN No 829 Sqn, Portland	
XT786	WS Wasp HAS1 [441]	RN Portland, ground instruction	
XT788	WS Wasp HAS1 [442] (G-BMIR)	Privately owned, Tattershall Thorpe	
XT790	WS Wasp HAS1 [608]	RN No 829 Sqn, Portland	
XT791	WS Wasp HAS1 [433]	RN No 829 Sqn, Portland	
XT793	WS Wasp HAS1 [456]	RN, stored Wroughton	
XT795	WS Wasp HAS1 [476/LE]	RN AES, Lee-on-Solent	
XT803	WS Sioux AH1 [Y]	Privately owned, Panshanger	
XT827	WS Sioux AH1 [D]	Army Apprentice College, Arborfield	
XT847	WS Sioux AH1 [F]	Privately owned, Fairoaks	
XT852	McD Phantom FGR2	MoD(PE) BAe Scampton	
XT853	McD Phantom FGR2	MoD(PE) BAe Scampton	
XT857	McD Phantom FG1 [C] (8913M)	RAF Leuchars ground instruction	
XT858	McD Phantom FG1	MoD(PE) BAe Brough (structures test)	
XT859	McD Phantom FG1 [BK]	RAF No 111 Sqn, Leuchars	
XT860	McD Phantom FG1 [AL]	RAF No 43 Sqn, Leuchars	
XT861	McD Phantom FG1 [AC]	Crashed 7 Sept 1987 into North Sea	
XT863	McD Phantom FG1 [BG]	RAF No 111 Sqn, Leuchars	
XT864	McD Phantom FG1 [BJ]	RAF No 111 Sqn, Leuchars	
XT865	McD Phantom FG1 [BU]	RAF No 111 Sqn, Leuchars	
XT867	McD Phantom FG1 [BH]	RAF No 111 Sqn, Leuchars	
XT870	McD Phantom FG1 [BS]	RAF No 111 Sqn, Leuchars	
XT872	McD Phantom FG1 [BT]	RAF No 111 Sqn, Leuchars	
XT873	McD Phantom FG1 [BA]	RAF No 111 Sqn, Leuchars	
XT874	McD Phantom FG1 [BE]	RAF No 111 Sqn, Leuchars	

Notes	Serial	Type (alternative identity)	Owner, Operator or Location
	XT875	McD Phantom FG1 [AK]	RAF No 43 Sqn, Leuchars
	XT891	McD Phantom FGR2 [CZ]	RAF No 64 Sqn/228 OCU, Leuchars
	XT892	McD Phantom FGR2 [X]	RAF No 56 Sqn, Wattisham
	XT893	McD Phantom FGR2 [CQ]	RAF No 64 Sqn/228 OCU, Leuchars
	XT894	McD Phantom FGR2 [CP]	RAF No 64 Sqn/228 OCU, Leuchars
	XT895	McD Phantom FGR2 [CH]	RAF, stored St Athan
	XT896	McD Phantom FGR2 [CY]	RAF No 64 Sqn/228 OCU, Leuchars
	XT897	McD Phantom FGR2 [Y]	RAF No 56 Sqn, Wattisham
	XT898	McD Phantom FGR2 [CE]	RAF No 64 Sqn/228 OCU, Leuchars
	XT899	McD Phantom FGR2 [K]	RAF No 19 Sqn, Wildenrath
	XT900	McD Phantom FGR2 [CO]	RAF No 64 Sqn/228 OCU, Leuchars
	XT901	McD Phantom FGR2	RAF No 56 Sqn, Wattisham
	XT902	McD Phantom FGR2 [CR]	RAF No 64 Sqn/228 OCU, Leuchars
	XT903	McD Phantom FGR2 [Y]	RAF No 92 Sqn, Wildenrath
	XT905	McD Phantom FGR2 [CU]	RAF No 64 Sqn/228 OCU, Leuchars
	XT906	McD Phantom FGR2 [CH]	RAF No 64 Sqn/228 OCU, Leuchars
	XT907	McD Phantom FGR2 [CT]	RAF No 64 Sqn/228 OCU, Leuchars
	XT908	McD Phantom FGR2 [AK]	RAF No 19 Sqn Wildenrath
	XT909	McD Phantom FGR2 [CS]	RAF No 64 Sqn/228 OCU, Leuchars
	XT910	McD Phantom FGR2 [CJ]	RAF No 64 Sqn/228 OCU, Leuchars
	XT911	McD Phantom FGR2 [T]	RAF No 92 Sqn, Wildenrath
	XT914	McD Phantom FGR2 [T]	RAF No 56 Sqn, Wattisham
	XV101	BAC VC10 C1	RAF No 10 Sqn, Brize Norton
	XV102	BAC VC10 C1	RAF No 10 Sqn, Brize Norton
	XV103	BAC VC10 C1	RAF No 10 Sqn, Brize Norton
	XV104	BAC VC10 C1	RAF No 10 Sqn, Brize Norton
	XV105	BAC VC10 C1	RAF No 10 Sqn, Brize Norton
	XV106	BAC VC10 C1	RAF No 10 Sqn, Brize Norton
	XV107	BAC VC10 C1	RAF No 10 Sqn, Brize Norton
	XV108	BAC VC10 C1	RAF No 10 Sqn, Brize Norton
	XV109	BAC VC10 C1	RAF No 10 Sqn, Brize Norton
	XV118	WS Scout AH1	AAC, stored Wroughton
	XV119	WS Scout AH1	AAC, stored Wroughton
	XV121	WS Scout AH1 [V]	AAC No 658 Sqn, Netheravon
	XV122	WS Scout AH1 [A]	AAC No 660 Sqn, Sek Kong
	XV123	WS Scout AH1	AAC, stored Wroughton
	XV124	WS Scout AH1	AAC, stored Wroughton
	XV126	WS Scout AH1	AAC, stored Wroughton
	XV127	WS Scout AH1	AAC D&TS, Middle Wallop
	XV128	WS Scout AH1	AAC D&TS, Middle Wallop
	XV129	WS Scout AH1 [V]	AAC No 666 (TA) Sqn, Netheravon
	XV130	WS Scout AH1 [R]	AAC No 666 (TA) Sqn, Netheravon
	XV131	WS Scout AH1 [X]	AAC No 660 Sqn, Brunei
	XV134	WS Scout AH1	AAC No 658 Sqn, Netheravon
	XV135	WS Scout AH1	AAC, stored Wroughton
	XV136	WS Scout AH1 [X]	AAC No 666 (TA) Sqn, Netheravon
	XV137	WS Scout AH1 [Z]	AAC No 658 Sqn, Netheravon
	XV138	WS Scout AH1	AAC No 658 Sqn, Netheravon
	XV139	WS Scout AH1	Army Apprentice College, Arborfield
	XV140	WS Scout AH1 [K]	AAC No 666 (TA) Sqn, Netheravon
	XV141	WS Scout AH1	Army Apprentice College, Arborfield
	XV147	HS Nimrod MR1 (Mod)	MoD(PE) stored RAE Farnborough
	XV148	HS Nimrod MR1 (Mod)	MoD(PE) BAe Woodford
	XV152	HS Buccaneer S2A (8776M) [A]	CSDE, RAF Swanton Morley
	XV154	HS Buccaneer S2A (8854M) [A]	RAF Lossiemouth, ground instruction
	XV155	HS Buccaneer S2B (8716M)	BAe Brough Apprentice School
	XV156	HS Buccaneer S2A (8773M)	RAF St Athan Fire Section
	XV157	HS Buccaneer S2B	RAF, stored Shawbury
	XV161	HS Buccaneer S2A	RAF No 12 Sqn, Lossiemouth
	XV163	HS Buccaneer S2A	RAF St Athan
	XV165	HS Buccaneer S2B	RAF No 12 Sqn, Lossiemouth
	XV168	HS Buccaneer S2B	RAF No 208 Sqn, Lossiemouth
	XV176	Lockheed Hercules C3	RAF Lyneham Transport Wing
	XV177	Lockheed Hercules C3	RAF Lyneham Transport Wing
	XV178	Lockheed Hercules C1P	RAF Lyneham Transport Wing
	XV179	Lockheed Hercules C1P	RAF Lyneham Transport Wing
	XV181	Lockheed Hercules C1	RAF Lyneham Transport Wing
	XV182	Lockheed Hercules C1P	RAF Lyneham Transport Wing
	XV183	Lockheed Hercules C3P	RAF Lyneham Transport Wing
	XV184	Lockheed Hercules C3P	RAF Lyneham Transport Wing
	XV185	Lockheed Hercules C1P	RAF Lyneham Transport Wing
	XV186	Lockheed Hercules C1P	RAF Lyneham Transport Wing
	XV187	Lockheed Hercules C1P	RAF Lyneham Transport Wing

Serial	Type (alternative identity)	Owner, Operator or Location	Notes
XV188	Lockheed Hercules C3P	RAF Lyneham Transport Wing	
XV189	Lockheed Hercules C3P	RAF Lyneham Transport Wing	
XV190	Lockheed Hercules C3	RAF Lyneham Transport Wing	
XV191	Lockheed Hercules C1P	RAF Lyneham Transport Wing	
XV192	Lockheed Hercules C1K	RAF Lyneham Transport Wing	
XV193	Lockheed Hercules C3P	RAF Lyneham Transport Wing	
XV195	Lockheed Hercules C1P	RAF Lyneham Transport Wing	
XV196	Lockheed Hercules C1P	RAF Lyneham Transport Wing	
XV197	Lockheed Hercules C3	RAF Lyneham Transport Wing	
XV199	Lockheed Hercules C3	RAF Lyneham Transport Wing	
XV200	Lockheed Hercules C1P	RAF Lyneham Transport Wing	
XV201	Lockheed Hercules C1K	RAF Lyneham Transport Wing/ 1312 Flt, Stanley	
XV202	Lockheed Hercules C3	RAF Lyneham Transport Wing	
XV203	Lockheed Hercules C1K	RAF Lyneham Transport Wing	
XV204	Lockheed Hercules C1K	RAF Lyneham Transport Wing/ 1312 Flt, Stanley	
XV205	Lockheed Hercules C1P	RAF Lyneham Transport Wing/ 1312 Flt, Stanley	
XV206	Lockheed Hercules C1P	RAF Lyneham Transport Wing	
XV207	Lockheed Hercules C3	RAF Lyneham Transport Wing	
XV208	Lockheed Hercules W2	MoD(PE) RAE Farnborough	
XV209	Lockheed Hercules C3	RAF Lyneham Transport Wing	
XV210	Lockheed Hercules C1P	MoD(PE) A&AEE Boscombe Down	
XV211	Lockheed Hercules C1P	RAF Lyneham Transport Wing	
XV212	Lockheed Hercules C3P	RAF Lyneham Transport Wing	
XV213	Lockheed Hercules C1K	RAF No 1312 Flt, Mount Pleasant	
XV214	Lockheed Hercules C3P	RAF Lyneham Transport Wing	
XV215	Lockheed Hercules C1P	RAF Lyneham Transport Wing	
XV217	Lockheed Hercules C3P	RAF Lyneham Transport Wing	
XV218	Lockheed Hercules C1P	RAF Lyneham Transport Wing	
XV219	Lockheed Hercules C3	RAF Lyneham Transport Wing	
XV220	Lockheed Hercules C3P	RAF Lyneham Transport Wing	
XV221	Lockheed Hercules C3	RAF Lyneham Transport Wing	
XV222	Lockheed Hercules C3	RAF Lyneham Transport Wing	
XV223	Lockheed Hercules C3	RAF Lyneham Transport Wing	
XV226	HS Nimrod MR2	RAF No 42 Sqn, St Mawgan	
XV227	HS Nimrod MR2P	RAF No 42 Sqn, St Mawgan	
XV228	HS Nimrod MR2P	RAF Kinloss MR Wing	
XV229	HS Nimrod MR2	RAF No 42 Sqn, St Mawgan	
XV230	HS Nimrod MR2P	RAF Kinloss MR Wing	
XV231	HS Nimrod MR2	RAF No 42 Sqn, St Mawgan	
XV232	HS Nimrod MR2P	RAF No 42 Sqn, St Mawgan	
XV233	HS Nimrod MR2	RAF No 42 Sqn, St Mawgan	
XV234	HS Nimrod MR2P	RAF Kinloss MR Wing	
XV235	HS Nimrod MR2	RAF No 42 Sqn, St Mawgan	
XV236	HS Nimrod MR2P	RAF No 42 Sqn, St Mawgan	
XV237	HS Nimrod MR2P	RAF No 42 Sqn, St Mawgan	
XV238	HS Nimrod MR2P	RAF Kinloss MR Wing	
XV239	HS Nimrod MR2P	RAF Kinloss MR Wing	
XV240	HS Nimrod MR2	RAF No 42 Sqn, St Mawgan	
XV241	HS Nimrod MR2	RAF Kinloss MR Wing	
XV242	HS Nimrod MR2	RAF No 42 Sqn, St Mawgan	
XV243	HS Nimrod MR2P	RAF No 42 Sqn, St Mawgan	
XV244	HS Nimrod MR2	RAF Kinloss MR Wing	
XV245	HS Nimrod MR2P	RAF No 42 Sqn, St Mawgan	
XV246	HS Nimrod MR2	RAF Kinloss MR Wing	
XV247	HS Nimrod MR2P	RAF Kinloss MR Wing	
XV248	HS Nimrod MR2P	RAF Kinloss MR Wing	
XV249	HS Nimrod MR2	RAF Kinloss MR Wing	
XV250	HS Nimrod MR2P	RAF No 42 Sqn, St Mawgan	
XV251	HS Nimrod MR2	RAF No 42 Sqn, St Mawgan	
XV252	HS Nimrod MR2	RAF Kinloss MR Wing	
XV253	HS Nimrod MR2P	RAF No 42 Sqn, St Mawgan	
XV254	HS Nimrod MR2P	RAF Kinloss MR Wing	
XV255	HS Nimrod MR2P	RAF Kinloss MR Wing	
XV257	HS Nimrod MR2	RAF at BAe Woodford on rebuild	
XV258	HS Nimrod MR2	RAF No 42 Sqn, St Mawgan	
XV259	BAe Nimrod AEW3	RAF, stored Waddington	
XV260	HS Nimrod MR2P	RAF Kinloss MR Wing	
XV261	BAe Nimrod AEW3	RAF, stored Abingdon	
XV262	BAe Nimrod AEW3	RAF, stored Abingdon	
XV263	BAe Nimrod AEW3P	RAF Finningley, ground instruction	
XV268	DHC Beaver AL1	AAC, stored Shawbury	

Notes	Serial	Type (alternative identity)	Owner, Operator or Location
	XV269	DHC Beaver AL1 (8011M)	AAC AETW, Middle Wallop
	XV270	DHC Beaver AL1	AAC, stored Shawbury
	XV271	DHC Beaver AL1	AAC, Aldergrove
	XV272	DHC Beaver AL1	AAC Middle Wallop, BDRT
	XV277	HS Harrier GR3	MoD(PE) Rolls-Royce, Filton
	XV279	HS Harrier GR1 [44] (8566M)	RAF Wittering
	XV281	HS Harrier GR3	Rolls-Royce, Filton
	XV290	Lockheed Hercules C3	RAF Lyneham Transport Wing
	XV291	Lockheed Hercules C1P	RAF Lyneham Transport Wing
	XV292	Lockheed Hercules C1P	RAF Lyneham Transport Wing
	XV293	Lockheed Hercules C1P	RAF Lyneham Transport Wing
	XV294	Lockheed Hercules C3	RAF Lyneham Transport Wing
	XV295	Lockheed Hercules C1	RAF Lyneham Transport Wing
	XV296	Lockheed Hercules C1K	RAF Lyneham Transport Wing
	XV297	Lockheed Hercules C1P	RAF Lyneham Transport Wing
	XV298	Lockheed Hercules C1P	RAF Lyneham Transport Wing
	XV299	Lockheed Hercules C3P	RAF Lyneham Transport Wing
	XV300	Lockheed Hercules C1P	RAF Lyneham Transport Wing
	XV301	Lockheed Hercules C3P	RAF Lyneham Transport Wing
	XV302	Lockheed Hercules C3	RAF Lyneham Transport Wing
	XV303	Lockheed Hercules C3	RAF Lyneham Transport Wing
	XV304	Lockheed Hercules C3P	RAF Lyneham Transport Wing
	XV305	Lockheed Hercules C3P	RAF Lyneham Transport Wing
	XV306	Lockheed Hercules C1P	RAF Lyneham Transport Wing
	XV307	Lockheed Hercules C3	RAF Lyneham Transport Wing
	XV328	EE Lightning T5 [BZ]	RAF No 11 Sqn, Binbrook
	XV332	HS Buccaneer S2B	RAF No 237 OCU, Lossiemouth
	XV333	HS Buccaneer S2B	RAF No 208 Sqn, Lossiemouth
	XV334	HS Buccaneer S2B [D]	RAF, stored Shawbury
	XV336	HS Buccaneer S2A	RAF, stored Shawbury
	XV337	HS Buccaneer S2C (8852M)	RAF Abingdon, BDRF
	XV338	HS Buccaneer S2A (fuselage etc) (8774M)	RAF St Athan (for RAF Honington ground instruction)
	XV338	HS Buccaneer S2A (nose only)	RAF Exhibition Flight, Abingdon
	XV341	HS Buccaneer S2A	RAF Lossiemouth Fire Section
	XV342	HS Buccaneer S2B [T]	RAF BAe Woodford
	XV344	HS Buccaneer S2C	MoD(PE) RAE Farnborough
	XV349	HS Buccaneer S2B	RAF, stored Shawbury
	XV350	HS Buccaneer S2B	MoD(PE) A&AEE, Boscombe Down
	XV352	HS Buccaneer S2B	RAF No 237 OCU, Lossiemouth
	XV353	HS Buccaneer S2B	RAF BAe Woodford
	XV355	HS Buccaneer S2B	RAF No 237 OCU, Lossiemouth
	XV356	HS Buccaneer S2A [B]	RAF, stored Shawbury
	XV359	HS Buccaneer S2B	RAF No 208 Sqn, Lossiemouth
	XV361	HS Buccaneer S2B	RAF No 208 Sqn, Lossiemouth
	XV370	Sikorsky SH-3D (G-ATYU)	MoD(PE) ETPS Boscombe Down
	XV371	WS61 Sea King HAS1	MoD(PE) RAE Farnborough
	XV372	WS61 Sea King HAS1	Westlands, Yeovil for ground instruction
	XV373	WS61 Sea King HAS1	MoD(PE) A&AEE Boscombe Down (wfu)
	XV393	McD Phantom FGR2 [CA]	RAF No 64 Sqn/228 OCU, Leuchars
	XV394	McD Phantom FGR2 [T]	RAF No 92 Sqn, Wildenrath
	XV396	McD Phantom FGR2 [CD]	RAF No 64 Sqn/228 OCU, Leuchars
	XV398	McD Phantom FGR2 [CI]	RAF No 64 Sqn/228 OCU, Leuchars
	XV399	McD Phantom FGR2 [L]	RAF No 56 Sqn, Wattisham
	XV400	McD Phantom FGR2 [D]	RAF No 56 Sqn, Wattisham
	XV401	McD Phantom FGR2 [A]	RAF No 23 Sqn, Mount Pleasant, FI
	XV402	McD Phantom FGR2 [A]	RAF
	XV404	McD Phantom FGR2 [I]	RAF No 19 Sqn, Wildenrath
	XV406	McD Phantom FGR2 [CK]	RAF No 64 Sqn/228 OCU, Leuchars
	XV407	McD Phantom FGR2 [CL]	RAF No 64 Sqn/228 OCU, Leuchars
	XV408	McD Phantom FGR2 [S]	RAF No 92 Sqn, Wildenrath
	XV409	McD Phantom FGR2 [A]	RAF
	XV410	McD Phantom FGR2 [E]	RAF No 56 Sqn, Wattisham
	XV411	McD Phantom FGR2 [O]	RAF No 56 Sqn, Wattisham
	XV412	McD Phantom FGR2 [S]	RAF, stored St Athan
	XV414	McD Phantom FGR2 [R]	RAF Wattisham, BDRT
	XV415	McD Phantom FGR2 [B]	RAF No 23 Sqn, Mount Pleasant, FI
	XV419	McD Phantom FGR2	RAF
	XV420	McD Phantom FGR2 [S]	RAF No 92 Sqn, Wildenrath
	XV421	McD Phantom FGR2	RAF
	XV422	McD Phantom FGR2 [J]	RAF No 19 Sqn, Wildenrath
	XV423	McD Phantom FGR2 [D]	RAF, stored St Athan
	XV424	McD Phantom FGR2 [GN]	RAF No 64 Sqn/228 OCU, Leuchars

Serial	Type (alternative identity)	Owner, Operator or Location	Notes
XV425	McD Phantom FGR2 [A]	RAF No 56 Sqn, Wattisham	
XV426	McD Phantom FGR2 [P]	RAF No 56 Sqn, Wattisham	
XV428	McD Phantom FGR2 [CC]	RAF No 64 Sqn/228 OCU, Leuchars	
XV429	McD Phantom FGR2 [K]	BAe Scampton (wfu)	
XV430	McD Phantom FGR2 [A]	RAF No 19 Sqn, Wildenrath	
XV432	McD Phantom FGR2 [H]	RAF No 56 Sqn, Wattisham	
XV433	McD Phantom FGR2 [F]	RAF No 56 Sqn, Wattisham	
XV435	McD Phantom FGR2 [R]	RAF No 92 Sqn, Wildenrath	
XV436	McD Phantom FGR2 [E] (8850M)	RAF Abingdon, BDRF	
XV437	McD Phantom FGR2 [Y]	RAF No 92 Sqn, Wildenrath	
XV438	McD Phantom FGR2 [R]	RAF No 92 Sqn, Wildenrath	
XV439	McD Phantom FGR2 [D]	RAF No 19 Sqn, Wildenrath	
XV442	McD Phantom FGR2 [H]	RAF No 19 Sqn, Wildenrath	
XV460	McD Phantom FGR2 [N]	RAF No 92 Sqn, Wildenrath	
XV461	McD Phantom FGR2 [G]	RAF No 56 Sqn, Wattisham	
XV462	McD Phantom FGR2 [B]	RAF No 19 Sqn, Wildenrath	
XV464	McD Phantom FGR2 [N]	RAF No 56 Sqn, Wattisham	
XV465	McD Phantom FGR2 [F]	RAF No 19 Sqn, Wildenrath	
XV466	McD Phantom FGR2 [CB]	RAF No 64 Sqn/228 OCU, Leuchars	
XV467	McD Phantom FGR2 [Q]	RAF No 92 Sqn, Wildenrath	
XV468	McD Phantom FGR2 [P]	RAF No 92 Sqn, Wildenrath	
XV469	McD Phantom FGR2 [T]	RAF No 56 Sqn, Wattisham	
XV470	McD Phantom FGR2 [CX]	RAF No 64 Sqn/228 OCU, Leuchars	
XV472	McD Phantom FGR2 [E]	RAF No 19 Sqn, Wildenrath	
XV473	McD Phantom FGR2	RAF St Athan	
XV474	McD Phantom FGR2 [M]	RAF No 56 Sqn, Wattisham	
XV475	McD Phantom FGR2 [Z]	RAF No 92 Sqn, Wildenrath	
XV476	McD Phantom FGR2 [G]	RAF No 19 Sqn, Wildenrath	
XV478	McD Phantom FGR2 [C]	RAF No 19 Sqn, Wildenrath	
XV480	McD Phantom FGR2	RAF	
XV481	McD Phantom FGR2 [F]	RAF No 23 Sqn, Mount Pleasant, FI	
XV482	McD Phantom FGR2 [C]	RAF No 56 Sqn, Wattisham	
XV485	McD Phantom FGR2 [M]	RAF No 19 Sqn, Wildenrath	
XV486	McD Phantom FGR2 [N]	RAF, stored St Athan	
XV487	McD Phantom FGR2 [AA]	RAF No 19 Sqn, Wildenrath	
XV488	McD Phantom FGR2 [O]	RAF No 92 Sqn, Wildenrath	
XV489	McD Phantom FGR2 [G]	RAF No 23 Sqn, Mount Plesant, FI	
XV490	McD Phantom FGR2 [CG]	RAF No 64 Sqn/228 OCU, Leuchars	
XV492	McD Phantom FGR2 [W]	RAF No 92 Sqn, Wildenrath	
XV494	McD Phantom FGR2 [L]	RAF No 19 Sqn, Wildenrath	
XV495	McD Phantom FGR2 [C]	RAF, stored St Athan	
XV496	McD Phantom FGR2 [V]	RAF No 92 Sqn, Wildenrath	
XV497	McD Phantom FGR2 [X]	RAF No 92 Sqn, Wildenrath	
XV498	McD Phantom FGR2 [U]	RAF No 92 Sqn, Wildenrath	
XV499	McD Phantom FGR2 [CF]	RAF No 64 Sqn/228 OCU, Leuchars	
XV500	McD Phantom FGR2 [J]	RAF No 56 Sqn, Wattisham	
XV501	McD Phantom FGR2 [B]	RAF No 56 Sqn, Wattisham	
XV555	HS Harrier GR1 (8566M)	*See XV279*	
XV567	McD Phantom FG1 [AI]	RAF No 43 Sqn, Leuchars	
XV568	McD Phantom FG1 [AT]	RAF No 43 Sqn, Leuchars	
XV569	McD Phantom FG1 [BQ]	RAF No 111 Sqn, Leuchars	
XV570	McD Phantom FG1 [BN]	RAF No 111 Sqn, Leuchars	
XV571	McD Phantom FG1 [AA]	RAF No 43 Sqn, Leuchars	
XV572	McD Phantom FG1 [AN]	RAF No 43 Sqn, Leuchars	
XV573	McD Phantom FG1 [BD]	RAF No 111 Sqn, Leuchars	
XV574	McD Phantom FG1 [BZ]	RAF No 111 Sqn, Leuchars	
XV575	McD Phantom FG1 [AS]	RAF No 43 Sqn, Leuchars	
XV576	McD Phantom FG1 [AD]	RAF No 43 Sqn, Leuchars	
XV577	McD Phantom FG1 [AM]	RAF No 43 Sqn, Leuchars	
XV579	McD Phantom FG1 [AR]	RAF No 43 Sqn, Leuchars	
XV581	McD Phantom FG1 [AE]	RAF No 43 Sqn, Leuchars	
XV582	McD Phantom FG1 [AF]	RAF No 43 Sqn, Leuchars	
XV583	McD Phantom FG1 [BB]	RAF No 111 Sqn, Leuchars	
XV584	McD Phantom FG1 [BF]	RAF No 111 Sqn, Leuchars	
XV585	McD Phantom FG1 [AP]	RAF No 43 Sqn, Leuchars	
XV586	McD Phantom FG1 [AJ]	RAF No 43 Sqn, Leuchars	
XV587	McD Phantom FG1 [AG]	RAF No 43 Sqn, Leuchars	
XV588	McD Phantom FG1 [007] (nose only)	RNAS Culdrose	
XV588	McD Phantom FG1 (fuselage, etc)	RAF Leuchars, BDRT	
XV590	McD Phantom FG1 [AX]	RAF No 43 Sqn, Leuchars	
XV591	McD Phantom FG1 [BM]	RAF No 111 Sqn, Leuchars	
XV592	McD Phantom FG1 [BL]	RAF No 111 Sqn, Leuchars	
XV615	BHC SR.N6 Winchester 2	RN Hong Kong	

Notes	Serial	Type (alternative identity)	Owner, Operator or Location
	XV623	WS Wasp HAS1 [601]	RN Porland, Fire Section
	XV624	WS Wasp HAS1	RN, stored Wroughton
	XV625	WS Wasp HAS1 [471/PB]	RNEC Manadon, for instruction
	XV626	WS Wasp HAS1 [325/HR]	RN, stored Wroughton
	XV629	WS Wasp HAS1	AAC Middle Wallop, BDRT
	XV631	WS Wasp HAS1	MoD(PE) RAE Farnborough
	XV632	WS Wasp HAS1 [610]	RN, stored Wroughton
	XV634	WS Wasp HAS1 [FIR 1]	RN No 829 Sqn, Portland
	XV636	WS Wasp HAS1 [325/HR]	RN, stored Wroughton
	XV638	WS Wasp HAS1 (8826M) [A/430]	RAF AMS, Brize Norton
	XV639	WS Wasp HAS1 [612]	RN, stored Wroughton
	XV642	WS61 Sea King HAS2A	MoD(PE) Westlands, Yeovil
	XV643	WS61 Sea King HAS5 [009/R]	RN No 820 Sqn, Culdrose
	XV644	WS61 Sea King HAS1 (A2664) [64]	RN AES, Lee-on-Solent
	XV647	WS61 Sea King HAS5 [820]	RN No 771 Sqn, Culdrose
	XV648	WS61 Sea King HAS5 [582]	RN No 706 Sqn, Culdrose
	XV649	WS61 Sea King AEW2A [183/R]	RN No 849 Sqn, Culdrose
	XV650	WS61 Sea King AEW2A [180]	RN No 849 Sqn, Culdrose
	XV651	WS61 Sea King HAS5 [131]	RN No 826 Sqn, Culdrose
	XV652	WS61 Sea King HAS5 [132]	RN No 826 Sqn, Culdrose
	XV653	WS61 Sea King HAS5 [509]	RN No 810 Sqn, Culdrose
	XV654	WS61 Sea King HAS5 [018/R]	RN No 820 Sqn, Culdrose
	XV655	WS61 Sea King HAS5 [253]	RN No 824 Sqn, Prestwick
	XV656	WS61 Sea King AEW2A [126]	RN No 849 Sqn, Culdrose
	XV657	WS61 Sea King HAS5 [132]	Westlands, Yeovil
	XV659	WS61 Sea King HAS5 [266/L]	RN No 814 Sqn, Culdrose
	XV660	WS61 Sea King HAS5 [507]	RN No 810 Sqn, Culdrose
	XV661	WS61 Sea King HAS5 AEW2A	RN No 826 Sqn, Culdrose
	XV663	WS61 Sea King HAS5 [705]	RN No 819 Sqn, Prestwick
	XV664	WS61 Sea King AEW2A [185]	RN No 849 Sqn, Culdrose
	XV665	WS61 Sea King HAS5 [508]	RN No 810 Sqn, Culdrose
	XV666	WS61 Sea King HAS5 [272]	RN No 814 Sqn, Culdrose
	XV668	WS61 Sea King HAS5 [586]	Ditched 24 Feb 87
	XV669	WS61 Sea King HAS1 [410/BL] (A2659)	RNAS Culdrose, Engineering Training School
	XV670	WS61 Sea King HAS5 [592]	RN No 706 Sqn, Culdrose
	XV671	WS61 Sea King AEW2A [185]	RN No 849 Sqn, Culdrose
	XV672	WS61 Sea King AEW2A [182/R]	RN No 849 Sqn, Culdrose
	XV673	WS61 Sea King HAS5 [588]	RN No 706 Sqn, Culdrose
	XV674	WS61 Sea King HAS5 [274/L]	RN No 814 Sqn, Culdrose
	XV675	WS61 Sea King HAS5	RN No 814 Sqn, Culdrose
	XV676	WS61 Sea King HAS6 [266/L]	RNAY Fleetlands
	XV677	WS61 Sea King HAS5 [707]	RN No 819 Sqn, Prestwick
	XV696	WS61 Sea King HAS5 [503]	RN No 810 Sqn, Culdrose
	XV697	WS61 Sea King AEW2A [184/R]	RN No 849 Sqn, Culdrose
	XV699	WS61 Sea King HAS5	RN No 826 Sqn, Culdrose
	XV700	WS61 Sea King HAS5 [011/R]	RN No 820 Sqn, Culdrose
	XV701	WS61 Sea King HAS5 [706]	RN No 819 Sqn, Prestwick
	XV703	WS61 Sea King HAS5 [586]	Crashed 23 September 1987
	XV704	WS61 Sea King HAS2A	RN NASU, Culdrose
	XV705	WS61 Sea King HAS5	RN No 771 Sqn, Culdrose
	XV706	WS61 Sea King HAS5 [597]	RN No 706 Sqn, Culdrose
	XV707	WS61 Sea King AEW2A [181]	RN No 849 Sqn, Culdrose
	XV708	WS61 Sea King HAS5 [596]	RN No 706 Sqn, Culdrose
	XV709	WS61 Sea King HAS5 [585]	RN No 706 Sqn, Culdrose
	XV710	WS61 Sea King HAS5 [267/L]	RN No 814 Sqn, Culdrose
	XV711	WS61 Sea King HAS5 [273/L]	RN No 706 Sqn, Culdrose
	XV712	WS61 Sea King HAS5	RN No 706 Sqn, Culdrose
	XV713	WS61 Sea King HAS5 [594]	RN No 706 Sqn, Culdrose
	XV714	WS61 Sea King AEW2A [187]	RN No 849 Sqn, Culdrose
	XV719	WS58 Wessex HC2 [B]	RAF No 72 Sqn, Aldergrove
	XV720	WS58 Wessex HC2	RAF No 22 Sqn SAR*
	XV721	WS58 Wessex HC2 [H]	RAF No 72 Sqn Aldergrove
	XV722	WS58 Wessex HC2 [WH]	RAF No 2 FTS, Shawbury
	XV723	WS58 Wessex HC2 [Q]	RAF No 72 Sqn, Aldergrove
	XV724	WS58 Wessex HC2	RAF No 22 Sqn SAR*
	XV725	WS58 Wessex HC2 [C]	RAF No 72 Sqn, Aldergrove
	XV726	WS58 Wessex HC2 [J]	RAF No 72 Sqn, Aldergrove
	XV728	WS58 Wessex HC2 [A]	RAF No 72 Sqn, Aldergrove
	XV729	WS58 Wessex HC2	RAF No 22 Sqn SAR*
	XV730	WS58 Wessex HC2	RAF No 22 Sqn SAR*
	XV731	WS58 Wessex HC2 [Y]	RAF No 72 Sqn, Aldergrove

Serial	Type (alternative identity)	Owner, Operator or Location	Notes
XV732	WS58 Wessex HCC4	RAF Queen's Flight, Benson	
XV733	WS58 Wessex HCC4	RAF Queen's Flight, Benson	
XV738	HS Harrier GR3 [B]	RAF No 4 Sqn, Gutersloh	
XV740	HS Harrier GR3 [05]	RAF No 1 Sqn, Wittering	
XV741	HS Harrier GR3 [F]	RAF No 233 OCU, Wittering	
XV744	HS Harrier GR3 [D]	RAF No 233 OCU, Wittering	
XV747	HS Harrier GR3 [G]	RAF No 233 OCU, Wittering	
XV748	HS Harrier GR3 [07]	RAF No 1 Sqn, Wittering	
XV751	HS Harrier GR3 [AU]	RAF No 3 Sqn, Gutersloh	
XV752	HS Harrier GR3 [G]	RAF No 3 Sqn, Gutersloh	
XV753	HS Harrier GR3 [06]	RAF No 1 Sqn, Wittering	
XV755	HS Harrier GR3 [M]	RAF No 233 OCU, Wittering	
XV758	HS Harrier GR3 [V]	RAF No 3 Sqn, Gutersloh	
XV759	HS Harrier GR3 [H]	RAF No 233 OCU, Wittering	
XV760	HS Harrier GR3 [C]	RAF No 4 Sqn, Gutersloh	
XV762	HS Harrier GR3 [09]	RAF ASF, Wittering	
XV778	HS Harrier GR3 [08]	RAF No 1 Sqn, Wittering	
XV779	HS Harrier GR3 [AA] (8931M)	RAF Wittering for/on display	
XV782	HS Harrier GR3 [F]	RAF No 4 Sqn, Gutersloh	
XV783	HS Harrier GR3 [N]	RAF No 233 OCU, Wittering	
XV784	HS Harrier GR3 (8909M) [C]	RAF Wittering, BDRT	
XV786	HS Harrier GR3 [E]	RAF No 4 Sqn, Gutersloh	
XV789	HS Harrier GR3	RAF	
XV790	HS Harrier GR3 [P]	Crashed Otterburn 2 November 1987	
XV793	HS Harrier GR3 [L]	RAF No 4 Sqn, Gutersloh	
XV804	HS Harrier GR3 [D]	RAF No 3 Sqn, Gutersloh	
XV806	HS Harrier GR3 [AN]	RAF No 3 Sqn, Gutersloh	
XV808	HS Harrier GR3 [L]	RAF No 233 OCU, Wittering	
XV809	HS Harrier GR3 [F]	RAF No 3 Sqn, Gutersloh	
XV810	HS Harrier GR3 [K]	RAF No 233 OCU, Wittering	
XV814	HS Comet 4C (G-APDF)	MoD(PE) RAE Farnborough	
XV859	BHC SR.N6 Winchester 6	RN NHTU, Lee-on-Solent	
XV863	HS Buccaneer S2B	RAF No 208 Sqn, Lossiemouth	
XV864	HS Buccaneer S2B	RAF No 12 Sqn, Lossiemouth	
XV865	HS Buccaneer S2B [BS]	RAF/BAe Woodford	
XV866	HS Buccaneer S2B	RAF, stored Shawbury	
XV867	HS Buccaneer S2B [EF]	RAF/BAe Woodford	
XV868	HS Buccaneer S2B	RAF No 208 Sqn, Lossiemouth	
XV869	HS Buccaneer S2B	RAF No 12 Sqn, Lossiemouth	
XW175	HS Harrier T4A	MoD(PE) RAE Bedford	
XW179	WS Sioux AH1 (composite)	Wessex Aviation Society, Wimborne	
XW198	WS Puma HC1 [DL]	RAF No 230 Sqn, Gutersloh	
XW199	WS Puma HC1 [DU]	RAF No 230 Sqn, Gutersloh	
XW200	WS Puma HC1 [FA]	RAF No 240 OCU, Odiham	
XW201	WS Puma HC1 [FB]	RAF No 240 OCU, Odiham	
XW202	WS Puma HC1 [FC]	RAF No 240 OCU, Odiham	
XW204	WS Puma HC1 [CA]	RAF No 33 Sqn, Odiham	
XW206	WS Puma HC1 [CC]	RAF No 33 Sqn, Odiham	
XW207	WS Puma HC1 [CD]	RAF No 33 Sqn, Odiham	
XW208	WS Puma HC1 [DP]	RAF No 230 Sqn, Gutersloh	
XW209	WS Puma HC1 [CF]	RAF No 33 Sqn, Odiham	
XW210	WS Puma HC1 [CG]	RAF No 33 Sqn, Odiham	
XW211	WS Puma HC1 [CH]	RAF No 33 Sqn, Odiham	
XW212	WS Puma HC1 [FD]	RAF No 240 OCU, Odiham	
XW213	WS Puma HC1 [CJ]	RAF No 33 Sqn, Odiham	
XW214	WS Puma HC1 [CK]	RAF No 33 Sqn, Odiham	
XW215	WS Puma HC1 [DM]	RAF No 230 Sqn, Gutersloh	
XW216	WS Puma HC1 [CL]	RAF No 1563 Flt, Belize	
XW217	WS Puma HC1 [DA]	RAF No 230 Sqn, Gutersloh	
XW218	WS Puma HC1 [DT]	RAF No 230 Sqn, Gutersloh	
XW219	WS Puma HC1 [DC]	RAF No 230 Sqn, Gutersloh	
XW220	WS Puma HC1 [DD]	RAF No 230 Sqn, Gutersloh	
XW221	WS Puma HC1 [DE]	RAF No 230 Sqn, Gutersloh	
XW222	WS Puma HC1 [DF]	RAF No 230 Sqn, Gutersloh	
XW223	WS Puma HC1 [DG]	RAF No 230 Sqn, Gutersloh	
XW224	WS Puma HC1 [DH]	RAF No 230 Sqn, Gutersloh	
XW225	WS Puma HC1 [FE]	RAF No 240 OCU, Odiham	
XW226	WS Puma HC1 [DK]	RAF No 230 Sqn, Gutersloh	
XW227	WS Puma HC1 [DN]	RAF No 230 Sqn, Gutersloh	
XW229	WS Puma HC1 [DB]	RAF No 230 Sqn, Gutersloh	
XW231	WS Puma HC1 [CM]	RAF No 33 Sqn, Odiham	
XW232	WS Puma HC1 [DJ]	RAF No 230 Sqn, Gutersloh	
XW233	WS Puma HC1 [CN]	RAF No 1563 Flt, Belize	

Notes	Serial	Type (alternative identity)	Owner, Operator or Location
	XW234	WS Puma HC1 [CO]	RAF No 33 Sqn, Odiham
	XW235	WS Puma HC1 [CP]	RAF No 33 Sqn, Odiham
	XW236	WS Puma HC1 [CQ]	RAF No 33 Sqn, Odiham
	XW237	WS Puma HC1 [CR]	RAF No 33 Sqn, Odiham
	XW241	Sud SA330E Puma (F-ZJUX)	MoD(PE) RAE Bedford
	XW249	Cushioncraft CC7	Cornwall Aero Park, Helston
	XW255	BHC BH-7 Wellington	RN NHTU, Lee-on-Solent
	XW264	HS Harrier T2 (forward fuselage)	CARG store, RAF Innsworth
	XW265	HS Harrier T4A [V]	RAF No 233 OCU, Wittering
	XW266	HS Harrier T4A [S]	RAF No 233 OCU, Wittering
	XW267	HS Harrier T4	MoD(PE) A&AEE, Boscombe Down
	XW268	HS Harrier T4A [U]	RAF No 233 OCU, Wittering
	XW269	HS Harrier T4	RAF No 233 OCU, Wittering
	XW270	HS Harrier T4 [T]	RAF No 4 Sqn, Gutersloh
	XW271	HS Harrier T4 [Z]	RAF No 3 Sqn, Gutersloh
	XW272	HS Harrier T4 (8783M) (nose only)	Cranfield Institute of Technology
	XW276	Aerospatiale SA341 (F-ZWRI)	Science Museum, Wroughton
	XW280	WS Scout AH1	AAC No 666 (TA) Sqn, Netheravon
	XW281	WS Scout AH1 [U]	AAC No 666 (TA) Sqn, Netheravon
	XW282	WS Scout AH1 [W]	AAC No 666 (TA) Sqn, Netheravon
	XW283	WS Scout AH1 [X]	AAC No 658 Sqn, Netheravon
	XW284	WS Scout AH1 [A]	AAC, stored Wroughton
	XW287	BAC Jet Provost T5 [P]	RAF No 6 FTS, Finningley
	XW289	BAC Jet Provost T5A [61]	RAF No 1 FTS, Linton-on-Ouse
	XW290	BAC Jet Provost T5A [41]	RAF College, Cranwell
	XW291	BAC Jet Provost T5 [N]	RAF No 6 FTS, Finningley
	XW292	BAC Jet Provost T5A [32]	RAF College, Cranwell
	XW293	BAC Jet Provost T5 [Z]	RAF No 6 FTS, Finningley
	XW294	BAC Jet Provost T5A [45]	RAF College, Cranwell
	XW295	BAC Jet Provost T5A [29]	RAF College, Cranwell
	XW296	BAC Jet Provost T5 [Q]	RAF No 6 FTS, Finningley
	XW298	BAC Jet Provost T5 [O]	RAF No 6 FTS, Finningley
	XW299	BAC Jet Provost T5A [60]	RAF No 1 FTS, Linton-on-Ouse
	XW301	BAC Jet Provost T5A [63]	RAF No 1 FTS, Linton-on-Ouse
	XW302	BAC Jet Provost T5 [T]	RAF No 6 FTS, Finningley
	XW303	BAC Jet Provost T5A [127]	RAF No 7 FTS, Church Fenton
	XW304	BAC Jet Provost T5 [X]	RAF No 6 FTS, Finningley
	XW305	BAC Jet Provost T5A [42]	RAF College, Cranwell
	XW306	BAC Jet Provost T5 [Y]	RAF No 6 FTS, Finningley
	XW307	BAC Jet Provost T5 [S]	RAF No 6 FTS, Finningley
	XW309	BAC Jet Provost T5 [V]	RAF No 6 FTS, Finningley
	XW310	BAC Jet Provost T5A [37]	RAF College, Cranwell
	XW311	BAC Jet Provost T5 [W]	RAF No 6 FTS, Finningley
	XW312	BAC Jet Provost T5A [64]	RAF No 1 FTS, Linton-on-Ouse
	XW313	BAC Jet Provost T5A [30]	RAF College, Cranwell
	XW315	BAC Jet Provost T5A [50]	RAF Abingdon, BDRF
	XW316	BAC Jet Provost T5A [28]	RAF College, Cranwell
	XW317	BAC Jet Provost T5A [25]	RAF College, Cranwell
	XW318	BAC Jet Provost T5A [12]	RAF College, Cranwell
	XW319	BAC Jet Provost T5A [57]	RAF No 3 FTS, Scampton
	XW320	BAC Jet Provost T5A [71]	RAF No 1 FTS, Linton-on-Ouse
	XW321	BAC Jet Provost T5A [132]	RAF No 7 FTS, Church Fenton
	XW322	BAC Jet Provost T5A [43]	RAF College, Cranwell
	XW323	BAC Jet Provost T5A [44]	RAF College, Cranwell
	XW324	BAC Jet Provost T5 [U]	RAF No 6 FTS, Finningley
	XW325	BAC Jet Provost T5A [33]	RAF College, Cranwell
	XW326	BAC Jet Provost T5A [62]	RAF No 1 FTS, Linton-on-Ouse
	XW327	BAC Jet Provost T5A [134]	RAF No 7 FTS, Church Fenton
	XW328	BAC Jet Provost T5A [22]	RAF College, Cranwell
	XW329	BAC Jet Provost T5A [48] (8741M)	RAF Church Fenton Fire Section
	XW330	BAC Jet Provost T5A [130]	RAF No 7 FTS, Church Fenton
	XW332	BAC Jet Provost T5A [34]	RAF College, Cranwell
	XW333	BAC Jet Provost T5A [61]	RAF No 3 FTS, Scampton
	XW334	BAC Jet Provost T5A [131]	RAF No 7 FTS, Church Fenton
	XW335	BAC Jet Provost T5A [27]	RAF College, Cranwell
	XW336	BAC Jet Provost T5A [6]	RAF College, Cranwell
	XW351	BAC Jet Provost T5A [31]	RAF College, Cranwell
	XW352	BAC Jet Provost T5 [R]	RAF No 6 FTS, Finningley
	XW353	BAC Jet Provost T5A [51]	RAF No 3 FTS, Scampton
	XW354	BAC Jet Provost T5A [7]	RAF College, Cranwell

Serial	Type (alternative identity)	Owner, Operator or Location	Notes
XW355	BAC Jet Provost T5A [20]	RAF College, Cranwell	
XW357	BAC Jet Provost T5A [5]	RAF College, Cranwell	
XW358	BAC Jet Provost T5A [18]	RAF College, Cranwell	
XW359	BAC Jet Provost T5A [65]	RAF No 1 FTS, Linton-on-Ouse	
XW360	BAC Jet Provost T5A [129]	RAF No 7 FTS, Church Fenton	
XW361	BAC Jet Provost T5A [21]	RAF College, Cranwell	
XW362	BAC Jet Provost T5A [17]	RAF College, Cranwell	
XW363	BAC Jet Provost T5A [36]	RAF College, Cranwell	
XW364	BAC Jet Provost T5A [35]	RAF College, Cranwell	
XW365	BAC Jet Provost T5A [73]	RAF No 1 FTS, Linton-on-Ouse	
XW366	BAC Jet Provost T5A [75]	RAF No 1 FTS, Linton-on-Ouse	
XW367	BAC Jet Provost T5A [26]	RAF College, Cranwell	
XW368	BAC Jet Provost T5A [L]	RAF No 6 FTS, Finningley	
XW369	BAC Jet Provost T5A [9]	RAF College, Cranwell	
XW370	BAC Jet Provost T5A [72]	RAF No 1 FTS, Linton-on-Ouse	
XW372	BAC Jet Provost T5A [M]	RAF No 6 FTS, Finningley	
XW373	BAC Jet Provost T5A [11]	RAF College, Cranwell	
XW374	BAC Jet Provost T5A [38]	RAF College, Cranwell	
XW375	BAC Jet Provost T5A [52]	RAF No 3 FTS, Scampton	
XW404	BAC Jet Provost T5A [77]	RAF No 1 FTS, Linton-on-Ouse	
XW405	BAC Jet Provost T5A [J]	RAF No 6 FTS, Finningley	
XW406	BAC Jet Provost T5A [23]	RAF College, Cranwell	
XW408	BAC Jet Provost T5A [24]	RAF College, Cranwell	
XW409	BAC Jet Provost T5A [123]	RAF No 7 FTS, Church Fenton	
XW410	BAC Jet Provost T5A [80]	RAF No 1 FTS, Linton-on-Ouse	
XW412	BAC Jet Provost T5A [15]	RAF College, Cranwell	
XW413	BAC Jet Provost T5A [69]	RAF No 1 FTS, Linton-on-Ouse	
XW415	BAC Jet Provost T5A [53]	RAF No 3 FTS, Scampton	
XW416	BAC Jet Provost T5A [19]	RAF College, Cranwell	
XW418	BAC Jet Provost T5A [126]	RAF No 7 FTS, Church Fenton	
XW419	BAC Jet Provost T5A [125]	RAF No 7 FTS, Church Fenton	
XW420	BAC Jet Provost T5A [8]	RAF College, Cranwell	
XW421	BAC Jet Provost T5A [60]	RAF No 3 FTS, Scampton	
XW422	BAC Jet Provost T5A [3]	RAF College, Cranwell	
XW423	BAC Jet Provost T5A [14]	RAF College, Cranwell	
XW424	BAC Jet Provost T5A [62]	Privately owned, Misson, Notts	
XW425	BAC Jet Provost T5A [H]	RAF No 6 FTS, Finningley	
XW427	BAC Jet Provost T5A [56]	RAF No 3 FTS, Scampton	
XW428	BAC Jet Provost T5A [39]	RAF College, Cranwell	
XW429	BAC Jet Provost T5A [66]	RAF No 1 FTS, Linton-on-Ouse	
XW430	BAC Jet Provost T5A [58]	RAF No 3 FTS, Scampton	
XW431	BAC Jet Provost T5A [59]	RAF No 3 FTS, Scampton	
XW432	BAC Jet Provost T5A [76]	RAF No 1 FTS, Linton-on-Ouse	
XW433	BAC Jet Provost T5A [124]	RAF No 7 FTS, Church Fenton	
XW434	BAC Jet Provost T5A [78]	RAF No 1 FTS, Linton-on-Ouse	
XW435	BAC Jet Provost T5A [4]	RAF College, Cranwell	
XW436	BAC Jet Provost T5A [62]	RAF No 3 FTS, Scampton	
XW437	BAC Jet Provost T5A [1]	RAF College, Cranwell	
XW438	BAC Jet Provost T5A [2]	RAF College, Cranwell	
XW527	HS Buccaneer S2B [527]	RAF No 12 Sqn, Lossiemouth	
XW528	HS Buccaneer S2B (8861M) [C]	RAF Coningsby, BDRT	
XW529	HS Buccaneer S2B	RAF	
XW530	HS Buccaneer S2B	RAF No 12 Sqn, Lossiemouth	
XW533	HS Buccaneer S2B	RAF No 208 Sqn, Lossiemouth	
XW534	HS Buccaneer S2B	MoD(PE)/A&AEE Boscombe Down	
XW538	HS Buccaneer S2B (8660M) [T]	RAF Lossiemouth Fire Section	
XW540	HS Buccaneer S2B	Crashed 22 April 1987, into North Sea	
XW541	HS Buccaneer S2B (8858M)	RAF Honington Fire Section	
XW542	HS Buccaneer S2B	RAF No 12 Sqn, Lossiemouth	
XW543	HS Buccaneer S2B	RAF No 12 Sqn, Lossiemouth	
XW544	HS Buccaneer S2B (8857M) [Y]	RAF No 2 SoTT, Cosford	
XW545	HS Buccaneer S2B (8859M)	RAF St Athan, BDRT	
XW546	HS Buccaneer S2B	MoD(PE) BAe Woodford	
XW547	HS Buccaneer S2B	RAF No 12 Sqn, Lossiemouth	
XW549	HS Buccaneer S2B (8860M)	RAF Kinloss, BDRT	
XW550	HS Buccaneer S2B [X]	RAF, stored St Athan	
XW566	SEPECAT Jaguar T2	MoD(PE) RAE Farnborough store	
XW612	WS Scout AH1 [X]	AAC No 658 Sqn, Netheravon	
XW613	WS Scout AH1 [V]	AAC, stored Wroughton	
XW614	WS Scout AH1	AAC, stored Wroughton	
XW615	WS Scout AH1	AAC, stored Wroughton	
XW616	WS Scout AH1	AAC Garrison Air Sqn, Falkland Islands	
XW626	HS Comet 4AEW (G-APDS)	MoD(PE), stored RAE Bedford	

Notes	Serial	Type (alternative identity)	Owner, Operator or Location
	XW630	HS Harrier GR3 [M]	RAF No 4 Sqn, Gutersloh
	XW635	Beagle D5/180 (G-AWSW)	RAF No 5 AEF, Teversham
	XW664	HS Nimrod R1P	RAF No 51 Sqn, Wyton
	XW665	HS Nimrod R1	RAF No 51 Sqn, Wyton
	XW666	HS Nimrod R1	RAF No 51 Sqn, Wyton
	XW750	HS748 Series 107 (G-ASJT)	MoD(PE) RAE Bedford
	XW763	HS Harrier GR3 [02]	RAF No 1 Sqn, Wittering
	XW764	HS Harrier GR3 [C]	RAF No 3 Sqn, Gutersloh
	XW768	HS Harrier GR3 [20]	RAF No 4 Sqn, Gutersloh
	XW788	HS125 CC1	RAF No 32 Sqn, Northolt
	XW789	HS125 CC1	RAF No 32 Sqn, Northolt
	XW790	HS125 CC1	RAF No 32 Sqn, Northolt
	XW791	HS125 CC1	RAF No 32 Sqn, Northolt
	XW795	WS Scout AH1	AAC, stored Wroughton
	XW796	WS Scout AH1 [V]	AAC No 660 Sqn, Sek Kong
	XW797	WS Scout AH1 [T]	AAC, stored Wroughton
	XW798	WS Scout AH1 [U]	AAC, stored Wroughton
	XW799	WS Scout AH1 [Z]	AAC No 658 Sqn, Netheravon
	XW836	WS Lynx	AAC Middle Wallop, BDRT
	XW838	WS Lynx [TAD 009]	AAC AETW, Middle Wallop
	XW839	WS Lynx	Rolls-Royce, Filton
	XW843	WS Gazelle AH1	AAC No 2 Flt, Netheravon
	XW844	WS Gazelle AH1	AAC No 661 Sqn, Hildesheim
	XW845	WS Gazelle HT2 [47/CU]	RN No 705 Sqn, Culdrose
	XW846	WS Gazelle AH1	AAC, stored Wroughton
	XW847	WS Gazelle AH1	AAC D&TS, Middle Wallop
	XW848	WS Gazelle AH1 [D]	AAC ARWS, Middle Wallop
	XW849	WS Gazelle AH1	RM 3 CBAS, Yeovilton
	XW851	WS Gazelle AH1 [33A]	RM 3 CBAS, Yeovilton
	XW852	WS Gazelle HT3	RAF No 32 Sqn, Northolt
	XW853	WS Gazelle HT2 [53/CU]	RN No 705 Sqn, Culdrose
	XW854	WS Gazelle HT2 [46/CU]	RN No 705 Sqn, Culdrose
	XW855	WS Gazelle HT3	RAF No 32 Sqn, Northolt
	XW856	WS Gazelle HT2 [47/CU]	RN No 705 Sqn, Culdrose
	XW857	WS Gazelle HT2 [55/CU]	RN No 705 Sqn, Culdrose
	XW858	WS Gazelle HT3 [C]	RAF No 2 FTS, Shawbury
	XW860	WS Gazelle HT2 [44/CU]	RN, stored Wroughton
	XW861	WS Gazelle HT2 [59/CU]	RN No 705 Sqn, Culdrose
	XW862	WS Gazelle HT3 [D]	RAF No 2 FTS, Shawbury
	XW863	WS Gazelle HT2 [42/CU]	RN, stored Wroughton
	XW864	WS Gazelle HT2 [54/CU]	RN, No 705 Sqn, Culdrose
	XW865	WS Gazelle AH1	AAC ARWS, Middle Wallop
	XW866	WS Gazelle HT3 [E]	RAF No 2 FTS, Shawbury
	XW868	WS Gazelle HT2 [50/CU]	RN No 705 Sqn, Culdrose
	XW870	WS Gazelle HT3 [F]	RAF No 2 FTS, Shawbury
	XW871	WS Gazelle HT2 [44/CU]	RN No 705 Sqn, Culdrose
	XW884	WS Gazelle HT2 [41/CU]	RN No 705 Sqn, Culdrose
	XW885	WS Gazelle AH1 [B]	AAC ARWS, Middle Wallop
	XW886	WS Gazelle HT2 [48/CU]	RN No 705 Sqn, Culdrose
	XW887	WS Gazelle HT2 [57/CU]	RN, stored Wroughton
	XW888	WS Gazelle AH1	AAC AETW, Middle Wallop
	XW889	WS Gazelle AH1	AAC AETW, Middle Wallop
	XW890	WS Gazelle HT2 [53/CU]	RN, stored Wroughton
	XW891	WS Gazelle HT2 [49/CU]	RN No 705 Sqn, Culdrose
	XW892	WS Gazelle AH1	AAC No 663 Sqn, Soest
	XW893	WS Gazelle AH1	AAC Garrison Air Sqn, Fl
	XW894	WS Gazelle HT2 [52/CU]	RN No 705 Sqn, Culdrose
	XW895	WS Gazelle HT2 [51/CU]	RN No 705 Sqn, Culdrose
	XW897	WS Gazelle AH1	AAC No 664 Sqn, Minden
	XW898	WS Gazelle HT3 [G]	RAF No 2 FTS, Shawbury
	XW899	WS Gazelle AH1	AAC, stored Wroughton
	XW900	WS Gazelle AH1 (TAD-900)	AAC AETW, Middle Wallop
	XW902	WS Gazelle HT3 [H]	RAF No 2 FTS, Shawbury
	XW903	WS Gazelle AH1 [E]	AAC ARWS, Middle Wallop
	XW904	WS Gazelle AH1	AAC No 664 Sqn, Minden
	XW906	WS Gazelle HT3 [J]	RAF No 2 FTS, Shawbury
	XW907	WS Gazelle HT2 [40/CU]	RN No 705 Sqn, Culdrose
	XW908	WS Gazelle AH1	AAC, stored Wroughton
	XW909	WS Gazelle AH1	AAC No 664 Sqn, Detmold
	XW910	WS Gazelle HT3 [K]	RAF No 2 FTS, Shawbury
	XW911	WS Gazelle AH1 [I]	AAC ARWS, Middle Wallop
	XW912	WS Gazelle AH1	AAC AETW, Middle Wallop
	XW913	WS Gazelle AH1	AAC No 664 Sqn, Minden
	XW916	HS Harrier GR3 [W]	RAF Wittering Fire Section

Serial	Type (alternative identity)	Owner, Operator or Location	Notes
XW917	HS Harrier GR3 [L]	RAF No 3 Sqn, Gutersloh	
XW919	HS Harrier GR3 [03]	RAF No 1 Sqn, Wittering	
XW921	HS Harrier GR3 [E]	RAF No 3 Sqn, Gutersloh	
XW922	HS Harrier GR3 (8885M) [B]	MoD ROF, Enfield	
XW923	HS Harrier GR3 (cockpit) (8724M)	RAF Wittering for rescue training	
XW924	HS Harrier GR3 [G]	RAF No 4 Sqn, Gutersloh	
XW925	HS Harrier T4 [R]	RAF No 233 OCU, Wittering	
XW927	HS Harrier T4 [Q]	RAF No 233 OCU, Wittering	
XW930	HS125 (G-ATPC)	MoD(PE) RAE Bedford	
XW934	HS Harrier T4 [12]	RAF No 1 Sqn, Wittering	
XW986	HS Buccaneer S2B	MoD(PE) RAE Farnborough	
XW987	HS Buccaneer S2B	MoD(PE) RAE West Freugh	
XW988	HS Buccaneer S2B	MoD(PE) RAE West Freugh	
XX101	Cushioncraft CC7	British Rotorcraft Museum, Weston-super-Mare	
XX102	Cushioncraft CC7	Museum of Army Transport, Beverley	
XX105	BAC 1-11/201 (G-ASJD)	MoD(PE) RAE Bedford	
XX108	SEPECAT Jaguar GR1 (G27-313)	MoD(PE) BAe Warton	
XX109	SEPECAT Jaguar GR1 (8918M)	RAF Coltishall, ground instruction	
XX110	SEPECAT Jaguar GR1 [EP]	RAF, stored Shawbury	
XX110	SEPECAT Jaguar GR1 Replica (BAPC 169)	RAF No 1 SoTT, Halton	
XX112	SEPECAT Jaguar GR1A [EA]	RAF No 6 Sqn, Coltishall	
XX115	SEPECAT Jaguar GR1 (JI005) (8821M)	RAF Abingdon, BDRF	
XX116	SEPECAT Jaguar GR1A [02] (JI008)	RAF No 226 OCU, Lossiemouth	
XX117	SEPECAT Jaguar GR1A [06] (JI004)	RAF No 226 OCU, Lossiemouth	
XX118	SEPECAT Jaguar GR1 (JI018) (8815M)	RAF No 1 SoTT, Halton	
XX119	SEPECAT Jaguar GR1 [01] (8898M)	RAF No 226 OCU, Lossiemouth	
XX121	SEPECAT Jaguar GR1 [EQ]	RAF, stored Shawbury	
XX139	SEPECAT Jaguar T2A [C]	RAF No 226 OCU, Lossiemouth	
XX140	SEPECAT Jaguar T2 [D]	RAF, stored Shawbury	
XX141	SEPECAT Jaguar T2A [ET]	RAF No 6 Sqn, Coltishall	
XX143	SEPECAT Jaguar T2A [GS] (JI002)	RAF No 54 Sqn, Coltishall	
XX144	SEPECAT Jaguar T2A [I]	RAF No 226 OCU, Lossiemouth	
XX145	SEPECAT Jaguar T2	MoD(PE) ETPS, Boscombe Down	
XX146	SEPECAT Jaguar T2A	RAF, stored Shawbury	
XX150	SEPECAT Jaguar T2 [AX]	RAF, stored Shawbury	
XX154	HS Hawk T1 [1]	MoD(PE) RAE Llanbedr	
XX156	HS Hawk T1 [1]	MoD(PE) RAE Bedford	
XX157	HS Hawk T1 [A]	RAF No 2 TWU/63 Sqn, Chivenor	
XX158	HS Hawk T1A	RAF No 2 TWU/63 Sqn, Chivenor	
XX159	HS Hawk T1A	RAF No 1 TWU/234 Sqn Brawdy	
XX160	HS Hawk T1	MoD(PE) RAE Llanbedr	
XX161	HS Hawk T1	RAF CFS, Valley	
XX162	HS Hawk T1 Replica (BAPC 152)	RAF Exhibition Flight, Abingdon	
XX162	HS Hawk T1	RAF No 4 FTS, Valley	
XX163	HS Hawk T1	RAF No 4 FTS, Valley	
XX164	HS Hawk T1	RAF No 4 FTS, Valley	
XX165	HS Hawk T1	RAF No 4 FTS, Valley	
XX167	HS Hawk T1	RAF No 4 FTS, Valley	
XX168	HS Hawk T1	RAF No 4 FTS, Valley	
XX169	HS Hawk T1	RAF No 4 FTS, Valley	
XX170	HS Hawk T1	RAF No 4 FTS, Valley	
XX171	HS Hawk T1	RAF No 4 FTS, Valley	
XX172	HS Hawk T1	RAF CFS Valley	
XX173	HS Hawk T1	RAF No 4 FTS, Valley	
XX174	HS Hawk T1	RAF No 4 FTS, Valley	
XX175	HS Hawk T1	RAF No 4 FTS, Valley	
XX176	HS Hawk T1	RAF No 4 FTS, Valley	
XX177	HS Hawk T1	RAF No 4 FTS, Valley	
XX178	HS Hawk T1	RAF No 4 FTS, Valley	
XX179	HS Hawk T1	RAF No 4 FTS, Valley	
XX181	HS Hawk T1	RAF CFS, Valley	
XX182	HS Hawk T1	RAF No 4 FTS, Valley	
XX183	HS Hawk T1	RAF No 4 FTS, Valley	

Notes	Serial	Type (alternative identity)	Owner, Operator or Location
	XX184	HS Hawk T1	RAF No 4 FTS, Valley
	XX185	HS Hawk T1	RAF No 4 FTS, Valley
	XX186	HS Hawk T1A	RAF No 2 TWU/63 Sqn, Chivenor
	XX187	HS Hawk T1A	RAF No 1 TWU/79 Sqn, Brawdy
	XX188	HS Hawk T1A	RAF No 1 TWU/234 Sqn, Brawdy
	XX189	HS Hawk T1A [J]	RAF No 2 TWU/151 Sqn, Chivenor
	XX190	HS Hawk T1A	RAF No 1 TWU/234 Sqn, Brawdy
	XX191	HS Hawk T1A	RAF No 1 TWU/79 Sqn, Brawdy
	XX192	HS Hawk T1A	RAF No 1 TWU/79 Sqn, Brawdy
	XX193	HS Hawk T1A	RAF No 1 TWU/234 Sqn, Brawdy
	XX194	HS Hawk T1A	RAF No 1 TWU/234 Sqn, Brawdy
	XX195	HS Hawk T1A	RAF No 2 TWU/63 Sqn, Chivenor
	XX196	HS Hawk T1A	RAF No 1 TWU/234 Sqn, Brawdy
	XX197	HS Hawk T1A	RAF No 1 TWU/79 Sqn, Brawdy
	XX198	HS Hawk T1A	RAF No 1 TWU/79 Sqn, Brawdy
	XX199	HS Hawk T1A	RAF No 1 TWU, Brawdy
	XX200	HS Hawk T1A	RAF No 1 TWU/79 Sqn, Brawdy
	XX201	HS Hawk T1A [N]	RAF No 2 TWU/151 Sqn, Chivenor
	XX202	HS Hawk T1A [P]	RAF No 2 TWU/151 Sqn, Chivenor
	XX203	HS Hawk T1A	RAF No 2 TWU/63 Sqn, Chivenor
	XX204	HS Hawk T1A [H]	RAF No 2 TWU/151 Sqn, Chivenor
	XX205	HS Hawk T1A	RAF No 2 TWU/151 Sqn, Chivenor
	XX217	HS Hawk T1A	RAF No 2 TWU/63 Sqn, Chivenor
	XX218	HS Hawk T1A	RAF No 1 TWU/234 Sqn, Brawdy
	XX219	HS Hawk T1A [T]	RAF No 2 TWU/151 Sqn, Chivenor
	XX220	HS Hawk T1A	RAF No 1 TWU/234 Sqn, Brawdy
	XX221	HS Hawk T1A	RAF No 1 TWU/79 Sqn, Brawdy
	XX222	HS Hawk T1A	RAF No 1 TWU/79 Sqn, Brawdy
	XX223	HS Hawk T1	Crashed Valley 7 July 1986
	XX224	HS Hawk T1	RAF CFS, Valley
	XX225	HS Hawk T1	RAF No 4 FTS, Valley
	XX226	HS Hawk T1	RAF No 4 FTS, Valley
	XX227	HS Hawk T1A	RAF Red Arrows, Scampton
	XX228	HS Hawk T1A [Q]	RAF No 2 TWU/151 Sqn, Chivenor
	XX230	HS Hawk T1A [M]	RAF No 2 TWU/151 Sqn, Chivenor
	XX231	HS Hawk T1	RAF No 4 FTS, Valley
	XX232	HS Hawk T1	RAF No 4 FTS, Valley
	XX233	HS Hawk T1	RAF No 4 FTS, Valley
	XX234	HS Hawk T1	RAF CFS, Valley
	XX235	HS Hawk T1	RAF No 4 FTS, Valley
	XX236	HS Hawk T1	RAF No 4 FTS, Valley
	XX237	HS Hawk T1A	RAF Red Arrows, Scampton
	XX238	HS Hawk T1	RAF CFS, Valley
	XX239	HS Hawk T1	RAF No 4 FTS, Valley
	XX240	HS Hawk T1	RAF No 4 FTS, Valley
	XX241	HS Hawk T1	Crashed nr Scampton 16 November 1987
	XX242	HS Hawk T1	RAF No 4 FTS, Valley
	XX243	HS Hawk T1A	RAF Red Arrows, Scampton
	XX244	HS Hawk T1	RAF No 4 FTS, Valley
	XX245	HS Hawk T1	RAF No 4 FTS, Valley
	XX246	HS Hawk T1A	RAF No 2 TWU/63 Sqn, Chivenor
	XX247	HS Hawk T1A	RAF No 1 TWU/234 Sqn, Brawdy
	XX248	HS Hawk T1A [E]	RAF No 2 TWU/151 Sqn, Chivenor
	XX249	HS Hawk T1	RAF No 4 FTS, Valley
	XX250	HS Hawk T1	RAF No 4 FTS, Valley
	XX252	HS Hawk T1A	RAF Red Arrows, Scampton
	XX253	HS Hawk T1A	RAF Red Arrows, Scampton
	XX254	HS Hawk T1A	RAF No 2 TWU/63 Sqn, Chivenor
	XX255	HS Hawk T1A	RAF No 2 TWU/63 Sqn, Chivenor
	XX256	HS Hawk T1A	RAF No 2 TWU/63 Sqn, Chivenor
	XX257	HS Hawk T1	RAF Chivenor, BDRT
	XX258	HS Hawk T1A	RAF No 1 TWU/79 Sqn, Brawdy
	XX259	HS Hawk T1A	Crashed nr Scampton 16 November 1987
	XX260	HS Hawk T1A	RAF Red Arrows, Scampton
	XX261	HS Hawk T1A	RAF No 1 TWU/234 Sqn, Brawdy
	XX263	HS Hawk T1A	RAF No 2 TWU/63 Sqn, Chivenor
	XX264	HS Hawk T1A	RAF Red Arrows, Scampton
	XX265	HS Hawk T1A [U]	RAF No 2 TWU/151 Sqn, Chivenor
	XX266	HS Hawk T1A	RAF Red Arrows, Scampton
	XX278	HS Hawk T1A	RAF No 2 TWU/63 Sqn, Chivenor
	XX280	HS Hawk T1A	RAF No 1 TWU/79 Sqn, Brawdy
	XX281	HS Hawk T1A [O]	RAF No 2 TWU/151 Sqn, Chivenor

Serial	Type (alternative identity)	Owner, Operator or Location	Notes
XX282	HS Hawk T1A	RAF No 2 TWU/63 Sqn, Chivenor	
XX283	HS Hawk T1A	RAF No 2 TWU/63 Sqn, Chivenor	
XX284	HS Hawk T1A	RAF No 2 TWU/63 Sqn, Chivenor	
XX285	HS Hawk T1A [R]	RAF No 2 TWU/151 Sqn, Chivenor	
XX286	HS Hawk T1A	RAF No 1 TWU/79 Sqn, Brawdy	
XX287	HS Hawk T1A	RAF No 2 TWU/63 Sqn, Chivenor	
XX288	HS Hawk T1A	RAF No 2 TWU/63 Sqn, Chivenor	
XX289	HS Hawk T1A	RAF No 2 TWU/63 Sqn, Chivenor	
XX290	HS Hawk T1	RAF No 4 FTS, Valley	
XX291	HS Hawk T1	RAF No 4 FTS, Valley	
XX292	HS Hawk T1	RAF No 4 FTS, Valley	
XX293	HS Hawk T1	Scrapped 1987	
XX294	HS Hawk T1	RAF No 4 FTS, Valley	
XX295	HS Hawk T1	RAF No 4 FTS, Valley	
XX296	HS Hawk T1	RAF No 4 FTS, Valley	
XX297	HS Hawk T1A (8933M)	RAF Finningley Fire Section	
XX297	HS Hawk T1 Replica (BAPC171)	RAF Exhibition Flight, Abingdon	
XX299	HS Hawk T1	RAF No 4 FTS, Valley	
XX300	HS Hawk T1 [S] (8827M)	Scrapped at Valley July 1987	
XX301	HS Hawk T1A [L]	RAF No 2 TWU/151 Sqn, Chivenor	
XX302	HS Hawk T1A	RAF No 1 TWU/234 Sqn, Brawdy	
XX303	HS Hawk T1A	RAF No 1 TWU/234 Sqn, Brawdy	
XX304	HS Hawk T1A	RAF Red Arrows, Scampton	
XX306	HS Hawk T1A	RAF Red Arrows, Scampton	
XX307	HS Hawk T1	RAF No 4 FTS, Valley	
XX308	HS Hawk T1A	RAF Red Arrows, Scampton	
XX309	HS Hawk T1	RAF No 4 FTS, Valley	
XX310	HS Hawk T1	RAF CFS, Valley	
XX311	HS Hawk T1	RAF No 4 FTS, Valley	
XX312	HS Hawk T1	RAF CFS, Valley	
XX313	HS Hawk T1	RAF No 4 FTS, Valley	
XX314	HS Hawk T1 [S]	RAF No 2 TWU/151 Sqn, Chivenor	
XX315	HS Hawk T1A	RAF No 1 TWU/234 Sqn, Brawdy	
XX316	HS Hawk T1A	RAF No 1 TWU/79 Sqn, Brawdy	
XX317	HS Hawk T1A	RAF No 1 TWU/234 Sqn, Brawdy	
XX318	HS Hawk T1A	RAF No 1 TWU/79 Sqn, Brawdy	
XX319	HS Hawk T1A	RAF No 1 TWU/79 Sqn, Brawdy	
XX320	HS Hawk T1A	RAF No 2 TWU/63 Sqn, Chivenor	
XX321	HS Hawk T1A	RAF No 2 TWU/63 Sqn, Chivenor	
XX322	HS Hawk T1A [W]	RAF No 2 TWU/151 Sqn, Chivenor	
XX323	HS Hawk T1A	RAF No 1 TWU/234 Sqn, Brawdy	
XX324	HS Hawk T1A	RAF No 1 TWU/234 Sqn, Brawdy	
XX325	HS Hawk T1A [X]	RAF No 2 TWU/151 Sqn, Chivenor	
XX326	HS Hawk T1A [A]	RAF No 2 TWU/151 Sqn, Chivenor	
XX327	HS Hawk T1A [B]	RAF No 2 TWU/151 Sqn, Chivenor	
XX329	HS Hawk T1A [C]	RAF No 2 TWU/151 Sqn, Chivenor	
XX330	HS Hawk T1A [D]	RAF No 2 TWU/151 Sqn, Chivenor	
XX331	HS Hawk T1A	RAF No 2 TWU/63 Sqn, Chivenor	
XX332	HS Hawk T1A [F]	RAF No 2 TWU/151 Sqn, Chivenor	
XX334	HS Hawk T1A	RAF No 2 TWU/63 Sqn, Chivenor	
XX335	HS Hawk T1A [I]	RAF No 2 TWU/151 Sqn, Chivenor	
XX337	HS Hawk T1A [K]	RAF No 2 TWU/151 Sqn, Chivenor	
XX338	HS Hawk T1	RAF No 4 FTS, Valley	
XX339	HS Hawk T1A	RAF No 1 TWU/234 Sqn, Brawdy	
XX341	HS Hawk T1 ASTRA [1]	MoD(PE) Institute of Technology, Cranfield	
XX342	HS Hawk T1 [2]	MoD(PE) ETPS Boscombe Down	
XX343	HS Hawk T1 [3]	MoD(PE) ETPS Boscombe Down	
XX344	HS Hawk T1 (8847M)	RAF Abingdon, BDRF	
XX345	HS Hawk T1A [Y]	RAF No 2 TWU/151 Sqn, Chivenor	
XX346	HS Hawk T1A	RAF No 2 TWU/63 Sqn, Chivenor	
XX347	HS Hawk T1	RAF No 4 FTS, Valley	
XX348	HS Hawk T1A	RAF No 1 TWU/234 Sqn, Brawdy	
XX349	HS Hawk T1	RAF No 2 TWU/63 Sqn, Chivenor	
XX350	HS Hawk T1A	RAF No 1 TWU/234 Sqn, Brawdy	
XX351	HS Hawk T1A	RAF No 1 TWU/234 Sqn, Brawdy	
XX352	HS Hawk T1A	RAF No 2 TWU/63 Sqn, Chivenor	
XX370	WS Gazelle AH1 [A]	AAC No 658 Sqn, Netheravon	
XX371	WS Gazelle AH1	AAC No 12 Flt, Wildenrath	
XX372	WS Gazelle AH1 [B]	AAC No 658 Sqn, Netheravon	
XX373	WS Gazelle AH1	AAC No 663 Sqn, Soest	
XX375	WS Gazelle AH1 [C]	AAC No 658 Sqn, Netheravon	
XX376	WS Gazelle AH1 [D]	Written off 29 September 1983	

Notes	Serial	Type (alternative identity)	Owner, Operator or Location
	XX377	WS Gazelle AH1 [L]	Written off 6 June 1982
	XX378	WS Gazelle AH1	AAC, stored Wroughton
	XX379	WS Gazelle AH1 [D]	AAC No 658 Sqn, Netheravon
	XX380	WS Gazelle AH1	RM 3 CBAS, Yeovilton
	XX381	WS Gazelle AH1	AAC No 2 Flt, Netheravon
	XX382	WS Gazelle HT3 [M]	RAF No 2 FTS, Shawbury
	XX383	WS Gazelle AH1 [E]	AAC No 658 Sqn, Netheravon
	XX384	WS Gazelle AH1	AAC No 661 Sqn, Hildesheim
	XX385	WS Gazelle AH1 [W]	AAC No 663 Sqn, Soest
	XX386	WS Gazelle AH1	AAC No 12 Flt, Wildenrath
	XX387	WS Gazelle AH1	AAC No 661 Sqn, Hildesheim
	XX388	WS Gazelle AH1	AAC No 652 Sqn, Hildesheim
	XX389	WS Gazelle AH1	AAC No 652 Sqn, Hildesheim
	XX391	WS Gazelle HT2 [56/CU]	RN No 705 Sqn, Culdrose
	XX392	WS Gazelle AH1 [W]	AAC ARWS, Middle Wallop
	XX393	WS Gazelle AH1	AAC No 2 Flt, Netheravon
	XX394	WS Gazelle AH1	AAC No 2 Flt, Netheravon
	XX395	WS Gazelle AH1	AAC No 663 Sqn, Soest
	XX396	WS Gazelle HT3 (8718M) [N]	RAF Exhibition Flight, Henlow
	XX398	WS Gazelle AH1	AAC No 661 Sqn, Hildesheim
	XX399	WS Gazelle AH1	RM, stored Wroughton
	XX403	WS Gazelle AH1 [Y]	AAC ARWS, Middle Wallop
	XX405	WS Gazelle AH1	AAC No 669 Sqn, Detmold
	XX406	WS Gazelle HT3 [P]	RAF No 2 FTS, Shawbury
	XX407	WS Gazelle AH1	AAC No 661 Sqn, Hildesheim
	XX408	WS Gazelle AH1	AAC Garrison Air Sqn, Falklands
	XX409	WS Gazelle AH1	AAC No 656 Sqn, Netheravon
	XX410	WS Gazelle HT2 [58/CU]	RN AES, Lee-on-Solent
	XX411	WS Gazelle AH1 [X]	AAC Middle Wallop, BDRT
	XX411	WS Gazelle AH1 (tail only)	FAA Museum, RNAS Yeovilton
	XX412	WS Gazelle AH1 [33C]	RM 3 CBAS, Yeovilton
	XX413	WS Gazelle AH1 [13A]	RM 3 CBAS, Yeovilton
	XX414	WS Gazelle AH1	AAC No 663 Sqn, Soest
	XX416	WS Gazelle AH1	AAC No 664 Sqn, Minden
	XX417	WS Gazelle AH1 [C]	AAC No 665 Sqn, Aldergrove
	XX418	WS Gazelle AH1	AAC No 664 Sqn, Minden
	XX419	WS Gazelle AH1	AAC No 663 Sqn, Soest
	XX431	WS Gazelle HT2 [43/CU]	RN No 705 Sqn, Culdrose
	XX432	WS Gazelle AH1	AAC No 664 Sqn, Minden
	XX433	WS Gazelle AH1 [D]	AAC No 665 Sqn, Aldergrove
	XX434	WS Gazelle AH1	RAF Abingdon, BDRF
	XX435	WS Gazelle AH1	AAC No 663 Sqn, Soest
	XX436	WS Gazelle HT2 [39/CU]	RN No 705 Sqn, Culdrose
	XX437	WS Gazelle AH1	AAC No 663 Sqn, Soest
	XX438	WS Gazelle AH1	AAC No 664 Sqn, Minden
	XX439	WS Gazelle AH1	AAC No 651 Sqn, Hildesheim
	XX440	WS Gazelle AH1 (G-BCHN) [E]	AAC No 665 Sqn, Aldergrove
	XX441	WS Gazelle HT2 [38/CU]	RN No 705 Sqn, Culdrose
	XX442	WS Gazelle AH1	AAC No 664 Sqn, Detmold
	XX443	WS Gazelle AH1 [X]	AAC No 653 Sqn, Soest
	XX444	WS Gazelle AH1	AAC No 658 Sqn, Netheravon
	XX445	WS Gazelle AH1	AAC No 659 Sqn, Detmold
	XX446	WS Gazelle HT2 [57/CU]	RN No 705 Sqn, Culdrose
	XX447	WS Gazelle AH1 [Y]	AAC No 653 Sqn, Soest
	XX448	WS Gazelle AH1	AAC No 659 Sqn, Detmold
	XX449	WS Gazelle AH1	AAC No 669 Sqn, Detmold
	XX450	WS Gazelle AH1 [13B]	RM 3 CBAS, Yeovilton
	XX451	WS Gazelle HT2 [58/CU]	RN No 705 Sqn, Culdrose
	XX452	WS Gazelle AH1	AAC Middle Wallop Fire Section
	XX453	WS Gazelle AH1	AAC No 661 Sqn, Detmold
	XX454	WS Gazelle AH1	AAC No 664 Sqn, Detmold
	XX455	WS Gazelle AH1	AAC No 661 Sqn, Hildesheim
	XX456	WS Gazelle AH1	AAC No 12 Flt, Wildenrath
	XX457	WS Gazelle AH1 [H]	AAC ARWS, Middle Wallop
	XX460	WS Gazelle AH1	AAC No 661 Sqn, Hildesheim
	XX462	WS Gazelle AH1	AAC No 652 Sqn, Hildesheim
	XX466	HS Hunter T66B/T7 [830/DD]	RNAS Culdrose, SAH
	XX467	HS Hunter T66B/T7 [86]	Air Service Training, Perth
	XX469	WS Lynx HAS2 (G-BNCL)	Helicopter Museum of GB, Blackpool
	XX475	SA Jetstream T2 [572/CU] (G-AWVJ/N1036S)	RN No 750 Sqn, Culdrose
	XX476	SA Jetstream T2 [561/CU] (G-AXGL/N1037S)	RN No 750 Sqn, Culdrose
	XX477	SA Jetstream T1 (8462M) (G-AXXS)	RAF Finningley — ground instruction

Serial	Type (alternative identity)	Owner, Operator or Location	Notes
XX478	SA Jetstream T2 [564/CU] (G-AXXT)	RN No 750 Sqn, Culdrose	
XX479	SA Jetstream T2 [563/CU] (G-AXUR)	RN No 750 Sqn, Culdrose	
XX480	SA Jetstream T2 [565/CU] (G-AXXU)	RN No 750 Sqn, Culdrose	
XX481	SA Jetstream T2 [560/CU] (G-AXUP)	RN No 750 Sqn, Culdrose	
XX482	SA Jetstream T1 [J]	RAF No 6 FTS, Finningley	
XX483	SA Jetstream T2 [562/CU]	RN No 750 Sqn, Culdrose	
XX484	SA Jetstream T2 [566/CU]	RN No 750 Sqn, Culdrose	
XX485	SA Jetstream T2 [567/CU]	RN No 750 Sqn, Culdrose	
XX486	SA Jetstream T2 [569/CU]	RN No 750 Sqn, Culdrose	
XX487	SA Jetstream T2 [568/CU]	RN No 750 Sqn, Culdrose	
XX488	SA Jetstream T2 [571/CU]	RN No 750 Sqn, Culdrose	
XX489	SA Jetstream T2 [575/CU]	RN No 750 Sqn, Culdrose	
XX490	SA Jetstream T2 [570/CU]	RN No 750 Sqn, Culdrose	
XX491	SA Jetstream T1 [K]	RAF No 6 FTS, Finningley	
XX492	SA Jetstream T1 [A]	RAF No 6 FTS, Finningley	
XX493	SA Jetstream T1 [L]	RAF No 6 FTS, Finningley	
XX494	SA Jetstream T1 [B]	RAF No 6 FTS, Finningley	
XX495	SA Jetstream T1 [C]	RAF No 6 FTS, Finningley	
XX496	SA Jetstream T1 [D]	RAF No 6 FTS, Finningley	
XX497	SA Jetstream T1 [E]	RAF No 6 FTS, Finningley	
XX498	SA Jetstream T1 [F]	RAF No 6 FTS, Finningley	
XX499	SA Jetstream T1 [G]	RAF No 6 FTS, Finningley	
XX500	SA Jetstream T1 [H]	RAF No 6 FTS, Finningley	
XX507	HS125 CC2	RAF No 32 Sqn, Northolt	
XX508	HS125 CC2	RAF No 32 Sqn, Northolt	
XX513	SA Bulldog T1 [A]	RAF No 1 FTS/RNEFTS, Topcliffe	
XX515	SA Bulldog T1 [7]	RAF CFS, Scampton	
XX516	SA Bulldog T1 [C]	RAF No 1 FTS/RNEFTS, Topcliffe	
XX517	SA Bulldog T1 [S]	RAF No 1 FTS/RNEFTS, Topcliffe	
XX518	SA Bulldog T1 [Z]	RAF, Cambridge UAS, Teversham	
XX519	SA Bulldog T1 [I]	RAF No 1 FTS/RNEFTS, Topcliffe	
XX520	SA Bulldog T1 [2]	RAF CFS, Scampton	
XX521	SA Bulldog T1 [01]	RAF, East Lowlands UAS, Turnhouse	
XX522	SA Bulldog T1 [E]	RAF No 1 FTS/RNEFTS, Topcliffe	
XX523	SA Bulldog T1 [F]	RAF No 1 FTS/RNEFTS, Topcliffe	
XX524	SA Bulldog T1 [04]	RAF, London UAS, Abingdon	
XX525	SA Bulldog T1 [03]	RAF, East Lowlands UAS, Turnhouse	
XX526	SA Bulldog T1 [C]	RAF, Oxford UAS, Abingdon	
XX527	SA Bulldog T1 [G]	RAF No 1 FTS/RNEFTS, Topcliffe	
XX528	SA Bulldog T1 [D]	RAF, Oxford UAS, Abingdon	
XX529	SA Bulldog T1 [H]	RAF No 1 FTS/RNEFTS, Topcliffe	
XX530	SA Bulldog T1 [12]	CTE, RAF Manston	
XX531	SA Bulldog T1 [B]	RAF No 1 FTS/RNEFTS, Topcliffe	
XX532	SA Bulldog T1 [J]	RAF, Yorkshire UAS, Finningley	
XX533	SA Bulldog T1 [J]	RAF No 1 FTS/RNEFTS, Topcliffe	
XX534	SA Bulldog T1 [04]	RAF, East Lowlands UAS, Turnhouse	
XX535	SA Bulldog T1 [10]	RAF, London UAS, Abingdon	
XX536	SA Bulldog T1 [D]	RAF No 1 FTS/RNEFTS, Topcliffe	
XX537	SA Bulldog T1 [02]	RAF, East Lowlands UAS, Turnhouse	
XX538	SA Bulldog T1 [E]	RAF, stored Shawbury	
XX539	SA Bulldog T1 [1]	RAF CFS, Scampton	
XX540	SA Bulldog T1 [K]	RAF No 1 FTS/RNEFTS, Topcliffe	
XX541	SA Bulldog T1 [L]	RAF No 1 FTS/RNEFTS, Topcliffe	
XX543	SA Bulldog T1 [F]	RAF, Yorkshire UAS, Finningley	
XX544	SA Bulldog T1 [01]	RAF, London UAS, Abingdon	
XX545	SA Bulldog T1 PAX [02]	RAF, East Lowlands UAS, Turnhouse	
XX546	SA Bulldog T1 [03]	RAF, London UAS, Abingdon	
XX547	SA Bulldog T1 [05]	RAF, London UAS, Abingdon	
XX548	SA Bulldog T1 [06]	RAF, London UAS, Abingdon	
XX549	SA Bulldog T1 [T]	RAF No 1 FTS/RNEFTS, Topcliffe	
XX550	SA Bulldog T1 [08]	RAF, Northumbria UAS, Teesside	
XX551	SA Bulldog T1 [M]	RAF No 1 FTS/RNEFTS, Topcliffe	
XX552	SA Bulldog T1 [08]	RAF, London UAS, Abingdon	
XX553	SA Bulldog T1 [07]	RAF, London UAS, Abingdon	
XX554	SA Bulldog T1 [09]	RAF, London UAS, Abingdon	
XX555	SA Bulldog T1 [10]	RAF CFS, Scampton	
XX556	SA Bulldog T1 [S]	RAF, East Midlands UAS, Newton	
XX557	SA Bulldog T1 PAX	RAF Topcliffe, ground instruction	
XX558	SA Bulldog T1 [A]	RAF, Birmingham UAS, Cosford	
XX559	SA Bulldog T1	RAF, Glasgow & Strathclyde UAS, Glasgow	

Notes	Serial	Type (alternative identity)	Owner, Operator or Location
	XX560	SA Bulldog T1	RAF, Glasgow & Strathclyde UAS, Glasgow
	XX561	SA Bulldog T1 [A]	RAF, Aberdeen, Dundee & St Andrews UAS, Leuchars
	XX562	SA Bulldog T1 [E]	RAF No 13 AEF, Sydenham
	XX611	SA Bulldog T1	RAF, Glasgow & Strathclyde UAS, Glasgow
	XX612	SA Bulldog T1 [05]	RAF, Wales UAS, St Athan
	XX613	SA Bulldog T1 [A]	RAF, Queen's UAS, Sydenham
	XX614	SA Bulldog T1 [1]	RAF, stored Shawbury
	XX615	SA Bulldog T1 [2]	RAF, Manchester UAS, Woodvale
	XX616	SA Bulldog T1 [3]	RAF, Manchester UAS, Woodvale
	XX617	SA Bulldog T1 [4]	RAF, Manchester UAS, Woodvale
	XX619	SA Bulldog T1 [B]	RAF, Yorkshire UAS, Finningley
	XX620	SA Bulldog T1 [C]	RAF, Yorkshire UAS, Finningley
	XX621	SA Bulldog T1 [D]	RAF, Yorkshire UAS, Finningley
	XX622	SA Bulldog T1 [E]	RAF, Yorkshire UAS, Finningley
	XX623	SA Bulldog T1 [M]	RAF, East Midlands UAS, Newton
	XX624	SA Bulldog T1 [G]	RAF, Yorkshire UAS, Finningley
	XX625	SA Bulldog T1 [01]	RAF, Wales UAS, St Athan
	XX626	SA Bulldog T1 [02]	RAF, Wales UAS, St Athan
	XX627	SA Bulldog T1 [03]	RAF, Wales UAS, St Athan
	XX628	SA Bulldog T1 [04]	RAF, Wales UAS, St Athan
	XX629	SA Bulldog T1 [V]	RAF, Northumbria UAS, Teesside
	XX630	SA Bulldog T1 [A]	RAF, Liverpool UAS, Woodvale
	XX631	SA Bulldog T1 [W]	RAF, Northumbria UAS, Teesside
	XX632	SA Bulldog T1 [D]	RAF, Bristol UAS, Filton
	XX633	SA Bulldog T1 [X]	RAF, Northumbria UAS, Teesside
	XX634	SA Bulldog T1 [C]	RAF, Cambridge UAS, Teversham
	XX635	SA Bulldog T1 (8767M) [S]	RAF St Athan, CTTS
	XX636	SA Bulldog T1 [Y]	RAF, Northumbria UAS, Teesside
	XX637	SA Bulldog T1 [Z]	RAF, Northumbria UAS, Teesside
	XX638	SA Bulldog T1 [N]	RAF No 1 FTS/RNEFTS, Topcliffe
	XX639	SA Bulldog T1 [02]	RAF, London UAS, Abingdon
	XX640	SA Bulldog T1 [U]	RAF, Queen's UAS, Sydenham
	XX653	SA Bulldog T1 [5]	RAF, CFS Scampton
	XX654	SA Bulldog T1 [A]	RAF, Bristol UAS, Filton
	XX655	SA Bulldog T1 [B]	RAF, Bristol UAS, Filton
	XX656	SA Bulldog T1 [C]	RAF, Bristol UAS, Filton
	XX657	SA Bulldog T1 [U]	RAF, Cambridge UAS, Teversham
	XX658	SA Bulldog T1 [A]	RAF, Cambridge UAS, Teversham
	XX659	SA Bulldog T1 [S]	RAF, Cambridge UAS, Teversham
	XX660	SA Bulldog T1 [A]	BAe Prestwick, spares recovery
	XX661	SA Bulldog T1 [B]	RAF, Oxford UAS, Abingdon
	XX663	SA Bulldog T1 [B]	RAF, Aberdeen, Dundee & St Andrews UAS, Leuchars
	XX664	SA Bulldog T1 [05]	RAF, East Lowlands UAS, Turnhouse
	XX665	SA Bulldog T1 [E]	RAF, Aberdeen, Dundee & St Andrews UAS, Leuchars
	XX666	SA Bulldog T1	RAF
	XX667	SA Bulldog T1 [D]	RAF, Aberdeen, Dundee & St Andrews UAS, Leuchars
	XX668	SA Bulldog T1 [P]	RAF No 1 FTS/RNEFTS, Topcliffe
	XX669	SA Bulldog T1 [B]	RAF, Birmingham UAS, Cosford
	XX670	SA Bulldog T1 [C]	RAF, Birmingham UAS, Cosford
	XX671	SA Bulldog T1 [D]	RAF, Birmingham UAS, Cosford
	XX672	SA Bulldog T1 [E]	RAF, Birmingham UAS, Cosford
	XX685	SA Bulldog T1 [L]	RAF, Liverpool UAS, Woodvale
	XX686	SA Bulldog T1 [U]	RAF, Liverpool UAS, Woodvale
	XX687	SA Bulldog T1 [A]	RAF, East Midlands UAS, Newton
	XX688	SA Bulldog T1 [S]	RAF, Liverpool UAS, Woodvale
	XX689	SA Bulldog T1 [3]	RAF CFS, Scampton
	XX690	SA Bulldog T1 [A]	RAF, Yorkshire UAS, Finningley
	XX691	SA Bulldog T1 [H]	RAF, Yorkshire UAS, Finningley
	XX692	SA Bulldog T1 [5]	RAF CFS, Scampton
	XX693	SA Bulldog T1 [11]	RAF CFS, Scampton
	XX694	SA Bulldog T1 [E]	RAF, East Midlands UAS, Newton
	XX695	SA Bulldog T1 [A]	RAF, Oxford UAS, Abingdon
	XX696	SA Bulldog T1 [8]	RAF CFS, Scampton
	XX697	SA Bulldog T1 [Q]	RAF, Queen's UAS, Sydenham
	XX698	SA Bulldog T1 [9]	RAF CFS, Scampton
	XX699	SA Bulldog T1 [Q]	RAF No 1 FTS/RNEFTS, Topcliffe
	XX700	SA Bulldog T1 [R]	RAF No 1 FTS/RNEFTS, Topcliffe

Serial	Type (alternative identity)	Owner, Operator or Location	Notes
XX701	SA Bulldog T1 [02]	RAF, Southampton UAS, Hurn	
XX702	SA Bulldog T1 [bl]	RAF, Glasgow & Strathclyde UAS, Glasgow	
XX704	SA Bulldog T1 [U]	RAF, East Midlands UAS, Newton	
XX705	SA Bulldog T1 [05]	RAF, Southampton UAS, Hurn	
XX706	SA Bulldog T1 [01]	RAF, Southampton UAS, Hurn	
XX707	SA Bulldog T1 [04]	RAF, Southampton UAS, Hurn	
XX708	SA Bulldog T1 [03]	RAF, Southampton UAS, Hurn	
XX709	SA Bulldog T1 [C]	RAF, Aberdeen, Dundee & St Andrews UAS, Leuchars	
XX710	SA Bulldog T1 [5]	RAF, Manchester UAS, Woodvale	
XX711	SA Bulldog T1 [S]	RAF, Queen's UAS, Sydenham	
XX712	SA Bulldog T1 [1]	RAF, Manchester UAS, Woodvale	
XX713	SA Bulldog T1 [6]	RAF CFS, Scampton	
XX714	SA Bulldog T1	MoD(PE) BAe Prestwick	
XX718	SEPECAT Jaguar GR1 Replica (BAPC150)	RAF Exhibition Flight, Abingdon	
XX719	SEPECAT Jaguar GR1A [EQ]	RAF No 6 Sqn, Coltishall	
XX720	SEPECAT Jaguar GR1A (JI003)	RAF No Sqn, Coltishall	
XX722	SEPECAT Jaguar GR1 [EF]	RAF, stored Shawbury	
XX723	SEPECAT Jaguar GR1A [07]	RAF No 226 OCU, Lossiemouth	
XX724	SEPECAT Jaguar GR1A [GA]	RAF No 54 Sqn, Coltishall	
XX725	SEPECAT Jaguar GR1A [EL] (JI010)	RAF No 6 Sqn, Coltishall	
XX726	SEPECAT Jaguar GR1 [EB]	RAF, stored Shawbury	
XX727	SEPECAT Jaguar GR1 [ER]	RAF, stored Shawbury	
XX729	SEPECAT Jaguar GR1A (JI012)	RAF No 6 Sqn, Coltishall	
XX730	SEPECAT Jaguar GR1 [EC]	RAF stored, Shawbury	
XX732	SEPECAT Jaguar GR1A [03]	Written off 27 November 1986	
XX733	SEPECAT Jaguar GR1A [EF]	RAF No 6 Sqn, Coltishall	
XX734	SEPECAT Jaguar GR1 (JI014) (8816M)	RAF Coltishall, BDRT	
XX736	SEPECAT Jaguar GR1 (JI013)	BAe Warton	
XX737	SEPECAT Jaguar GR1A [GG] (JI015)	RAF No 54 Sqn, Coltishall	
XX738	SEPECAT Jaguar GR1A [GJ] (JI016)	RAF No 54 Sqn, Coltishall	
XX739	SEPECAT Jaguar GR1 (8902M) [I]	RAF No 1 SoTT, Halton	
XX741	SEPECAT Jaguar GR1A [EJ]	RAF No 6 Sqn, Coltishall	
XX743	SEPECAT Jaguar GR1 [EG]	RAF, stored Shawbury	
XX744	SEPECAT Jaguar GR1 [DJ]	RAF, stored Shawbury	
XX745	SEPECAT Jaguar GR1A [03]	RAF No 226 OCU, Lossiemouth	
XX746	SEPECAT Jaguar GR1A [09] (8895M)	RAF No 1 SoTT, Halton	
XX747	SEPECAT Jaguar GR1 [B] (8903M)	RAF No 1 SoTT, Halton	
XX748	SEPECAT Jaguar GR1A [GD]	RAF No 54 Sqn, Coltishall	
XX751	SEPECAT Jaguar GR1 [10] (89--M)	RAF No 2 SoTT, Cosford	
XX752	SEPECAT Jaguar GR1A [GF]	RAF No 54 Sqn, Coltishall	
XX753	SEPECAT Jaguar GR1 [05]	RAF, stored Shawbury	
XX754	SEPECAT Jaguar GR1A [GR]	RAF No 54 Sqn, Coltishall	
XX756	SEPECAT Jaguar GR1 [AM] (8899M)	RAF No 2 SoTT, Cosford	
XX757	SEPECAT Jaguar GR1 [CU]	RAF, stored Shawbury	
XX763	SEPECAT Jaguar GR1 [24]	RAF, stored Shawbury	
XX764	SEPECAT Jaguar GR1 [3]	RAF, No 226 OCU, Lossiemouth	
XX765	SEPECAT Jaguar ACT	MoD(PE) BAe, stored Warton	
XX766	SEPECAT Jaguar GR1A [GP]	RAF No 54 Sqn, Coltishall	
XX767	SEPECAT Jaguar GR1A [GE]	RAF No 54 Sqn, Coltishall	
XX818	SEPECAT Jaguar GR1 [DE]	RAF, stored Shawbury	
XX819	SEPECAT Jaguar GR1 [CE] (8923M)	RAF No 2 SoTT, Cosford	
XX821	SEPECAT Jaguar GR1 [P] (8896M)	RAFC Cranwell Engineering School	
XX824	SEPECAT Jaguar GR1 [AD]	RAF, stored Shawbury	
XX825	SEPECAT Jaguar GR1 [BN]	RAF, stored Shawbury	
XX826	SEPECAT Jaguar GR1 [34]	RAF, stored Shawbury	
XX829	SEPECAT Jaguar T2A [D]	RAF No 226 OCU, Lossiemouth	
XX830	SEPECAT Jaguar T2	MoD(PE) ETPS, Boscombe Down	
XX832	SEPECAT Jaguar T2A [S]	RAF No 226 OCU, Lossiemouth	
XX833	SEPECAT Jaguar T2A [Z]	RAF No 41 Sqn, Coltishall	
XX834	SEPECAT Jaguar T2A [34]	RAF No 2 Sqn, Laarbruch	
XX835	SEPECAT Jaguar T2	MoD(PE) RAE Farnborough	
XX836	SEPECAT Jaguar T2A [ER]	RAF No 6 Sqn, Coltishall	

Notes	Serial	Type (alternative identity)	Owner, Operator or Location
	XX837	SEPECAT Jaguar T2 [Z]	RAF, stored Shawbury
	XX838	SEPECAT Jaguar T2A [X]	RAF No 226 OCU, Lossiemouth
	XX839	SEPECAT Jaguar T2 [Y]	RAF, stored Shawbury
	XX840	SEPECAT Jaguar T2A [T]	RAF No 226 OCU, Lossiemouth
	XX841	SEPECAT Jaguar T2 [S]	RAF, stored Shawbury
	XX842	SEPECAT Jaguar T2A [33]	RAF No 2 Sqn, Laarbruch
	XX843	SEPECAT Jaguar T2A [GT]	RAF No 54 Sqn, Coltishall
	XX844	SEPECAT Jaguar T2 [F]	MoD(PE) ETPS, Boscombe Down
	XX845	SEPECAT Jaguar T2 [AZ]	RAF Abingdon
	XX846	SEPECAT Jaguar T2A [A]	RAF No 226 OCU, Lossiemouth
	XX847	SEPECAT Jaguar T2 [G]	RAF, stored Shawbury
	XX885	HS Buccaneer S2B	RAF No 208 Sqn, Lossiemouth
	XX886	HS Buccaneer S2B	RAF Honington, WLT instructional use
	XX887	HS Buccaneer S2B	RAF, stored Shawbury
	XX888	HS Buccaneer S2B	RAF, stored Shawbury
	XX889	HS Buccaneer S2B	RAF No 12 Sqn, Lossiemouth
	XX892	HS Buccaneer S2B	RAF No 208 Sqn, Lossiemouth
	XX893	HS Buccaneer S2B	RAF No 237 OCU, Lossiemouth
	XX894	HS Buccaneer S2B	RAF No 208 Sqn, Lossiemouth
	XX895	HS Buccaneer S2B	RAF No 12 OCU, Lossiemouth
	XX896	HS Buccaneer S2B	RAF, stored Shawbury
	XX897	HS Buccaneer S2B	MoD(PE) RS&RE Bedford
	XX899	HS Buccaneer S2B	RAF No 237 OCU, Lossiemouth
	XX900	HS Buccaneer S2B	RAF No 208 Sqn, Lossiemouth
	XX901	HS Buccaneer S2B	RAF No 208 Sqn, Lossiemouth
	XX907	WS Lynx AH1	RAE, stored Farnborough
	XX910	WS Lynx HAS2	RAE, stored Farnborough
	XX914	BAC VC10 srs 1103 (G-ATDJ/ 8777M)	RAF AMS, Brize Norton
	XX919	BAC 1-11/402 (PI-C 1121)	MoD(PE) RAE Farnborough
	XX946	Panavia Tornado (P02) (8883M)	RAF Honington for ground instruction/ Saudi Support Unit
	XX947	Panavia Tornado (P03) (8797M)	RAF Marham for ground instruction
	XX948	Panavia Tornado (P06) (8879M)	RAF No 2 SoTT, Cosford
	XX955	SEPECAT Jaguar GR1A [GK]	RAF No 54 Sqn, Coltishall
	XX956	SEPECAT Jaguar GR1 [BE]	RAF, stored Shawbury
	XX958	SEPECAT Jaguar GR1 [BK]	RAF, stored Shawbury
	XX959	SEPECAT Jaguar GR1 [CJ]	RAF, stored Shawbury
	XX962	SEPECAT Jaguar GR1A [EK]	RAF No 6 Sqn, Coltishall
	XX965	SEPECAT Jaguar GR1A [04]	RAF No 226 OCU, Lossiemouth
	XX966	SEPECAT Jaguar GR1A (8904M) [EL]	RAF No 1 SoTT, Halton
	XX967	SEPECAT Jaguar GR1 [AC]	RAF, stored Shawbury
	XX968	SEPECAT Jaguar GR1 [AJ]	RAF, stored Shawbury
	XX969	SEPECAT Jaguar GR1A (8897M) [01]	RAF No 2 SoTT, Cosford
	XX970	SEPECAT Jaguar GR1A [EH]	RAF No 6 Sqn, Coltishall
	XX974	SEPECAT Jaguar GR1A [EG]	RAF No 6 Sqn, Coltishall
	XX975	SEPECAT Jaguar GR1 [07] (8905M)	RAF No 1 SoTT, Halton
	XX976	SEPECAT Jaguar GR1 (8906M) [BD]	RAF No 1 SoTT, Halton
	XX977	SEPECAT Jaguar GR1 [DL]	RAF, stored Shawbury
	XX979	SEPECAT Jaguar GR1A	MoD(PE) A&AEE Boscombe Down
	XZ101	SEPECAT Jaguar GR1A [Q]	RAF No 41 Sqn, Coltishall
	XZ103	SEPECAT Jaguar GR1A [23]	RAF No 2 Sqn, Laarbruch
	XZ104	SEPECAT Jaguar GR1A [24]	RAF No 2 Sqn, Laarbruch
	XZ106	SEPECAT Jaguar GR1A [26]	RAF No 2 Sqn, Laarbruch
	XZ107	SEPECAT Jaguar GR1A [H]	RAF No 41 Sqn, Coltishall
	XZ108	SEPECAT Jaguar GR1A [28]	RAF No 2 Sqn, Laarbruch
	XZ109	SEPECAT Jaguar GR1A [29]	RAF No 2 Sqn, Laarbruch
	XZ111	SEPECAT Jaguar GR1A [31]	RAF No 2 Sqn, Laarbruch
	XZ112	SEPECAT Jaguar GR1A [32]	RAF No 2 Sqn, Laarbruch
	XZ113	SEPECAT Jaguar GR1A [30]	RAF No 2 Sqn, Laarbruch
	XZ114	SEPECAT Jaguar GR1A [B]	RAF No 41 Sqn, Coltishall
	XZ115	SEPECAT Jaguar GR1A [C]	RAF No 41 Sqn, Coltishall
	XZ116	SEPECAT Jaguar GR1A [D]	Crashed 17 June 1987, Cumbria
	XZ117	SEPECAT Jaguar GR1A [E]	RAF No 41 Sqn, Coltishall
	XZ118	SEPECAT Jaguar GR1A [F]	RAF No 41 Sqn, Coltishall
	XZ119	SEPECAT Jaguar GR1A [G]	RAF No 41 Sqn, Coltishall
	XZ129	HS Harrier GR3 [09]	RAF No 1 Sqn, Wittering
	XZ130	HS Harrier GR3 [H]	RAF No 3 Sqn, Gutersloh

Serial	Type (alternative identity)	Owner, Operator or Location	Notes
XZ131	HS Harrier GR3 [D]	RAF No 1417 Flt, Belize	
XZ132	HS Harrier GR3 [04]	RAF No 1 Sqn, Wittering	
XZ133	HS Harrier GR3 [10]	RAF No 1 Sqn, Wittering	
XZ135	HS Harrier GR3 [P] (8848M) (nose only)	RAF Exhibition Flight, Abingdon	
XZ136	HS Harrier GR3 [O]	Crashed Otterburn 2 November 1987	
XZ138	HS Harrier GR3 [14]	RAF No 1 Sqn, Wittering	
XZ145	HS Harrier T4 [T]	RAF No 233 OCU, Wittering	
XZ146	HS Harrier T4 [W]	RAF No 233 OCU, Wittering	
XZ147	HS Harrier T4A [Z]	RAF No 233 OCU, Wittering	
XZ170	WS Lynx AH7	MoD(PE) Westlands, Yeovil	
XZ171	WS Lynx AH1	MoD(PE) Rolls-Royce, Filton	
XZ172	WS Lynx AH1 [K]	AAC ARW/LCF, Middle Wallop	
XZ173	WS Lynx AH1	AAC No 651 Sqn, Hildesheim	
XZ174	WS Lynx AH1	AAC No 651 Sqn, Hildesheim	
XZ175	WS Lynx AH1 [A]	AAC OTS/LCF, Middle Wallop	
XZ176	WS Lynx AH1 [A]	AAC ARW/LCF, Middle Wallop	
XZ177	WS Lynx AH1	AAC No 652 Sqn, Hildesheim	
XZ178	WS Lynx AH1	AAC No 654 Sqn, Detmold	
XZ179	WS Lynx AH1/5	MoD(PE) ETPS Boscombe Down	
XZ180	WS Lynx AH1	MoD(PE) Westlands, Yeovil	
XZ181	WS Lynx AH1	AAC No 663 Sqn, Soest	
XZ182	WS Lynx AH1 [23A]	RM 3 CBAS, Yeovilton	
XZ183	WS Lynx AH1	AAC No 669 Sqn, Detmold	
XZ184	WS Lynx AH1	AAC No 654 Sqn, Detmold	
XZ185	WS Lynx AH1	AAC No 663 Sqn, Soest	
XZ186	WS Lynx AH1	AAC No 662 Sqn, Soest	
XZ187	WS Lynx AH1	AAC No 655 Sqn, Aldergrove	
XZ188	WS Lynx AH1	AAC No 655 Sqn, Aldergrove	
XZ190	WS Lynx AH1	AAC No 651 Sqn, Hildesheim	
XZ191	WS Lynx AH1	AAC No 651 Sqn, Hildesheim	
XZ192	WS Lynx AH1	AAC No 651 Sqn, Hildesheim	
XZ193	WS Lynx AH1 [A]	AAC No 665 Sqn, Aldergrove	
XZ194	WS Lynx AH1	AAC No 663 Sqn, Soest	
XZ195	WS Lynx AH1 [X]	AAC No 665 Sqn, Aldergrove	
XZ196	WS Lynx AH1 [B]	AAC No 663 Sqn, Soest	
XZ197	WS Lynx AH1 [Y]	AAC No 665 Sqn, Aldergrove	
XZ198	WS Lynx AH1	AAC No 663 Sqn, Soest	
XZ199	WS Lynx AH1 [C]	AAC No 663 Sqn, Soest	
XZ203	WS Lynx AH1 [B]	AAC ARW/LCF, Middle Wallop	
XZ204	WS Lynx AH1	Written off 18 March 1987	
XZ205	WS Lynx AH1	AAC AETW, Middle Wallop	
XZ206	WS Lynx AH1	AAC No 655 Sqn, Aldergrove	
XZ207	WS Lynx AH1	AAC No 655 Sqn, Aldergrove	
XZ208	WS Lynx AH1	AAC No 655 Sqn, Aldergrove	
XZ209	WS Lynx AH1	AAC No 662 Sqn, Soest	
XZ210	WS Lynx AH1	AAC No 663 Sqn, Soest	
XZ211	WS Lynx AH1	AAC No 663 Sqn, Soest	
XZ212	WS Lynx AH1	AAC No 663 Sqn, Soest	
XZ213	WS Lynx AH1	AAC stored, Wroughton	
XZ214	WS Lynx AH1	AAC, stored Wroughton	
XZ215	WS Lynx AH1	AAC D&TS, Middle Wallop	
XZ216	WS Lynx AH1	AAC No 662 Sqn, Soest	
XZ217	WS Lynx AH1	AAC No 656 Sqn, Netheravon	
XZ218	WS Lynx AH1 [Z]	AAC No 665 Sqn, Aldergrove	
XZ219	WS Lynx AH1	AAC No 663 Sqn, Soest	
XZ220	WS Lynx AH1	AAC No 654 Sqn, Detmold	
XZ221	WS Lynx AH1	AAC No 657 Sqn, Oakington	
XZ222	WS Lynx AH1	AAC D&TS, Middle Wallop	
XZ227	WS Lynx HAS3 [407/YK]	RN No 815 Sqn, Portland	
XZ228	WS Lynx HAS3	RN No 702 Sqn, Portland	
XZ229	WS Lynx HAS3 [402/BX]	RN No 829 Sqn, Portland	
XZ230	WS Lynx HAS3	RN NASU, Yeovilton	
XZ231	WS Lynx HAS3 [417/NM]	RN No 815 Sqn, Portland	
XZ232	WS Lynx HAS2 [335]	RN No 815 Sqn, Portland	
XZ233	WS Lynx HAS3 [435/ED]	RN No 829 Sqn, Portland	
XZ234	WS Lynx HAS3 [305]	RN No 815 Sqn, Portland	
XZ235	WS Lynx HAS3 [605]	RN No 829 Sqn, Portland	
XZ236	WS Lynx HAS2	MoD(PE) A&AEE, Boscombe Down	
XZ237	WS Lynx HAS2 [604]	RN No 815 Sqn, Portland	
XZ238	WS Lynx HAS3 [645/PO]	RN No 702 Sqn, Portland	
XZ239	WS Lynx HAS2	RNAY Fleetlands	
XZ240	WS Lynx HAS2 [301]	RN No 815 Sqn, Portland	
XZ241	WS Lynx HAS2 [604]	RN No 829 Sqn, Portland	

Notes	Serial	Type (alternative identity)	Owner, Operator or Location
	XZ243	WS Lynx HAS3 [635/PO]	RN No 702 Sqn, Portland
	XZ244	WS Lynx HAS3 [472/AM]	RN No 815 Sqn, Portland
	XZ245	WS Lynx HAS3 [330/BZ]	RN No 829 Sqn, Portland
	XZ246	WS Lynx HAS3 [434/ED]	RN No 829 Sqn, Portland
	XZ248	WS Lynx HAS2 [345/NC]	RN No 815 Sqn, Portland
	XZ249	WS Lynx HAS2	RNEC Manadon for instruction
	XZ250	WS Lynx HAS3	RN No 815 Sqn, Portland
	XZ252	WS Lynx HAS3 [644/PO]	RN No 702 Sqn, Portland
	XZ254	WS Lynx HAS2 [333/BM]	RN No 815 Sqn, Portland
	XZ255	WS Lynx HAS3 [450/SS]	RN No 829 Sqn, Portland
	XZ256	WS Lynx HAS2	RN NASU, Yeovilton
	XZ257	WS Lynx HAS8	RNAY Fleetlands
	XZ280	BAe Nimrod AEW3	RAF, stored Waddington
	XZ281	BAe Nimrod AEW3	RAF, stored Waddington
	XZ282	BAe Nimrod AEW3	RAF, stored Waddington
	XZ283	BAe Nimrod AEW3	RAF, stored Waddington
	XZ284	HS Nimrod MR2	RAF No 42 Sqn, St Mawgan
	XZ285	BAe Nimrod AEW3	RAF, stored Waddington
	XZ286	BAe Nimrod AEW3	RAF, stored Abingdon
	XZ287	BAe Nimrod AEW3	RAF, stored Waddington
	XZ290	WS Gazelle AH1	AAC, stored Wroughton
	XZ291	WS Gazelle AH1	AAC No 12 Flt, Wildenrath
	XZ292	WS Gazelle AH1	AAC No 664 Sqn, Detmold
	XZ294	WS Gazelle AH1	AAC No 664 Sqn, Minden
	XZ295	WS Gazelle AH1	AAC No 12 Flt, Wildenrath
	XZ296	WS Gazelle AH1	AAC No 663 Sqn, Soest
	XZ297	WS Gazelle AH1	Crashed 12 July 1986, West Germany
	XZ298	WS Gazelle AH1	AAC No 664 Sqn, Detmold
	XZ299	WS Gazelle AH1	AAC No 657 Sqn, Oakington
	XZ300	WS Gazelle AH1	AAC No 664 Sqn, Minden
	XZ301	WS Gazelle AH1	AAC No 664 Sqn, Minden
	XZ302	WS Gazelle AH1 [L]	AAC No 665 Sqn, Aldergrove
	XZ303	WS Gazelle AH1	AAC No 663 Sqn, Soest
	XZ304	WS Gazelle AH1	AAC No 664 Sqn, Minden
	XZ305	WS Gazelle AH1 [A]	AAC No 665 Sqn, Aldergrove
	XZ307	WS Gazelle AH1 [B]	AAC No 665 Sqn, Aldergrove
	XZ308	WS Gazelle AH1 [L]	AAC ARWS, Middle Wallop
	XZ309	WS Gazelle AH1	AAC No 664 Sqn, Minden
	XZ310	WS Gazelle AH1	AAC No 661 Sqn, Hildesheim
	XZ311	WS Gazelle AH1	AAC No 664 Sqn, Minden
	XZ312	WS Gazelle AH1	AAC No 2 Flt, Netheravon
	XZ313	WS Gazelle AH1	AAC, stored Wroughton
	XZ314	WS Gazelle AH1	AAC No 656 Sqn, Netheravon
	XZ315	WS Gazelle AH1	AAC ARWS, Middle Wallop
	XZ316	WS Gazelle AH1 [R]	AAC ARWS, Middle Wallop
	XZ317	WS Gazelle AH1 [Q]	AAC ARWS, Middle Wallop
	XZ318	WS Gazelle AH1 [U]	AAC ARWS, Middle Wallop
	XZ319	WS Gazelle AH1 [S]	AAC ARWS, Middle Wallop
	XZ320	WS Gazelle AH1	MoD(PE) A&AEE, Boscombe Down
	XZ321	WS Gazelle AH1	AAC, stored Wroughton
	XZ322	WS Gazelle AH1 [N]	AAC ARWS, Middle Wallop
	XZ323	WS Gazelle AH1	AAC, stored Wroughton
	XZ324	WS Gazelle AH1	AAC Garrison Air Sqn, Falklands
	XZ325	WS Gazelle AH1	AAC, stored Wroughton
	XZ326	WS Gazelle AH1 [C]	RM, stored Wroughton
	XZ327	WS Gazelle AH1	AAC, stored Wroughton
	XZ328	WS Gazelle AH1	AAC No 657 Sqn, Oakington
	XZ329	WS Gazelle AH1 [J]	AAC ARWS, Middle Wallop
	XZ330	WS Gazelle AH1	AAC No 657 Sqn, Oakington
	XZ331	WS Gazelle AH1	AAC, No 657 Sqn, Oakington
	XZ332	WS Gazelle AH1 [O]	AAC ARWS, Middle Wallop
	XZ333	WS Gazelle AH1 [A]	AAC ARWS, Middle Wallop
	XZ334	WS Gazelle AH1	AAC No 657 Sqn, Oakington
	XZ335	WS Gazelle AH1	AAC No 3 Flt, Topcliffe
	XZ336	WS Gazelle AH1	Accident 29 April 1986
	XZ337	WS Gazelle AH1	AAC No 664 Sqn, Detmold
	XZ338	WS Gazelle AH1 [X]	AAC ARWS, Middle Wallop
	XZ339	WS Gazelle AH1	MoD(PE) Westlands, Weston-super-Mare
	XZ340	WS Gazelle AH1 [T]	AAC ARWS, Middle Wallop
	XZ341	WS Gazelle AH1	AAC D&TS, Middle Wallop
	XZ342	WS Gazelle AH1 [Z]	AAC No 663 Sqn, Soest
	XZ343	WS Gazelle AH1	AAC No 12 Flt, Wildenrath
	XZ344	WS Gazelle AH1	AAC No 656 Sqn, Netheravon

Serial	Type (alternative identity)	Owner, Operator or Location	Notes
XZ345	WS Gazelle AH1	AAC No 3 Flt, Topcliffe	
XZ346	WS Gazelle AH1	MoD(PE) A&AEE, Boscombe Down	
XZ347	WS Gazelle AH1	AAC No 3 Flt, Topcliffe	
XZ348	WS Gazelle AH1	AAC No 2 Flt, Netheravon	
XZ349	WS Gazelle AH1 [M]	AAC ARWS, Middle Wallop	
XZ355	SEPECAT Jaguar GR1A [J]	RAF No 41 Sqn, Coltishall	
XZ356	SEPECAT Jaguar GR1A [R]	RAF No 41 Sqn, Coltishall	
XZ357	SEPECAT Jaguar GR1A [K]	RAF No 41 Sqn, Coltishall	
XZ358	SEPECAT Jaguar GR1A [L]	RAF No 41 Sqn, Coltishall	
XZ359	SEPECAT Jaguar GR1A [M]	RAF No 41 Sqn, Coltishall	
XZ360	SEPECAT Jaguar GR1A [N]	RAF No 41 Sqn, Coltishall	
XZ361	SEPECAT Jaguar GR1A [25]	RAF No 2 Sqn, Laarbruch	
XZ362	SEPECAT Jaguar GR1A [27]	RAF No 2 Sqn, Laarbruch	
XZ363	SEPECAT Jaguar GR1A [A]	RAF No 41 Sqn, Coltishall	
XZ363	SEPECAT Jaguar GR1A Replica [A] (BAPC 151)	RAF Exhibition Flight, Abingdon	
XZ364	SEPECAT Jaguar GR1A [21]	RAF No 2 Sqn, Laarbruch	
XZ366	SEPECAT Jaguar GR1A [22]	RAF No 2 Sqn, Laarbruch	
XZ367	SEPECAT Jaguar GR1A [20]	RAF No 2 Sqn, Laarbruch	
XZ368	SEPECAT Jaguar GR1 [8900M] [AG]	RAF No 2 SoTT, Cosford	
XZ369	SEPECAT Jaguar GR1A [EE]	RAF No 6 Sqn, Coltishall	
XZ370	SEPECAT Jaguar GR1 [BN]	RAF, stored Shawbury	
XZ371	SEPECAT Jaguar GR1 (8907M) [AP]	RAF No 2 SoTT, Cosford	
XZ372	SEPECAT Jaguar GR1A [ED]	RAF No 6 Sqn, Coltishall	
XZ373	SEPECAT Jaguar GR1A [EC]	RAF No 6 Sqn, Coltishall	
XZ374	SEPECAT Jaguar GR1 [AD]	RAF, stored Shawbury	
XZ375	SEPECAT Jaguar GR1A [GB]	RAF No 54 Sqn, Coltishall	
XZ377	SEPECAT Jaguar GR1A [GC]	RAF No 54 Sqn, Coltishall	
XZ378	SEPECAT Jaguar GR1A [EP]	RAF No 6 Sqn, Coltishall	
XZ381	SEPECAT Jaguar GR1 [BL]	RAF, stored Shawbury	
XZ382	SEPECAT Jaguar GR1 (8908M) [AE]	RAF No 1 SoTT, Halton	
XZ383	SEPECAT Jaguar GR1 (8901M) [AF]	RAF No 2 SoTT, Cosford	
XZ384	SEPECAT Jaguar GR1 [BC]	RAF, stored Shawbury	
XZ385	SEPECAT Jaguar GR1A [GM]	RAF No 54 Sqn, Coltishall	
XZ386	SEPECAT Jaguar GR1A [05]	Crashed 24 June 1987, Powys	
XZ387	SEPECAT Jaguar GR1A [EB]	RAF No 6 Sqn, Coltishall	
XZ389	SEPECAT Jaguar GR1 [BL]	RAF, stored Shawbury	
XZ390	SEPECAT Jaguar GR1A [35]	RAF, stored Shawbury	
XZ391	SEPECAT Jaguar GR1A [GN]	RAF No 54 Sqn, Coltishall	
XZ392	SEPECAT Jaguar GR1A [GQ]	RAF No 54 Sqn, Coltishall	
XZ394	SEPECAT Jaguar GR1A [ES]	RAF No 6 Sqn, Coltishall	
XZ395	SEPECAT Jaguar GR1A [GJ]	Written off 22 August 1984	
XZ396	SEPECAT Jaguar GR1A [EM]	RAF No 6 Sqn, Coltishall	
XZ398	SEPECAT Jaguar GR1A [D] (JI007)	RAF No 41 Sqn, Coltishall	
XZ399	SEPECAT Jaguar GR1A [EN]	RAF No 6 Sqn, Coltishall	
XZ400	SEPECAT Jaguar GR1A [GH]	RAF No 54 Sqn, Coltishall	
XZ431	HS Buccaneer S2B	RAF No 208 Sqn, Lossiemouth	
XZ432	HS Buccaneer S2B	RAF No 237 OCU, Lossiemouth	
XZ439	BAe Sea Harrier FRS1 [2]	MoD(PE) BAe Dunsfold	
XZ440	BAe Sea Harrier FRS1 [40]	MoD(PE) A&AEE Boscombe Down	
XZ445	BAe Harrier T4A [723]	RN No 899 Sqn, Yeovilton	
XZ451	BAe Sea Harrier FRS1	RN No 899 Sqn, Yeovilton	
XZ455	BAe Sea Harrier FRS1 [127/L]	RN No 800 Sqn, Yeovilton	
XZ457	BAe Sea Harrier FRS1	RN No 899 Sqn, Yeovilton	
XZ459	BAe Sea Harrier FRS1 [22]	RN No 899 Sqn, Yeovilton	
XZ460	BAe Sea Harrier FRS1 [122/L]	RN No 800 Sqn, Yeovilton	
XZ492	BAe Sea Harrier FRS1 [128/L]	RN No 800 Sqn, Yeovilton	
XZ493	BAe Sea Harrier FRS1 [713]	RN No 899 Sqn, Yeovilton	
XZ494	BAe Sea Harrier FRS1 [004/R]	RN No 801 Sqn, Yeovilton	
XZ495	BAe Sea Harrier FRS1 [714]	RN No 899 Sqn, Yeovilton	
XZ497	BAe Sea Harrier FRS1 [4]	MoD(PE) BAe Dunsfold	
XZ498	BAe Sea Harrier FRS1 [002/R]	RN No 801 Sqn, Yeovilton	
XZ499	BAe Sea Harrier FRS1 [715]	RN No 899 Sqn, Yeovilton	
XZ550	Slingsby Venture T2	RAF No 642 VGS, Linton-on-Ouse	
XZ551	Slingsby Venture T2	RAF No 624 VGS, Chivenor	
XZ552	Slingsby Venture T2 [A]	RAF No 642 VGS, Linton-on-Ouse	
XZ553	Slingsby Venture T2 [Q]	RAF No 663 VGS, Kinloss	
XZ554	Slingsby Venture T2 [4]	RAF No 633 VGS, Cosford	
XZ555	Slingsby Venture T2	RAF ACCGS, Syerston	

Notes	Serial	Type (alternative identity)	Owner, Operator or Location
	XZ556	Slingsby Venture T2 [56]	RAF No 611 VGS, Swanton Morley
	XZ557	Slingsby Venture T2 [7]	RAF No 633 VGS, Cosford
	XZ558	Slingsby Venture T2 [8]	RAF No 613 VGS, Halton
	XZ559	Slingsby Venture T2 [3]	RAF No 613 VGS, Halton
	XZ560	Slingsby Venture T2 [60]	RAF No ???
	XZ561	Slingsby Venture T2 [B]	RAF No 632 VGS, Ternhill
	XZ562	Slingsby Venture T2 [2]	RAF No 635 VGS, Samlesbury
	XZ563	Slingsby Venture T2	RAF No 635 VGS, Samlesbury
	XZ564	Slingsby Venture T2 [4]	RAF No 635 VGS, Samlesbury
	XZ570	WS61 Sea King HAS5	MoD(PE) A&AEE Boscombe Down/ Westlands, Yeovil
	XZ571	WS61 Sea King HAS5 [136]	RN No 826 Sqn, Culdrose
	XZ574	WS61 Sea King HAS5 [506]	RN No 810 Sqn, Culdrose
	XZ575	WS61 Sea King HAS5 [271]	RN No 814 Sqn, Culdrose
	XZ576	WS61 Sea King HAS6	MoD(PE) Westlands, Yeovil
	XZ577	WS61 Sea King HAS5 [138]	RN No 826 Sqn, Culdrose
	XZ578	WS61 Sea King HAS5 [501]	RN No 810 Sqn, Culdrose
	XZ579	WS61 Sea King HAS5 [017/R]	RN No 820 Sqn, Culdrose
	XZ580	WS61 Sea King HAS6	MoD(PE) Westlands, Yeovil
	XZ581	WS61 Sea King HAS5	RN No ???
	XZ582	WS61 Sea King HAS5 [264/L]	RN No 814 Sqn, Culdrose
	XZ585	WS61 Sea King HAR3	RAF No 202 Sqn SAR*
	XZ586	WS61 Sea King HAR3	RAF SKTU, RNAS Culdrose
	XZ587	WS61 Sea King HAR3	RAF No 202 Sqn SAR*
	XZ588	WS61 Sea King HAR3	RAF No 202 Sqn SAR*
	XZ589	WS61 Sea King HAR3	RAF No 202 Sqn SAR*
	XZ590	WS61 Sea King HAR3	RAF No 202 Sqn SAR*
	XZ591	WS61 Sea King HAR3 [S]	RAF SKTU, RNAS Culdrose
	XZ592	WS61 Sea King HAR3	RAF No 78 Sqn, Mount Pleasant, Fl
	XZ593	WS61 Sea King HAR3	RAF No 202 Sqn SAR*
	XZ594	WS61 Sea King HAR3	RAF No 202 Sqn SAR*
	XZ595	WS61 Sea King HAR3	RAF No 202 Sqn SAR*
	XZ596	WS61 Sea King HAR3	RAF No 202 Sqn SAR*
	XZ597	WS61 Sea King HAR3 [S]	RAF No 78 Sqn, Mount Pleasant, Fl
	XZ598	WS61 Sea King HAR3	RAF No 202 Sqn SAR*
	XZ599	WS61 Sea King HAR3 [S]	RAF SKTU, RNAS Culdrose
	XZ605	WS Lynx AH1 [23B]	RM 3 CBAS, Yeovilton
	XZ606	WS Lynx AH1	RNAY Fleetlands
	XZ607	WS Lynx AH1	AAC No 654 Sqn, Detmold
	XZ608	WS Lynx AH1	AAC No 654 Sqn, Detmold
	XZ609	WS Lynx AH1	AAC, stored Wroughton
	XZ610	WS Lynx AH1	AAC No 654 Sqn, Detmold
	XZ611	WS Lynx AH1 [H]	AAC ARW/LCF, Middle Wallop
	XZ612	WS Lynx AH1 [23C]	RM 3 CBAS, Yeovilton
	XZ613	WS Lynx AH1	MoD(PE) A&AEE, Boscombe Down
	XZ614	WS Lynx AH1 [23D]	RM 3 CBAS, Yeovilton
	XZ615	WS Lynx AH1	AAC No 651 Sqn, Hildesheim
	XZ616	WS Lynx AH1	AAC, stored Wroughton
	XZ617	WS Lynx AH1	AAC, stored Wroughton
	XZ630	Panavia Tornado	BAe Warton
	XZ631	Panavia Tornado	BAe Warton
	XZ641	WS Lynx AH7	RNAY Fleetlands
	XZ642	WS Lynx AH1	AAC No 653 Sqn, Soest
	XZ643	WS Lynx AH1	AAC No 653 Sqn, Soest
	XZ644	WS Lynx AH1	AAC No 657 Sqn, Oakington
	XZ645	WS Lynx AH1	AAC No 669 Sqn, Detmold
	XZ646	WS Lynx AH1	AAC No 654 Sqn, Detmold
	XZ647	WS Lynx AH1	AAC No 669 Sqn, Detmold
	XZ648	WS Lynx AH1 [D]	AAC ARW/LCF, Middle Wallop
	XZ649	WS Lynx AH1 [E]	AAC ARW/LCF, Middle Wallop
	XZ650	WS Lynx AH1	AAC No 659 Sqn, Detmold
	XZ651	WS Lynx AH1	AAC No 659 Sqn, Detmold
	XZ652	WS Lynx AH1	AAC No 659 Sqn, Detmold
	XZ653	WS Lynx AH1	AAC No 654 Sqn, Detmold
	XZ654	WS Lynx AH1	AAC No 654 Sqn, Detmold
	XZ655	WS Lynx AH1	AAC No 652 Sqn, Hildesheim
	XZ661	WS Lynx AH1	AAC No 652 Sqn, Hildesheim
	XZ662	WS Lynx AH1	AAC No 652 Sqn, Hildesheim
	XZ663	WS Lynx AH1	AAC No 659 Sqn, Detmold

Note: *The SAR Wing and SAREW are based at RAF Finningley, with the SKTU at RNAS Culdrose and with No 202 Sqn SAR detached flights: A Flt—RAF Boulmer; B Flt—RAF Brawdy; C Flt—RAF Coltishall; D Flt—RAF Lossiemouth.

Serial	Type (alternative identity)	Owner, Operator or Location	Notes
XZ664	WS Lynx AH1	AAC No 655 Sqn, Aldergrove	
XZ665	WS Lynx AH1	AAC No 655 Sqn, Aldergrove	
XZ666	WS Lynx AH1 [X]	AAC No 665 Sqn, Aldergrove	
XZ667	WS Lynx AH1 [D]	AAC No 663 Sqn, Soest	
XZ668	WS Lynx AH1 [E]	AAC No 663 Sqn, Soest	
XZ669	WS Lynx AH1 [F]	AAC No 663 Sqn, Soest	
XZ670	WS Lynx AH1	AAC No 653 Sqn, Soest	
XZ671	WS Lynx AH1	AAC, stored Wroughton	
XZ672	WS Lynx AH1	AAC No 659 Sqn, Detmold	
XZ673	WS Lynx AH1	AAC No 652 Sqn, Hildesheim	
XZ674	WS Lynx AH1	AAC No 652 Sqn, Hildesheim	
XZ675	WS Lynx AH1	AAC No 663 Sqn, Detmold	
XZ676	WS Lynx AH1	AAC No 656 Sqn, Netheravon	
XZ677	WS Lynx AH1	AAC No 651 Sqn, Hildesheim	
XZ678	WS Lynx AH1	AAC No 651 Sqn, Hildesheim	
XZ679	WS Lynx AH1	AAC No 651 Sqn, Hildesheim	
XZ680	WS Lynx AH1 [F]	AAC ARW/LCF, Middle Wallop	
XZ681	WS Lynx AH1	AAC Middle Wallop, BDRT	
XZ689	WS Lynx HAS2 [300]	RN No 815 Sqn, Portland	
XZ690	WS Lynx HAS2 [600/PO]	RN No 829 Sqn, Portland	
XZ691	WS Lynx HAS2 [375/VB]	RN No 829 Sqn, Portland	
XZ692	WS Lynx HAS3 [643/PO]	RN No 702 Sqn, Portland	
XZ693	WS Lynx HAS3 [640]	RN No 702 Sqn, Portland	
XZ694	WS Lynx HAS3 [360]	RN No 815 Sqn, Portland	
XZ695	WS Lynx HAS2 [466/AT]	RN No 829 Sqn, Portland	
XZ696	WS Lynx HAS3 [344/GW]	RN No 815 Sqn, Portland	
XZ697	WS Lynx HAS3 [602]	RN No 829 Sqn, Portland	
XZ698	WS Lynx HAS2 [342]	RN No 815 Sqn, Portland	
XZ699	WS Lynx HAS2 [300/PO]	RN No 815 Sqn, Portland	
XZ719	WS Lynx HAS2 [431/CY]	RN No 815 Sqn, Portland	
XZ720	WS Lynx HAS2 [403/BX]	RN No 829 Sqn, Portland	
XZ721	WS Lynx HAS2 [475]	RN No 829 Sqn, Portland	
XZ722	WS Lynx HAS2 [420/EX]	RN No 815 Sqn, Portland	
XZ723	WS Lynx HAS3 [454/PN]	RN No 815 Sqn, Portland	
XZ724	WS Lynx HAS3 [376/XB]	RN No 829 Sqn, Portland	
XZ725	WS Lynx HAS2 [320/AZ]	RN No 815 Sqn, Portland	
XZ726	WS Lynx HAS3 [464/DN]	RN No 815 Sqn, Portland	
XZ727	WS Lynx HAS2	RN No 815 Sqn, Portland	
XZ728	WS Lynx HAS2 [443/JP]	RN No 815 Sqn, Portland	
XZ729	WS Lynx HAS3 [471/PB]	RN No 815 Sqn, Portland	
XZ730	WS Lynx HAS2 [326/AW]	RN No 815 Sqn, Portland	
XZ731	WS Lynx HAS3 [641]	RN No 702 Sqn, Portland	
XZ732	WS Lynx HAS2 [601/PO]	RN No 829 Sqn, Portland	
XZ733	WS Lynx HAS3 [410/GC]	RN No 815 Sqn, Portland	
XZ734	WS Lynx HAS3 [405/LO]	RN No 829 Sqn, Portland	
XZ735	WS Lynx HAS3 [322/AV]	RN No 815 Sqn, Portland	
XZ736	WS Lynx HAS2	RN No 815 Sqn, Portland	
XZ916	WS61 Sea King HAS5 [130]	RN No 826 Sqn, Culdrose	
XZ918	WS61 Sea King HAS5 [020/R]	RN No 820 Sqn, Culdrose	
XZ920	WS61 Sea King HAS5 [510]	RN No 810 Sqn, Culdrose	
XZ921	WS61 Sea King HAS5 [593/R]	RN No 706 Sqn, Culdrose	
XZ922	WS61 Sea King HAS5 [500]	RN No 810 Sqn, Culdrose	
XZ930	WS Gazelle HT3 [Q]	RAF No 2 FTS, Shawbury	
XZ931	WS Gazelle HT3 [R]	RAF No 2 FTS, Shawbury	
XZ932	WS Gazelle HT3 [S]	RAF No 2 FTS, Shawbury	
XZ933	WS Gazelle HT3 [T]	RAF No 2 FTS, Shawbury	
XZ934	WS Gazelle HT3 [U]	RAF No 2 FTS, Shawbury	
XZ935	WS Gazelle HT3	RAF No 32 Sqn, Northolt	
XZ936	WS Gazelle HT3	MoD(PE) ETPS Boscombe Down	
XZ937	WS Gazelle HT3 [Y]	RAF No 2 FTS, Shawbury	
XZ938	WS Gazelle HT2 [45/CU]	RN No 705 Sqn, Culdrose	
XZ939	WS Gazelle HT3 [Z]	MoD(PE) ETPS, Boscombe Down	
XZ940	WS Gazelle HT3 [O]	RAF No 2 FTS, Shawbury	
XZ941	WS Gazelle HT3 [B]	RAF No 2 FTS, Shawbury	
XZ942	WS Gazelle HT2 [42/CU]	RN No 705 Sqn, Culdrose	
XZ964	BAe Harrier GR3 [F]	RAF No 1417 Flt, Belize	
XZ965	BAe Harrier GR3 [M]	RAF No 3 Sqn, Gutersloh	
XZ966	BAe Harrier GR3 [K]	RAF No 4 Sqn, Gutersloh	
XZ967	BAe Harrier GR3 [B]	RAF No 3 Sqn, Gutersloh	
XZ968	BAe Harrier GR3 [01]	RAF No 1 Sqn, Wittering	
XZ969	BAe Harrier GR3	RAF No 4 Sqn, Gutersloh	
XZ970	BAe Harrier GR3 [R]	RAF No 3 Sqn, Gutersloh	
XZ971	BAe Harrier GR3 [G]	RAF No 1417 Flt, Belize	
XZ987	BAe Harrier GR3 [O]	RAF No 4 Sqn, Gutersloh	

Notes	Serial	Type (alternative identity)	Owner, Operator or Location
	XZ990	BAe Harrier GR3 [H]	RAF No 4 Sqn, Gutersloh
	XZ991	BAe Harrier GR3 [P]	RAF No 4 Sqn, Gutersloh
	XZ992	BAe Harrier GR3 [T]	Written off 29 November 1984
	XZ993	BAe Harrier GR3 [11]	RAF No 1 Sqn, Wittering
	XZ994	BAe Harrier GR3	RAF No 1417 Flt, Belize
	XZ995	BAe Harrier GR3 [V]	RAF No 4 Sqn, Gutersloh
	XZ996	BAe Harrier GR3 [C]	RAF No 1417 Flt, Belize
	XZ997	BAe Harrier GR3 [E]	RAF No 233 OCU, Wittering
	XZ998	BAe Harrier GR3 [J]	RAF No 233 OCU, Wittering
	XZ999	BAe Harrier GR3 [H]	RAF No 4 Sqn, Gutersloh
	ZA101	BAe Hawk 100 (G-HAWK)	BAe Dunsfold
	ZA105	WS61 Sea King HAR3 [S]	RAF No 202 Sqn SAR*
	ZA110	BAe Jetstream T2 [573/CU] (G-AXUO)	RN No 750 Sqn, Culdrose
	ZA111	BAe Jetstream T2 [574/CU] (G-AXFV)	RN No 750 Sqn, Culdrose
	ZA126	WS61 Sea King HAS5 [591/R]	RN No 706 Sqn, Culdrose
	ZA127	WS61 Sea King HAS5 [504]	RN No 810 Sqn, Culdrose
	ZA128	WS61 Sea King HAS5	RNAY Fleetlands
	ZA129	WS61 Sea King HAS5 [139]	RN No 826 Sqn, Culdrose
	ZA130	WS61 Sea King HAS5 [253]	RN No 824 Sqn, Culdrose
	ZA131	WS61 Sea King HAS5 [133]	RN No 826 Sqn, Culdrose
	ZA133	WS61 Sea King HAS5 [252]	RNAY Fleetlands
	ZA134	WS61 Sea King HAS5 [252]	RN No 824 Sqn, Prestwick
	ZA135	WS61 Sea King HAS5 [505]	RN No 810 Sqn, Culdrose
	ZA136	WS61 Sea King HAS6	RNAY Fleetlands
	ZA137	WS61 Sea King HAS5 [589]	RN No 706 Sqn, Culdrose
	ZA140	BAe VC10 K2 (G-ARVL) [A]	RAF No 101 Sqn, Brize Norton
	ZA141	BAe VC10 K2 (G-ARVG) [B]	RAF No 101 Sqn, Brize Norton
	ZA142	BAe VC10 K2 (G-ARVI) [C]	RAF No 101 Sqn, Brize Norton
	ZA143	BAe VC10 K2 (G-ARVK) [D]	RAF No 101 Sqn, Brize Norton
	ZA144	BAe VC10 K2 (G-ARVC) [E]	RAF No 101 Sqn, Brize Norton
	ZA147	BAe VC10 K3 (5H-MMT) [F]	RAF No 101 Sqn, Brize Norton
	ZA148	BAe VC10 K3 (5Y-ADA) [G]	RAF No 101 Sqn, Brize Norton
	ZA149	BAe VC10 K3 (5X-UVJ) [H]	RAF No 101 Sqn, Brize Norton
	ZA150	BAe VC10 K3 (5H-MOG) [J]	RAF No 101 Sqn, Brize Norton
	ZA166	WS61 Sea King HAS5 [590/R]	RN No 706 Sqn, Culdrose
	ZA167	WS61 Sea King HAS5 [265]	RN No 814 Sqn, Culdrose
	ZA168	WS61 Sea King HAS5	RN No 820 Sqn, Culdrose
	ZA169	WS61 Sea King HAS5 [587/R]	RN No 706 Sqn, Culdrose
	ZA170	WS61 Sea King HAS5 [584]	RN No 706 Sqn, Culdrose
	ZA175	BAe Sea Harrier FRS1 [713]	RN No 899 Sqn, Yeovilton
	ZA176	BAe Sea Harrier FRS1 [716]	RN No 899 Sqn, Yeovilton
	ZA190	BAe Sea Harrier FRS1 [006/R]	Crashed 15 October 1987 off HMS *Ark Royal*
	ZA191	BAe Sea Harrier FRS1 [123/L]	RN No 800 Sqn, Yeovilton
	ZA193	BAe Sea Harrier FRS1 [003/R]	RN No 801 Sqn, Yeovilton
	ZA195	BAe Sea Harrier FRS1	MoD(PE) BAe Dunsfold
	ZA250	BAe Harrier T52 (G-VTOL)	BAe Dunsfold
	ZA254	Panavia Tornado F2	MoD(PE) BAe Warton
	ZA267	Panavia Tornado F2T	MoD(PE) BAe Warton
	ZA283	Panavia Tornado F2	MoD(PE) BAe Warton
	ZA291	WS61 Sea King HC4 [VO]	RN No 846 Sqn, Yeovilton
	ZA292	WS61 Sea King HC4 [E]	RN No 845 Sqn, Yeovilton
	ZA293	WS61 Sea King HC4 [VK]	RN No 846 Sqn, Yeovilton
	ZA295	WS61 Sea King HC4 [ZU]	RN No 707 Sqn, Yeovilton
	ZA296	WS61 Sea King HC4	RNAY Fleetlands
	ZA297	WS61 Sea King HC4 [F]	RN No 845 Sqn, Yeovilton
	ZA298	WS61 Sea King HC4 [G] (G-BJNM)	RN, stored Wroughton
	ZA299	WS61 Sea King HC4 [ZV]	RN No 707 Sqn, Yeovilton
	ZA310	WS61 Sea King HC4 [VQ]	RN No 846 Sqn, Yeovilton
	ZA312	WS61 Sea King HC4 [ZT]	RN No 707 Sqn, Yeovilton
	ZA313	WS61 Sea King HC4 [VR]	RN No 846 Sqn, Yeovilton
	ZA314	WS61 Sea King HC4 [VN]	RN No 846 Sqn, Yeovilton
	ZA319	Panavia Tornado GR1T [B-11]	RAF TTTE, Cottesmore
	ZA320	Panavia Tornado GR1T [B-01]	RAF TTTE, Cottesmore
	ZA321	Panavia Tornado GR1 [B-58]	RAF TTTE, Cottesmore
	ZA322	Panavia Tornado GR1 [B-50]	RAF TTTE, Cottesmore
	ZA323	Panavia Tornado GR1T [B-14]	RAF TTTE, Cottesmore
	ZA324	Panavia Tornado GR1T [B-02]	RAF TTTE, Cottesmore
	ZA325	Panavia Tornado GR1T [B-03]	RAF TTTE, Cottesmore
	ZA326	Panavia Tornado GR1T	MoD(PE) RAE Bedford

Serial	Type (alternative identity)	Owner, Operator or Location	Notes
ZA327	Panavia Tornado GR1 [B-51]	RAF TTTE, Cottesmore	
ZA328	Panavia Tornado GR1	BAe Warton	
ZA329	Panavia Tornado GR1 [B-52)	RAF TTTE, Cottesmore	
ZA330	Panavia Tornado GR1T [B-08]	RAF TTTE, Cottesmore	
ZA352	Panavia Tornado GR1T [B-04)	RAF TTTE, Cottesmore	
ZA353	Panavia Tornado GR1 [B-53)	RAF TTTE, Cottesmore	
ZA354	Panavia Tornado GR1	MoD(PE) BAe Warton	
ZA355	Panavia Tornado GR1 [B-54]	RAF TTTE, Cottesmore	
ZA356	Panavia Tornado GR1T [B-07]	RAF TTTE, Cottesmore	
ZA357	Panavia Tornado GR1T [B-05]	RAF TTTE, Cottesmore	
ZA358	Panavia Tornado GR1T [B-06]	RAF TTTE, Cottesmore	
ZA359	Panavia Tornado GR1 [B-55]	RAF TTTE, Cottesmore	
ZA360	Panavia Tornado GR1 [B-56]	RAF TTTE, Cottesmore	
ZA361	Panavia Tornado GR1 [B-57]	RAF TTTE, Cottesmore	
ZA362	Panavia Tornado GR1T [B-09]	RAF TTTE, Cottesmore	
ZA365	Panavia Tornado GR1T [GZ]	RAF No 20 Sqn, Laarbruch	
ZA366	Panavia Tornado GR1T	Crashed 3 June 1987, Manby	
ZA367	Panavia Tornado GR1T	RAF TWCU/45 Sqn, Honington	
ZA368	Panavia Tornado GR1T	RAF TWCU/45 Sqn, Honington	
ZA369	Panavia Tornado GR1 [BR-61]	RAF TTTE, Cottesmore	
ZA370	Panavia Tornado GR1	RAF TWCU/45 Sqn, Honington	
ZA371	Panavia Tornado GR1 [GF]	RAF No 20 Sqn, Laarbruch	
ZA372	Panavia Tornado GR1	RAF TWCU/45 Sqn, Honington	
ZA373	Panavia Tornado GR1	RAF TTTE, Cottesmore	
ZA374	Panavia Tornado GR1	RAF TWCU/45 Sqn, Honington	
ZA375	Panavia Tornado GR1	RAF TWCU/45 Sqn, Honington	
ZA376	Panavia Tornado GR1 [E]	MoD(PE) TOEU Boscombe Down	
ZA392	Panavia Tornado GR1 [EK]	RAF No 15 Sqn, Laarbruch	
ZA393	Panavia Tornado GR1	RAF TWCU/45 Sqn, Honington	
ZA394	Panavia Tornado GR1 [GP]	RAF No 20 Sqn, Laarbruch	
ZA395	Panavia Tornado GR1 [FP]	RAF No 16 Sqn, Laarbruch	
ZA396	Panavia Tornado GR1 [GE]	RAF No 20 Sqn, Laarbruch	
ZA397	Panavia Tornado GR1 [EN]	RAF No 15 Sqn, Laarbruch	
ZA398	Panavia Tornado GR1	RAF TWCU/45 Sqn, Honington	
ZA399	Panavia Tornado GR1 [GA]	RAF No 20 Sqn, Laarbruch	
ZA400	Panavia Tornado GR1	RAF No 9 Sqn, Bruggen	
ZA401	Panavia Tornado GR1 [GJ]	RAF No 20 Sqn, Laarbruch	
ZA402	Panavia Tornado GR1	BAe Warton	
ZA403	Panavia Tornado GR1	BAe Warton	
ZA404	Panavia Tornado GR1	RAF TWCU/45 Sqn, Honington	
ZA405	Panavia Tornado GR1	RAF TTTE, Cottesmore	
ZA406	Panavia Tornado GR1	RAF TWCU/45 Sqn, Honington	
ZA407	Panavia Tornado GR1	RAF TWCU/45 Sqn, Honington	
ZA409	Panavia Tornado GR1T [EW]	RAF No 15 Sqn, Laarbruch	
ZA410	Panavia Tornado GR1T [EX]	RAF No 15 Sqn, Laarbruch	
ZA411	Panavia Tornado GR1T [GY]	RAF No 20 Sqn, Laarbruch	
ZA412	Panavia Tornado GR1T [GT]	Accident 14 April 1987	
ZA446	Panavia Tornado GR1 [F]	RAF No 15 Sqn, Laarbruch	
ZA447	Panavia Tornado GR1 [EA]	RAF No 15 Sqn, Laarbruch	
ZA448	Panavia Tornado GR1 [EB]	RAF No 15 Sqn, Laarbruch	
ZA449	Panavia Tornado GR1	BAe Warton	
ZA450	Panavia Tornado GR1 [EC]	RAF No 15 Sqn, Laarbruch	
ZA452	Panavia Tornado GR1 [GK]	RAF No 20 Sqn, Laarbruch	
ZA453	Panavia Tornado GR1 [EG]	RAF No 15 Sqn, Laarbruch	
ZA454	Panavia Tornado GR1 [EH]	RAF No 15 Sqn, Laarbruch	
ZA455	Panavia Tornado GR1 [EJ]	RAF No 15 Sqn, Laarbruch	
ZA456	Panavia Tornado GR1 [GB]	RAF No 20 Sqn, Laarbruch	
ZA457	Panavia Tornado GR1 [AJ]	RAF No 9 Sqn, Bruggen	
ZA458	Panavia Tornado GR1 [FB]	RAF No 16 Sqn, Laarbruch	
ZA459	Panavia Tornado GR1 [EL]	RAF No 15 Sqn, Laarbruch	
ZA460	Panavia Tornado GR1 [FD]	RAF No 16 Sqn, Laarbruch	
ZA461	Panavia Tornado GR1 [AM]	RAF No 9 Sqn, Bruggen	
ZA462	Panavia Tornado GR1 [EM]	RAF No 15 Sqn, Laarbruch	
ZA463	Panavia Tornado GR1 [GL]	RAF No 20 Sqn, Laarbruch	
ZA464	Panavia Tornado GR1 [GM]	RAF No 20 Sqn, Laarbruch	
ZA465	Panavia Tornado GR1 [FK]	RAF No 16 Sqn, Laarbruch	
ZA466	Panavia Tornado GR1 [FH]	RAF No 16 Sqn, Laarbruch	
ZA467	Panavia Tornado GR1 [FF]	RAF No 16 Sqn, Laarbruch	
ZA468	Panavia Tornado GR1 [FN]	RAF No 16 Sqn, Laarbruch	
ZA469	Panavia Tornado GR1 [GD]	RAF No 20 Sqn, Laarbruch	
ZA470	Panavia Tornado GR1 [FL]	RAF No 16 Sqn, Laarbruch	
ZA471	Panavia Tornado GR1 [FJ]	RAF No 16 Sqn, Laarbruch	
ZA472	Panavia Tornado GR1 [EE]	RAF No 15 Sqn, Laarbruch	
ZA473	Panavia Tornado GR1 [FM]	RAF No 16 Sqn, Laarbruch	

Notes	Serial	Type (alternative identity)	Owner, Operator or Location
	ZA474	Panavia Tornado GR1 [FG]	RAF No 16 Sqn, Laarbruch
	ZA475	Panavia Tornado GR1 [FC]	RAF No 16 Sqn, Laarbruch
	ZA490	Panavia Tornado GR1 [GG]	RAF No 20 Sqn, Laarbruch
	ZA491	Panavia Tornado GR1 [GC]	RAF No 20 Sqn, Laarbruch
	ZA492	Panavia Tornado GR1 [FE]	RAF No 16 Sqn, Laarbruch
	ZA493	Panavia Tornado GR1 [GH]	Crashed 17 June 1987, Cumbria
	ZA494	Panavia Tornado GR1 [15]	RAF Honington BDRT
	ZA540	Panavia Tornado GR1T [06]	RAF No 27 Sqn, Marham
	ZA541	Panavia Tornado GR1T [S]	RAF No 617 Sqn, Marham
	ZA542	Panavia Tornado GR1 [04]	RAF No 27 Sqn, Marham
	ZA543	Panavia Tornado GR1	RAF TWCU/45 Sqn, Honington
	ZA544	Panavia Tornado GR1T	RAF TWCU/45 Sqn, Honington
	ZA545	Panavia Tornado GR1	RAF TWCU/45 Sqn, Honington
	ZA546	Panavia Tornado GR1 [05]	RAF No 27 Sqn, Marham
	ZA547	Panavia Tornado GR1 [03]	RAF No 27 Sqn, Marham
	ZA548	Panavia Tornado GR1T	RAF TWCU/45 Sqn, Honington
	ZA549	Panavia Tornado GR1T [08]	RAF No 27 Sqn, Marham
	ZA550	Panavia Tornado GR1	RAF No 27 Sqn, Marham
	ZA551	Panavia Tornado GR1T [T]	RAF No 617 Sqn, Marham
	ZA552	Panavia Tornado GR1T	RAF TWCU/45 Sqn, Honington
	ZA553	Panavia Tornado GR1 [01]	RAF No 27 Sqn, Marham
	ZA554	Panavia Tornado GR1 [11]	RAF No 27 Sqn, Marham
	ZA555	Panavia Tornado GR1T (remains)	RAF Honington. Crashed 2 December 1986
	ZA556	Panavia Tornado GR1	RAF TWCU/45 Sqn, Honington
	ZA557	Panavia Tornado GR1 [12]	RAF No 27 Sqn, Marham
	ZA559	Panavia Tornado GR1	RAF No 617 Sqn, Marham
	ZA560	Panavia Tornado GR1 [C]	RAF No 617 Sqn, Marham
	ZA561	Panavia Tornado GR1 [02]	RAF No 27 Sqn, Marham
	ZA562	Panavia Tornado GR1T [B-15]	RAF TTTE, Cottesmore
	ZA563	Panavia Tornado GR1 [10]	RAF No 27 Sqn, Marham
	ZA564	Panavia Tornado GR1 [14]	RAF No 27 Sqn, Marham
	ZA585	Panavia Tornado GR1 [G]	RAF No 617 Sqn, Marham
	ZA587	Panavia Tornado GR1	RAF TWCU/45 Sqn, Honington
	ZA588	Panavia Tornado GR1	RAF TWCU/45 Sqn, Honington
	ZA589	Panavia Tornado GR1	RAF TWCU/45 Sqn, Honington
	ZA590	Panavia Tornado GR1	RAF TWCU/45 Sqn, Honington
	ZA591	Panavia Tornado GR1	RAF TWCU/45 Sqn, Honington
	ZA592	Panavia Tornado GR1 [B]	RAF No 617 Sqn, Marham
	ZA593	Panavia Tornado GR1 [F]	RAF No 617 Sqn, Marham
	ZA594	Panavia Tornado GR1T	RAF TWCU/45 Sqn, Honington
	ZA595	Panavia Tornado GR1T	RAF TWCU/45 Sqn, Honington
	ZA596	Panavia Tornado GR1	RAF TWCU/45 Sqn, Honington
	ZA597	Panavia Tornado GR1 [M]	RAF No — Honington
	ZA598	Panavia Tornado GR1T	RAF TWCU/45 Sqn, Honington
	ZA599	Panavia Tornado GR1T	RAF TWCU/45 Sqn, Honington
	ZA600	Panavia Tornado GR1 [07]	RAF No 27 Sqn, Marham
	ZA600	Panavia Tornado GR1 Replica (BAPC 155)	RAF Exhibition Flight, Abingdon
	ZA601	Panavia Tornado GR1 [M]	RAF No 617 Sqn, Marham
	ZA602	Panavia Tornado GR1T [B-13]	RAF TTTE, Cottesmore
	ZA604	Panavia Tornado GR1T	RAF TWCU/45 Sqn, Honington
	ZA605	Panavia Tornado GR1 [G]	Written off 10 December 1986
	ZA606	Panavia Tornado GR1 [09]	RAF No 27 Sqn, Marham
	ZA607	Panavia Tornado GR1 [P]	RAF No 617 Sqn, Marham
	ZA608	Panavia Tornado GR1 [Z]	RAF No 617 Sqn, Marham
	ZA609	Panavia Tornado GR1 [J]	RAF No 617 Sqn, Marham
	ZA611	Panavia Tornado GR1 [A]	RAF No 617 Sqn, Marham
	ZA612	Panavia Tornado GR1T	RAF TWCU/45 Sqn, Honington
	ZA613	Panavia Tornado GR1 [N]	RAF No 617 Sqn, Marham
	ZA614	Panavia Tornado GR1 [ME]	RAF No 617 Sqn, Marham
	ZA625	Slingsby Venture T2 [1]	RAF No 616 VGS, Henlow
	ZA626	Slingsby Venture T2 [C]	RAF No 624 VGS, Chivenor
	ZA627	Slingsby Venture T2	RAF No 612 VGS, Benson
	ZA628	Slingsby Venture T2 [B]	RAF No 637 VGS, Little Rissington
	ZA629	Slingsby Venture T2 [9]	RAF No 664 VGS, Bishops Court, NI
	ZA630	Slingsby Venture T2	RAF No 616 VGS, Henlow
	ZA631	Slingsby Venture T2 [1]	RAF ACCGS, Syerston
	ZA632	Slingsby Venture T2 [2]	RAF No 632 VGS, Ternhill
	ZA633	Slingsby Venture T2 [3]	RAF No 616 VGS, Henlow
	ZA634	Slingsby Venture T2 [C]	RAF No 635 VGS, Samlesbury
	ZA652	Slingsby Venture T2 [6]	RAF No 642 VGS, Linton-on-Ouse
	ZA653	Slingsby Venture T2 [1]	RAF No 612 VGS, Benson
	ZA654	Slingsby Venture T2 [2]	RAF No —

Serial	Type (alternative identity)	Owner, Operator or Location	Notes
ZA655	Slingsby Venture T2 [V]	RAF No 644 VGS, Syerston	
ZA656	Slingsby Venture T2 [6]	RAF No 624 VGS, Chivenor	
ZA657	Slingsby Venture T2	RAF No 644 VGS, Syerston	
ZA658	Slingsby Venture T2	RAF ACCGS/644 VGS, Syerston	
ZA659	Slingsby Venture T2	RAF No 642 VGS, Linton-on-Ouse	
ZA660	Slingsby Venture T2 [6]	RAF No 612 VGS, Benson	
ZA661	Slingsby Venture T2 [3]	RAF No 637 VGS, Little Rissington	
ZA662	Slingsby Venture T2 [62]	RAF No 633 VGS, Cosford	
ZA663	Slingsby Venture T2 [3]	RAF ACCGS, Syerston	
ZA664	Slingsby Venture T2 [4]	RAF No 663 VGS, Kinloss	
ZA665	Slingsby Venture T2	RAF No 637 VGS, Little Rissington	
ZA666	Slingsby Venture T2 [6]	RAF No 613 VGS, Halton	
ZA670	B-V Chinook HC1 [BG]	RAF No 18 Sqn, Gutersloh	
ZA671	B-V Chinook HC1 [EO]	RAF No 7 Sqn, Odiham	
ZA672	B-V Chinook HC1 [BH]	RAF No 18 Sqn, Gutersloh	
ZA673	B-V Chinook HC1 [BL]	RAF No 18 Sqn, Gutersloh	
ZA674	B-V Chinook HC1 [BA]	RAF No 18 Sqn, Gutersloh	
ZA675	B-V Chinook HC1 [BB]	RAF No 18 Sqn, Gutersloh	
ZA676	B-V Chinook HC1 [FG]	RAF, stored Wroughton	
ZA677	B-V Chinook HC1 [EU]	RAF No 7 Sqn, Odiham	
ZA678	B-V Chinook HC1 [EZ]	RAF No 7 Sqn, Odiham	
ZA679	B-V Chinook HC1 [BC]	RAF No 18 Sqn, Gutersloh	
ZA680	B-V Chinook HC1 [T]	RAF No 78 Sqn, Mount Pleasant, FI	
ZA681	B-V Chinook HC1 [ES]	RAF No 7 Sqn, Odiham	
ZA682	B-V Chinook HC1 [BN]	RAF No 18 Sqn, Gutersloh	
ZA683	B-V Chinook HC1 [EW]	RAF No 7 Sqn, Odiham	
ZA684	B-V Chinook HC1 [F]	RAF No 78 Sqn, Mount Pleasant, FI	
ZA704	B-V Chinook HC1 [BJ]	RAF No 18 Sqn, Gutersloh	
ZA705	B-V Chinook HC1 [D]	RAF No 78 Sqn, Mount Pleasant, FI	
ZA707	B-V Chinook HC1 [FH]	RAF No 240 OCU, Odiham	
ZA708	B-V Chinook HC1 [BK]	RAF No 18 Sqn, Gutersloh	
ZA709	B-V Chinook HC1	RNAY Fleetlands	
ZA710	B-V Chinook HC1 [EY]	RAF No 7 Sqn, Odiham	
ZA711	B-V Chinook HC1 [ET]	RAF No 7 Sqn, Odiham	
ZA712	B-V Chinook HC1 [ER]	RAF No 7 Sqn, Odiham	
ZA713	B-V Chinook HC1 [EN]	RAF No 7 Sqn, Odiham	
ZA714	B-V Chinook HC1 [EX]	RAF No 7 Sqn, Odiham	
ZA717	B-V Chinook HC1 [EM]	RAF No 7 Sqn, Odiham	
ZA718	B-V Chinook HC1 [EQ]	RAF No 7 Sqn, Odiham	
ZA720	B-V Chinook HC1 [EP]	RAF No 7 Sqn, Odiham	
ZA721	B-V Chinook HC1 [EP]	Written off 27 February 1987	
ZA726	WS Gazelle AH1	AAC No 663 Sqn, Soest	
ZA727	WS Gazelle AH1	Crashed 7 October 1986	
ZA728	WS Gazelle AH1 [33D]	RM 3 CBAS, Yeovilton	
ZA729	WS Gazelle AH1	AAC No 661 Sqn, Detmold	
ZA730	WS Gazelle AH1 [F]	RM, stored Wroughton	
ZA731	WS Gazelle AH1 [C]	AAC No 29 Flt, Suffield, Canada	
ZA732	WS Gazelle AH1 [D]	Crashed 16 July 1987	
ZA733	WS Gazelle AH1 [J]	AAC No 665 Sqn, Aldergrove	
ZA734	WS Gazelle AH1	AAC No 25 Flt, Belize	
ZA735	WS Gazelle AH1	AAC, No 25 Flt, Belize	
ZA736	WS Gazelle AH1 [A]	AAC No 29 Flt, Suffield, Canada	
ZA737	WS Gazelle AH1 [V]	AAC ARWS, Middle Wallop	
ZA765	WS Gazelle AH1	AAC No 25 Flt, Belize	
ZA766	WS Gazelle AH1	AAC No 663 Sqn, Soest	
ZA767	WS Gazelle AH1	AAC No 25 Flt, Belize	
ZA768	WS Gazelle AH1 [F]	AAC ARWS, Middle Wallop	
ZA769	WS Gazelle AH1 [K]	AAC ARWS, Middle Wallop	
ZA771	WS Gazelle AH1 [Z]	AAC ARWS, Middle Wallop	
ZA772	WS Gazelle AH1	AAC No 656 Sqn, Netheravon	
ZA773	WS Gazelle AH1	AAC No 665 Sqn, Aldergrove	
ZA774	WS Gazelle AH1	AAC No 655 Sqn, Aldergrove	
ZA775	WS Gazelle AH1	AAC No 656 Sqn, Netheravon	
ZA776	WS Gazelle AH1 [13D]	RM 3 CBAS, Yeovilton	
ZA777	WS Gazelle AH1	AAC No 661 Sqn, Hildesheim	
ZA801	WS Gazelle HT3 [V]	RAF Abingdon Fire Section	
ZA802	WS Gazelle HT3 [W]	RAF No 2 FTS, Shawbury	
ZA803	WS Gazelle HT3 [X]	RAF No 2 FTS, Shawbury	
ZA804	WS Gazelle HT3 [I]	RAF No 2 FTS, Shawbury	
ZA934	WS Puma HC1 [FC]	RAF No 240 OCU, Odiham	
ZA935	WS Puma HC1 [CT]	RAF No 1563 Flt, Belize	
ZA936	WS Puma HC1 [CU]	RAF No 33 Sqn, Odiham	
ZA937	WS Puma HC1 [CV]	RAF No 33 Sqn, Odiham	
ZA938	WS Puma HC1 [CW]	RAF No 1563 Flt, Belize	

Notes	Serial	Type (alternative identity)	Owner, Operator or Location
	ZA939	WS Puma HC1 [CX]	RAF No 33 Sqn, Odiham
	ZA940	WS Puma HC1 [CY]	RAF No 33 Sqn, Odiham
	ZA941	WS Puma HC1	MoD(PE) RAE Farnborough
	ZA947	Douglas Dakota C3	MoD(PE) RAE Farnborough
	ZB500	WS Lynx (G-LYNX)	Westlands, Yeovil
	ZB506	WS61 Sea King Mk 4X	MoD(PE) RAE Bedford
	ZB507	WS61 Sea King Mk 4X	MoD(PE) RAE Farnborough
	ZB600	BAe Harrier T4A [R]	RAF No 4 Sqn, Gutersloh
	ZB601	BAe Harrier T4A	RAF No —
	ZB602	BAe Harrier T4A [Y]	RAF No 233 OCU, Wittering
	ZB603	BAe Harrier T4A	RAF No 3 Sqn, Gutersloh
	ZB604	BAe Harrier T4N [717]	RN No 899 Sqn, Yeovilton
	ZB605	BAe Harrier T4N [718]	RN No 899 Sqn, Yeovilton
	ZB615	SEPECAT Jaguar T2	MoD(PE) IAM Farnborough
	ZB625	WS Gazelle HT3 [N]	RAF No 2 FTS, Shawbury
	ZB626	WS Gazelle HT3 [L]	RAF No 2 FTS, Shawbury
	ZB627	WS Gazelle HT3 [A]	RAF No 2 FTS, Shawbury
	ZB628	WS Gazelle HT3 [V]	RAF No 2 FTS, Shawbury
	ZB629	WS Gazelle HT3	RAF No 32 Sqn, Northolt
	ZB646	WS Gazelle HT2 [CU]	RN, stored Wroughton
	ZB647	WS Gazelle HT2 [CU]	RN, stored Wroughton
	ZB648	WS Gazelle HT3	MoD(PE) RAE Farnborough
	ZB649	WS Gazelle HT2 [FL]	RNAY Fleetlands
	ZB665	WS Gazelle AH1	AAC, stored Wroughton
	ZB666	WS Gazelle AH1 [G]	AAC ARWS, Middle Wallop
	ZB667	WS Gazelle AH1	AAC No 664 Sqn, Detmold
	ZB668	WS Gazelle AH1	AAC, 665 Sqn, Aldergrove
	ZB669	WS Gazelle AH1	AAC, stored Wroughton
	ZB670	WS Gazelle AH1	AAC No 665 Sqn, Aldergrove
	ZB671	WS Gazelle AH1 [E]	AAC No 29 Flt, Suffield, Canada
	ZB672	WS Gazelle AH1	AAC No 3 Flt, Topcliffe
	ZB673	WS Gazelle AH1 [P]	AAC ARWS, Middle Wallop
	ZB674	WS Gazelle AH1	AAC Garrison Air Sqn, Falklands
	ZB675	WS Gazelle AH1	AAC Garrison Air Sqn, Falklands
	ZB676	WS Gazelle AH1	AAC, stored Wroughton
	ZB677	WS Gazelle AH1	AAC No 661 Sqn, Hildesheim
	ZB678	WS Gazelle AH1	AAC, stored Wroughton
	ZB679	WS Gazelle AH1	AAC, stored Wroughton
	ZB680	WS Gazelle AH1 [B]	AAC No 29 Flt, Suffield, Canada
	ZB681	WS Gazelle AH1 [G]	AAC No 655 Sqn, Aldergrove
	ZB682	WS Gazelle AH1	AAC No 655 Sqn, Aldergrove
	ZB683	WS Gazelle AH1	AAC No 655 Sqn, Aldergrove
	ZB684	WS Gazelle AH1	AAC No 655 Sqn, Aldergrove
	ZB685	WS Gazelle AH1	AAC No 655 Sqn, Aldergrove
	ZB686	WS Gazelle AH1	AAC No 655 Sqn, Aldergrove
	ZB687	WS Gazelle AH1	AAC No 655 Sqn, Aldergrove
	ZB688	WS Gazelle AH1	AAC, stored Wroughton
	ZB689	WS Gazelle AH1	AAC, stored Wroughton
	ZB690	WS Gazelle AH1	AAC, stored Wroughton
	ZB691	WS Gazelle AH1	AAC, stored Wroughton
	ZB692	WS Gazelle AH1	AAC, stored Wroughton
	ZB693	WS Gazelle AH1	AAC, stored Wroughton
	ZD230	BAC Super VC10 (G-ASGA)	RAF, stored Abingdon
	ZD231	BAC Super VC10 (G-ASGB)	Scrapped Abingdon April 1987
	ZD232	BAC Super VC10 (G-ASGD) (8699M)	RAF Brize Norton Fire Section
	ZD233	BAC Super VC10 (G-ASGE)	RAF FF&SS, Catterick
	ZD234	BAC Super VC10 (G-ASGF) (8700M)	RAF Brize Norton Fire Section
	ZD235	BAC Super VC10 (G-ASGG)	RAF, stored Abingdon
	ZD236	BAC Super VC10 (G-ASGH)	Scrapped Abingdon July 1987
	ZD237	BAC Super VC10 (G-ASGI)	Scrapped Abingdon July 1987
	ZD238	BAC Super VC10 (G-ASGJ)	Scrapped Abingdon July 1987
	ZD239	BAC Super VC10 (G-ASGK)	RAF, stored Abingdon
	ZD240	BAC Super VC10 (G-ASGL)	RAF, stored Abingdon
	ZD241	BAC Super VC10 (G-ASGM)	RAF, stored Abingdon
	ZD242	BAC Super VC10 (G-ASGP)	Scrapped Abingdon August 1987
	ZD243	BAC Super VC10 (G-ASGR)	RAF, stored Abingdon
	ZD249	WS Lynx HAS3	MoD(PE) Westlands, Yeovil
	ZD250	WS Lynx HAS3 [346/BW]	RN No 829 Sqn, Portland
	ZD251	WS Lynx HAS3 [327]	RN No 815 Sqn, Portland
	ZD252	WS Lynx HAS3 [301/PO]	RN No 815 Sqn, Portland

Serial	Type (alternative identity)	Owner, Operator or Location	Notes
ZD253	WS Lynx HAS3 [304/PO]	RN No 815 Sqn, Portland	
ZD254	WS Lynx HAS3 [632/PO]	RN No 702 Sqn, Portland	
ZD255	WS Lynx HAS3 [479]	RN No 815 Sqn, Portland	
ZD256	WS Lynx HAS3 [432/SC]	RN No 815 Sqn, Portland	
ZD257	WS Lynx HAS3 [346/BW]	RN No 815 Sqn, Portland	
ZD258	WS Lynx HAS3 [GIB]	RN No 815 Sqn (208 Flt), Gibraltar	
ZD259	WS Lynx HAS3 [323/AB]	RN No 815 Sqn, Portland	
ZD260	WS Lynx HAS3 [303]	RN No 815 Sqn, Portland	
ZD261	WS Lynx HAS3	RN No 815 Sqn, Portland	
ZD262	WS Lynx HAS3 [632]	RN No 702 Sqn, Portland	
ZD263	WS Lynx HAS3 [630]	RNAY Fleetlands	
ZD264	WS Lynx HAS3 [304/PO]	RN No 815 Sqn, Portland	
ZD265	WS Lynx HAS3 [328/BA]	RN No 829 Sqn, Portland	
ZD266	WS Lynx HAS3	MoD(PE) Westlands, Yeovil	
ZD267	WS Lynx HAS3	MoD(PE) A&AEE Boscombe Down	
ZD268	WS Lynx HAS3 [342/BT]	RN No 829 Sqn, Portland	
ZD272	WS Lynx AH1 [A]	AAC No 663 Sqn, Soest	
ZD273	WS Lynx AH1	AAC No 656 Sqn, Netheravon	
ZD274	WS Lynx AH1	AAC No 656 Sqn, Netheravon	
ZD275	WS Lynx AH1	AAC No 657 Sqn, Oakington	
ZD276	WS Lynx AH1	AAC No 652 Sqn, Hildesheim	
ZD277	WS Lynx AH1	AAC No 655 Sqn, Aldergrove	
ZD278	WS Lynx AH1	AAC, stored Wroughton	
ZD279	WS Lynx AH1 [L]	AAC ARW/LCF, Middle Wallop	
ZD280	WS Lynx AH1	AAC No 663 Sqn, Soest	
ZD281	WS Lynx AH1	AAC No 657 Sqn, Oakington	
ZD282	WS Lynx AH1 [24A]	RM 3 CBAS, Yeovilton	
ZD283	WS Lynx AH1 [M]	AAC ARW/LCF, Middle Wallop	
ZD284	WS Lynx AH1 [24B]	RM 3 CBAS, Yeovilton	
ZD285	WS Lynx AH5	MoD(PE) RAE Farnborough	
ZD318	BAe Harrier GR5	MoD(PE) BAe Dunsfold	
ZD319	BAe Harrier GR5	MoD(PE) BAe Dunsfold	
ZD320	BAe Harrier GR5	MoD(PE) A&AEE Boscombe Down	
ZD321	BAe Harrier GR5	MoD(PE) A&AEE Boscombe Down/BAe Dunsfold	
ZD322	BAe Harrier GR5	MoD(PE) A&AEE Boscombe Down/BAe Dunsfold	
ZD323	BAe Harrier GR5 [A]	RAF No 233 OCU, Wittering	
ZD324	BAe Harrier GR5	RAF No 233 OCU, Wittering	
ZD325	BAe Harrier GR5	Crashed in Atlantic Ocean 23 October 1987	
ZD326	BAe Harrier GR5	RAF No 233 OCU, Wittering	
ZD327	BAe Harrier GR5	RAF No 233 OCU, Wittering	
ZD328	BAe Harrier GR5	RAF No 233 OCU, Wittering	
ZD329	BAe Harrier GR5	RAF No 233 OCU, Wittering	
ZD330	BAe Harrier GR5	RAF No 233 OCU, Wittering	
ZD345	BAe Harrier GR5	RAF No 233 OCU, Wittering	
ZD472	Harrier GR5 Replica [01] (BAPC---)	RAF Exhibition Flight, Abingdon	
ZD476	WS61 Sea King HC4 [ZS]	RN No 707 Sqn, Yeovilton	
ZD477	WS61 Sea King HC4 [VL]	RN No 846 Sqn, Yeovilton	
ZD478	WS61 Sea King HC4 [VM]	RN No 846 Sqn, Yeovilton	
ZD479	WS61 Sea King HC4 [ZW]	RN No 707 Sqn, Yeovilton	
ZD480	WS61 Sea King HC4 [VP]	RN No 846 Sqn, Yeovilton	
ZD485	FMA IA58 Pucara (A-515)	RAF Cosford Aerospace Museum	
ZD493	BAC VC10 (G-ARVJ)	RAF Fire Section Brize Norton	
ZD559	WS Lynx AH1/5	MoD(PE) RAE Bedford	
ZD560	WS Lynx Mk 7	MoD(PE) ETPS Boscombe Down	
ZD565	WS Lynx HAS3 [633]	RN No 702 Sqn, Portland	
ZD566	WS Lynx HAS3 [637]	RN No 702 Sqn, Portland	
ZD567	WS Lynx HAS3 [636/PO]	RN No 702 Sqn, Portland	
ZD574	B-V Chinook HC1 [FH]	RAF No 240 OCU, Odiham	
ZD575	B-V Chinook HC1 [FF]	RAF No 240 OCU, Odiham	
ZD576	B-V Chinook HC1 [FG]	RAF No 240 OCU, Odiham	
ZD578	BAe Sea Harrier FRS1 [125/L]	RN No 800 Sqn, Yeovilton	
ZD579	BAe Sea Harrier FRS1 [126/L]	RN No 800 Sqn, Yeovilton	
ZD580	BAe Sea Harrier FRS1 [716]	RN No 899 Sqn, Yeovilton	
ZD581	BAe Sea Harrier FRS1 [721]	RN No 899 Sqn, Yeovilton	
ZD582	BAe Sea Harrier FRS1 [127/L]	RN No 800 Sqn, Yeovilton	
ZD607	BAe Sea Harrier FRS1 [123/L]	RN No 800 Sqn, Yeovilton	
ZD608	BAe Sea Harrier FRS1 [000/R]	RN No 801 Sqn, Yeovilton	
ZD609	BAe Sea Harrier FRS1 [712]	RN No 899 Sqn, Yeovilton	
ZD610	BAe Sea Harrier FRS1 [711]	RN No 899 Sqn, Yeovilton	
ZD611	BAe Sea Harrier FRS1 [001/R]	RN No 801 Sqn, Yeovilton	

Notes	Serial	Type (alternative identity)	Owner, Operator or Location
	ZD612	BAe Sea Harrier FRS1 [002/R]	RN No 801 Sqn, Yeovilton
	ZD613	BAe Sea Harrier FRS1 [710]	RN No 899 Sqn, Yeovilton
	ZD614	BAe Sea Harrier FRS1 [124/L]	RN No 800 Sqn, Yeovilton
	ZD615	BAe Sea Harrier FRS1 [005/R]	RN No 801 Sqn, Yeovilton
	ZD620	BAe 125 CC3	RAF No 32 Sqn, Northolt
	ZD621	BAe 125 CC3	RAF No 32 Sqn, Northolt
	ZD625	WS61 Sea King HC4 [ZX]	RN No 707 Sqn, Yeovilton
	ZD626	WS61 Sea King HC4 [ZY]	RN No 707 Sqn, Yeovilton
	ZD627	WS61 Sea King HC4 [ZZ]	RN No 707 Sqn, Yeovilton
	ZD630	WS61 Sea King HAS5 [013]	RN No 820 Sqn, Culdrose
	ZD631	WS61 Sea King HAS5 [019/R]	RN No 820 Sqn, Culdrose
	ZD632	WS61 Sea King HAS5	Crashed 15 October 1986 off Gibraltar
	ZD633	WS61 Sea King HAS5 [012/R]	RN No 820 Sqn, Culdrose
	ZD634	WS61 Sea King HAS5 [702/PW]	RN No 819 Sqn, Prestwick
	ZD635	WS61 Sea King HAS5 [703]	Burned at Predannack
	ZD636	WS61 Sea King HAS5 [701/PW]	RN No 819 Sqn, Prestwick
	ZD637	WS61 Sea King HAS5 [704]	RN No 819 Sqn, Prestwick
	ZD643	Schleicher Vanguard TX1 (BGA2884)	RAF No 618 VGS, West Malling
	ZD644	Schleicher Vanguard TX1 (BGA2883)	RAF, stored Dunstable
	ZD645	Schleicher Vanguard TX1 (BGA2885)	RAF No 618 VGS, West Malling
	ZD646	Schleicher Vanguard TX1 (BGA2886)	RAF, stored Dunstable
	ZD647	Schleicher Vanguard TX1 (BGA2887)	RAF No 618 VGS, West Malling
	ZD648	Schleicher Vanguard TX1 (BGA2888)	RAF, stored Dunstable
	ZD649	Schleicher Vanguard TX1 (BGA2889)	RAF No 618 VGS, West Malling
	ZD650	Schleicher Vanguard TX1 (BGA2890)	RAF No 618 VGS, West Malling
	ZD651	Schleicher Vanguard TX1 (BGA2891)	RAF No 618 VGS, West Malling
	ZD652	Schleicher Vanguard TX1 (BGA2892)	RAF No 618 VGS, West Malling
	ZD657	Schleicher Valiant TX1 (BGA2893)	RAF No 631 VGS, Sealand
	ZD658	Schleicher Valiant TX1 (BGA2894)	RAF No 614 VGS, Wethersfield
	ZD659	Schleicher Valiant TX1 (BGA2895)	RAF No 618 VGS, West Malling
	ZD660	Schleicher Valiant TX1 (BGA2896)	RAF No 645 VGS, Catterick
	ZD661	Schleicher Valiant TX1 (BGA2897)	RAF ACCGS, Syerston
	ZD667	BAe Harrier GR3 [U]	RAF No 4 Sqn, Gutersloh
	ZD668	BAe Harrier GR3 [J]	RAF No 4 Sqn, Gutersloh
	ZD669	BAe Harrier GR3 [A]	RAF No 3 Sqn, Gutersloh
	ZD670	BAe Harrier GR3 [W]	RAF No 3 Sqn, Gutersloh
	ZD703	BAe 125 CC3	RAF No 32 Sqn, Northolt
	ZD704	BAe 125 CC3	RAF No 32 Sqn, Northolt
	ZD707	Panavia Tornado GR1 [BK]	RAF No 14 Sqn, Bruggen
	ZD708	Panavia Tornado GR1	BAe Warton
	ZD709	Panavia Tornado GR1 [AH]	RAF No 9 Sqn, Bruggen
	ZD710	Panavia Tornado GR1 [BJ]	RAF No 14 Sqn, Bruggen
	ZD711	Panavia Tornado GR1 [BG]	RAF No 14 Sqn, Bruggen
	ZD711	Panavia Tornado GR1T [DY]	RAF No 31 Sqn, Bruggen
	ZD712	Panavia Tornado GR1T [BY]	RAF No 14 Sqn, Bruggen
	ZD713	Panavia Tornado GR1T	RAF TWCU/45 Sqn, Honington
	ZD714	Panavia Tornado GR1 [BE]	RAF No 14 Sqn, Bruggen
	ZD715	Panavia Tornado GR1 [DB]	RAF No 31 Sqn, Bruggen
	ZD716	Panavia Tornado GR1 [O]	MoD(PE) TOEU Boscombe Down
	ZD717	Panavia Tornado GR1 [CD]	RAF No 17 Sqn, Bruggen
	ZD718	Panavia Tornado GR1 [BH]	RAF No 14 Sqn, Bruggen
	ZD719	Panavia Tornado GR1 [AD]	RAF No 9 Sqn, Bruggen
	ZD720	Panavia Tornado GR1 [CK]	RAF No 17 Sqn, Bruggen
	ZD738	Panavia Tornado GR1 [DD]	Crashed 27 July 1987, North Yorkshire
	ZD739	Panavia Tornado GR1 [AC]	RAF No 9 Sqn, Bruggen
	ZD740	Panavia Tornado GR1 [DA]	RAF No 31 Sqn, Bruggen
	ZD741	Panavia Tornado GR1T [AY]	RAF No 9 Sqn, Bruggen
	ZD742	Panavia Tornado GR1T [CY]	RAF No 17 Sqn, Bruggen
	ZD743	Panavia Tornado GR1T [CZ]	RAF No 17 Sqn, Bruggen

Serial	Type (alternative identity)	Owner, Operator or Location	Notes
ZD744	Panavia Tornado GR1 [BD]	RAF No 14 Sqn, Bruggen	
ZD745	Panavia Tornado GR1 [AB]	RAF No 9 Sqn, Bruggen	
ZD746	Panavia Tornado GR1 [DJ]	RAF No 31 Sqn, Bruggen	
ZD747	Panavia Tornado GR1 [DK]	RAF No 31 Sqn, Bruggen	
ZD748	Panavia Tornado GR1 [DG]	RAF No 31 Sqn, Bruggen	
ZD749	Panavia Tornado GR1 [U]	MoD(PE) TOEU Boscombe Down	
ZD788	Panavia Tornado GR1 [CB]	RAF No 17 Sqn, Bruggen	
ZD789	Panavia Tornado GR1 [CE]	RAF No 17 Sqn, Bruggen	
ZD790	Panavia Tornado GR1 [DL]	RAF No 31 Sqn, Bruggen	
ZD792	Panavia Tornado GR1 [CF]	RAF No 17 Sqn, Bruggen	
ZD793	Panavia Tornado GR1 [CA]	RAF No 17 Sqn, Bruggen	
ZD808	Panavia Tornado GR1 [CJ]	RAF No 17 Sqn, Bruggen	
ZD809	Panavia Tornado GR1 [AA]	RAF No 9 Sqn, Bruggen	
ZD810	Panavia Tornado GR1 [CG]	RAF No 17 Sqn, Bruggen	
ZD811	Panavia Tornado GR1 [DF]	RAF No 31 Sqn, Bruggen	
ZD812	Panavia Tornado GR1T [FV]	RAF No 16 Sqn, Laarbruch	
ZD842	Panavia Tornado GR1T [BZ]	RAF No 14 Sqn, Bruggen	
ZD843	Panavia Tornado GR1 [DH]	RAF No 31 Sqn, Bruggen	
ZD844	Panavia Tornado GR1 [DE]	RAF No 31 Sqn, Bruggen	
ZD845	Panavia Tornado GR1 [BA]	RAF No 14 Sqn, Bruggen	
ZD846	Panavia Tornado GR1 [BL]	RAF No 14 Sqn, Bruggen	
ZD847	Panavia Tornado GR1 [CH]	RAF No 17 Sqn, Bruggen	
ZD848	Panavia Tornado GR1 [BC]	RAF No 14 Sqn, Bruggen	
ZD849	Panavia Tornado GR1 [CC]	RAF No 17 Sqn, Bruggen	
ZD850	Panavia Tornado GR1 [CL]	RAF No 17 Sqn, Bruggen	
ZD851	Panavia Tornado GR1 [DC]	RAF No 31 Sqn, Bruggen	
ZD890	Panavia Tornado GR1 [AE]	RAF No 9 Sqn, Bruggen	
ZD891	Panavia Tornado GR1 [BB]	RAF No 14 Sqn, Bruggen	
ZD892	Panavia Tornado GR1 [AF]	RAF No 9 Sqn, Bruggen	
ZD893	Panavia Tornado GR1 [AG]	RAF No 9 Sqn, Bruggen	
ZD894	Panavia Tornado GR1 [BE]	Crashed 30 March 1987	
ZD895	Panavia Tornado GR1 [BF]	RAF No 14 Sqn, Bruggen	
ZD899	Panavia Tornado F2T	MoD(PE) BAe Warton	
ZD900	Panavia Tornado F2T	MoD(PE) BAe Samlesbury	
ZD901	Panavia Tornado F2T [AB]	RAF No 229 OCU/65 Sqn, Coningsby	
ZD902	Panavia Tornado F2T [AC]	RAF No 229 OCU/65 Sqn, Coningsby	
ZD903	Panavia Tornado F2T	RAF, stored St Athan	
ZD904	Panavia Tornado F2T [AE]	RAF No 229 OCU/65 Sqn, Coningsby	
ZD905	Panavia Tornado F2 [AV]	RAF, stored St Athan	
ZD906	Panavia Tornado F2 [AN]	RAF, stored St Athan	
ZD932	Panavia Tornado F2 [AM]	RAF, stored St Athan	
ZD933	Panavia Tornado F2 [AO]	RAF, stored St Athan	
ZD934	Panavia Tornado F2T [AD]	RAF, stored St Athan	
ZD935	Panavia Tornado F2T [AF]	RAF No 229 OCU/65 Sqn, Coningsby	
ZD936	Panavia Tornado F2	RAF, stored St Athan	
ZD937	Panavia Tornado F2 [AQ]	RAF, stored St Athan	
ZD938	Panavia Tornado F2	RAF, stored St Athan	
ZD939	Panavia Tornado F2	RAF, stored St Athan	
ZD940	Panavia Tornado F2 [AT]	RAF, stored St Athan	
ZD941	Panavia Tornado F2 [AU]	RAF, stored St Athan	
ZD948	Lockheed TriStar KC1 (G-BFCA)	RAF No 216 Sqn, Brize Norton	
ZD949	Lockheed TriStar K1 (G-BFCB)	RAF No 216 Sqn, Brize Norton	
ZD950	Lockheed TriStar KC1 (G-BFCC)	RAF No 216 Sqn, Brize Norton	
ZD951	Lockheed TriStar K1 (G-BFCD)	RAF No 216 Sqn, Brize Norton	
ZD952	Lockheed TriStar KC1 (G-BFCE)	RAF No 216 Sqn, Brize Norton	
ZD953	Lockheed TriStar KC1 (G-BFCF)	RAF No 216 Sqn, Brize Norton	
ZD974	Schempp-Hirth Janus C (BGA2875)	RAF ACCGS, Syerston	
ZD975	Schempp-Hirth Janus C (BGA2876)	RAF ACCGS, Syerston	
ZD980	B-V Chinook HC1 [FJ]	RAF No 240 OCU, Odiham	
ZD981	B-V Chinook HC1 [BD]	RAF No 18 Sqn, Gutersloh	
ZD982	B-V Chinook HC1 [FI]	RAF No 240 OCU, Odiham	
ZD983	B-V Chinook HC1 [BF]	RAF No 18 Sqn, Gutersloh	
ZD984	B-V Chinook HC1 [BE]	RAF No 18 Sqn, Gutersloh	
ZD990	BAe Harrier T4A [X]	RAF No 3 Sqn, Gutersloh	
ZD991	BAe Harrier T4A [S]	RAF No 4 Sqn, Gutersloh	
ZD992	BAe Harrier T4A [P]	RAF No 233 OCU, Wittering	
ZD993	BAe Harrier T4A [O]	RAF No 233 OCU, Wittering	
ZD996	Panavia Tornado GR1(R) [AK]	RAF No 9 Sqn, Bruggen	
ZE116	Panavia Tornado GR1(R) [AL]	RAF No 9 Sqn, Bruggen	
ZE154	Panavia Tornado F3T [AK]	RAF No 229 OCU/65 Sqn, Coningsby	
ZE155	Panavia Tornado F3	MoD(PE), BAe Warton	

Notes	Serial	Type (alternative identity)	Owner, Operator or Location
	ZE156	Panavia Tornado F3 [AV]	RAF No 229 OCU/65 Sqn, Coningsby
	ZE157	Panavia Tornado F3T [AH]	RAF No 229 OCU/65 Sqn, Coningsby
	ZE158	Panavia Tornado F3 [AP]	RAF No 229 OCU/65 Sqn, Coningsby
	ZE159	Panavia Tornado F3 [AW]	RAF No 229 OCU/65 Sqn, Cgningsby
	ZE160	Panavia Tornado F3T [AG]	RAF No 229 OCU/65 Sqn, Coningsby
	ZE161	Panavia Tornado F3 [AX]	RAF No 229 OCU/65 Sqn, Coningsby
	ZE162	Panavia Tornado F3 [AY]	RAF No 229 OCU/65 Sqn, Coningsby
	ZE163	Panavia Tornado F3T	RAF No 229 OCU/65 Sqn, Coningsby
	ZE164	Panavia Tornado F3 [AN]	RAF No 229 OCU/65 Sqn, Coningsby
	ZE165	Panavia Tornado F3 [AZ]	RAF No 229 OCU/65 Sqn, Coningsby
	ZE166	Panavia Tornado F3T [AI]	RAF No 229 OCU/65 Sqn, Coningsby
	ZE167	Panavia Tornado F3 [AR]	RAF No 229 OCU/65 Sqn, Coningsby
	ZE168	Panavia Tornado F3 [AO]	RAF No 229 OCU/65 Sqn, Coningsby
	ZE199	Panavia Tornado F3T [AJ]	RAF No 229 OCU/65 Sqn, Coningsby
	ZE200	Panavia Tornado F3 [AS]	RAF No 229 OCU/65 Sqn, Coningsby
	ZE201	Panavia Tornado F3 [AQ]	RAF No 229 OCU/65 Sqn, Coningsby
	ZE202	Panavia Tornado F3T	MoD(PE) A&AEE, Boscombe Down
	ZE203	Panavia Tornado F3 [BA]	RAF No 29 Sqn, Coningsby
	ZE204	Panavia Tornado F3 [BB]	RAF No 29 Sqn, Coningsby
	ZE205	Panavia Tornado F3T [AA]	RAF No 229 OCU/65 Sqn, Coningsby
	ZE206	Panavia Tornado F3 [BF]	RAF No 29 Sqn, Coningsby
	ZE207	Panavia Tornado F3	RAF No 229 OCU/65 Sqn, Coningsby
	ZE208	Panavia Tornado F3T [BT]	RAF No 29 Sqn, Coningsby
	ZE209	Panavia Tornado F3 [BC]	RAF No 29 Sqn, Coningsby
	ZE210	Panavia Tornado F3	RAF TOEU, Coningsby
	ZE250	Panavia Tornado F3T [AP]	RAF No 229 OCU/65 Sqn, Coningsby
	ZE251	Panavia Tornado F3	RAF TOEU, Coningsby
	ZE252	Panavia Tornado F3	RAF TOEU, Coningsby
	ZE253	Panavia Tornado F3T	MoD(PE) BAe Warton
	ZE254	Panavia Tornado F3 [BG]	RAF No 29 Sqn, Coningsby
	ZE255	Panavia Tornado F3 [BH]	RAF No 29 Sqn, Coningsby
	ZE256	Panavia Tornado F3T [CT]	RAF No 5 Sqn, Coningsby
	ZE257	Panavia Tornado F3 [BD]	RAF No 29 Sqn, Coningsby
	ZE258	Panavia Tornado F3 [BE]	RAF No 29 Sqn, Coningsby
	ZE287	Panavia Tornado F3T [AE]	RAF No 229 OCU/65 Sqn, Coningsby
	ZE288	Panavia Tornado F3 [BI]	RAF No 29 Sqn, Coningsby
	ZE289	Panavia Tornado F3 [BJ]	RAF No 29 Sqn, Coningsby
	ZE290	Panavia Tornado F3T [AD]	RAF No 229 OCU/65 Sqn, Coningsby
	ZE291	Panavia Tornado F3 [BK]	RAF No 29 Sqn, Coningsby
	ZE292	Panavia Tornado F3	RAF No 5 Sqn, Coningsby
	ZE293	Panavia Tornado F3T	MoD(PE), BAe Warton
	ZE294	Panavia Tornado F3	RAF No 5 Sqn, Coningsby
	ZE295	Panavia Tornado F3	RAF No 5 Sqn, Coningsby
	ZE296	Panavia Tornado F3T	RAF No 5 Sqn, Coningsby
	ZE338	Panavia Tornado F3	MoD(PE), BAe Warton
	ZE339	Panavia Tornado F3	MoD(PE), BAe Warton
	ZE340	Panavia Tornado F3T	MoD(PE), BAe Warton
	ZE341	Panavia Tornado F3	MoD(PE), BAe Warton
	ZE342	Panavia Tornado F3	MoD(PE), BAe Warton
	ZE343	Panavia Tornado F3T	MoD(PE), BAe Warton
	ZE350	McD Phantom F-4J(UK) [T]	RAF No 74 Sqn, Wattisham
	ZE351	McD Phantom F-4J(UK) [I]	RAF No 74 Sqn, Wattisham
	ZE352	McD Phantom F-4J(UK) [G]	RAF No 74 Sqn, Wattisham
	ZE353	McD Phantom F-4J(UK) [E]	RAF No 74 Sqn, Wattisham
	ZE354	McD Phantom F-4J(UK) [R]	RAF No 74 Sqn, Wattisham
	ZE355	McD Phantom F-4J(UK) [S]	RAF No 74 Sqn, Wattisham
	ZE356	McD Phantom F-4J(UK) [Q]	RAF No 74 Sqn, Wattisham
	ZE357	McD Phantom F-4J(UK) [N]	RAF No 74 Sqn, Wattisham
	ZE358	McD Phantom F-4J(UK) [H]	Crashed 26 August 1987 nr Aberystwyth
	ZE359	McD Phantom F-4J(UK) [J]	RAF No 74 Sqn, Wattisham
	ZE360	McD Phantom F-4J(UK) [O]	RAF No 74 Sqn, Wattisham
	ZE361	McD Phantom F-4J(UK) [P]	RAF No 74 Sqn, Wattisham
	ZE362	McD Phantom F-4J(UK) [V]	RAF No 74 Sqn, Wattisham
	ZE363	McD Phantom F-4J(UK) [W]	RAF No 74 Sqn, Wattisham
	ZE364	McD Phantom F-4J(UK) [Z]	RAF No 74 Sqn, Wattisham
	ZE368	WS61 Sea King HAR3	RAF No 202 Sqn SAR*
	ZE369	WS61 Sea King HAR3	RAF No 202 Sqn SAR*
	ZE370	WS61 Sea King HAR3	RAF No 202 Sqn SAR*
	ZE375	WS Lynx AH5	MoD(PE) Rolls-Royce, Filton
	ZE376	WS Lynx AH7	MoD(PE) Westlands, Yeovil
	ZE377	WS Lynx AH7	AAC Wroughton
	ZE378	WS Lynx AH7	AAC Wroughton
	ZE379	WS Lynx AH7	AAC Wroughton
	ZE380	WS Lynx AH7	AAC Wroughton

Serial	Type (alternative identity)	Owner, Operator or Location	Notes
ZE381	WS Lynx AH7	AAC Wroughton	
ZE382	WS Lynx AH7	AAC Wroughton	
ZE383	WS Lynx AH7	AAC Wroughton	
ZE395	BAe 125 CC3	RAF No 32 Sqn, Northolt	
ZE396	BAe 125 CC3	RAF No 32 Sqn, Northolt	
ZE410	Agusta A109A (AE-334)	AAC 7 Regt HQ Flt, Netheravon	
ZE411	Agusta A109A (AE-331)	AAC 7 Regt HQ Flt, Netheravon	
ZE412	Agusta A109A	AAC 7 Regt HQ Flt, Netheravon	
ZE413	Agusta A109A	AAC 7 Regt HQ Flt, Netheravon	
ZE418	WS61 Sea King HAS5 [512]	RN No 810 Sqn, Culdrose	
ZE419	WS61 Sea King HAS5 [014/R]	RN No 820 Sqn, Culdrose	
ZE420	WS61 Sea King HAS5 [010]	RN No 820 Sqn, Culdrose	
ZE421	WS61 Sea King HAS5 [502]	RN No 810 Sqn, Culdrose	
ZE422	WS61 Sea King HAS5 [270/L]	RN No 814 Sqn, Culdrose	
ZE425	WS61 Sea King HC4 [A]	RN No 845 Sqn, Yeovilton	
ZE426	WS61 Sea King HC4 [B]	RN No 845 Sqn, Yeovilton	
ZE427	WS61 Sea King HC4 [C]	RN No 845 Sqn, Yeovilton	
ZE428	WS61 Sea King HC4 [D]	RN No 845 Sqn, Yeovilton	
ZE432	BAC 1-11/479 (DQ-FBV)	MoD(PE) ETPS Boscombe Down	
ZE433	BAC 1-11/479 (DQ-FBQ)	MoD(PE) RAE Bedford	
ZE438	BAe Jetstream T3 [576]	RN No 750 Sqn, Culdrose	
ZE439	BAe Jetstream T3 [577/CU]	RN No 750 Sqn, Culdrose	
ZE440	BAe Jetstream T3 [578]	RN No 750 Sqn, Culdrose	
ZE441	BAe Jetstream T3 [579]	RN No 750 Sqn, Culdrose	
ZE449	Sud SA330L Puma HC1 (PA-12)	MoD(PE) Westlands, Weston-super-Mare	
ZE472	HS Hawk T63	To Abu Dhabi AF, 1014	
ZE477	WS Lynx 3	MoD(PE) Westlands, Yeovil	
ZE495	Grob Viking T1 (BGA3000)	RAF No 644 VGS, Syerston	
ZE496	Grob Viking T1 (BGA3001)	RAF No 631 VGS, Sealand	
ZE497	Grob Viking T1 (BGA3002)	RAF No 622 VGS, Upavon	
ZE498	Grob Viking T1 (BGA3003)	RAF ACCGS, Syerston	
ZE499	Grob Viking T1 (BGA3004)	RAF ACCGS, Syerston	
ZE500	Grob Viking T1 (BGA3005)	RAF No 631 VGS, Sealand	
ZE501	Grob Viking T1 (BGA3006)	RAF ACCGS, Syerston	
ZE502	Grob Viking T1 (BGA3007)	RAF No 645 VGS, Catterick	
ZE503	Grob Viking T1 (BGA3008)	RAF No 625 VGS, South Cerney	
ZE504	Grob Viking T1 (BGA3009)	RAF No 645 VGS, Catterick	
ZE520	Grob Viking T1 (BGA3010)	RAF No 645 VGS, Catterick	
ZE521	Grob Viking T1 (BGA3011)	RAF No 662 VGS, Arbroath	
ZE522	Grob Viking T1 (BGA3012)	RAF No 662 VGS, Arbroath	
ZE523	Grob Viking T1 (BGA3013)	RAF No 631 VGS, Sealand	
ZE524	Grob Viking T1 (BGA3014)	RAF No 611 VGS, Swanton Morley	
ZE525	Grob Viking T1 (BGA3015)	RAF No 622 VGS, Upavon	
ZE526	Grob Viking T1 (BGA3016)	RAF No 631 VGS, Sealand	
ZE527	Grob Viking T1 (BGA3017)	RAF No 611 VGS, Swanton Morley	
ZE528	Grob Viking T1 (BGA3018)	RAF No 631 VGS, Sealand	
ZE529	Grob Viking T1 (BGA3019)	RAF No 631 VGS, Sealand	
ZE530	Grob Viking T1 (BGA3020)	RAF No 645 VGS, Catterick	
ZE531	Grob Viking T1 (BGA3021)	RAF No 645 VGS, Catterick	
ZE532	Grob Viking T1 (BGA3022)	RAF ACCGS, Syerston	
ZE533	Grob Viking T1 (BGA3023)	RAF No 622 VGS, Upavon	
ZE534	Grob Viking T1 (BGA3024)	RAF No 662 VGS, Arbroath	
ZE550	Grob Viking T1 (BGA3025)	RAF No 622 VGS, Upavon	
ZE551	Grob Viking T1 (BGA3026)	RAF No 611 VGS, Swanton Morley	
ZE552	Grob Viking T1 (BGA3027)	RAF No 662 VGS, Arbroath	
ZE553	Grob Viking T1 (BGA3028)	RAF No 643 VGS, Scampton	
ZE554	Grob Viking T1 (BGA3029)	RAF No 631 VGS, Sealand	
ZE555	Grob Viking T1 (BGA3030)	RAF No ???	
ZE556	Grob Viking T1 (BGA3031)	RAF No 622 VGS, Upavon	
ZE557	Grob Viking T1 (BGA3032)	RAF No 661 VGS, Kirknewton	
ZE558	Grob Viking T1 (BGA3033)	RAF No 634 VGS, St Athan	
ZE559	Grob Viking T1 (BGA3034)	RAF No 661 VGS, Kirknewton	
ZE560	Grob Viking T1 (BGA3035)	RAF No 634 VGS, St Athan	
ZE561	Grob Viking T1 (BGA3036)	RAF No 661 VGS, Kirknewton	
ZE562	Grob Viking T1 (BGA3037)	RAF No 611 VGS, Swanton Morley	
ZE563	Grob Viking T1 (BGA3038)	RAF No 615 VGS, Kenley	
ZE564	Grob Viking T1 (BGA3039)	RAF No 661 VGS, Kirknewton	
ZE584	Grob Viking T1 (BGA3040)	RAF No 661 VGS, Kirknewton	
ZE585	Grob Viking T1 (BGA3041)	RAF No 614 VGS, Wethersfield	
ZE586	Grob Viking T1 (BGA3042)	RAF No 625 VGS, South Cerney	
ZE587	Grob Viking T1 (BGA3043)	RAF No 634 VGS, St Athan	
ZE588	Grob Viking T1 (BGA3044)	RAF No 614 VGS, Wethersfield	
ZE589	Grob Viking T1 (BGA3045)	RAF No 635 VGS, Samlesbury	

Notes	Serial	Type (alternative identity)	Owner, Operator or Location
	ZE590	Grob Viking T1 (BGA3046)	RAF No 635 VGS, Samlesbury
	ZE591	Grob Viking T1 (BGA3047)	RAF No 636 VGS, Swansea
	ZE592	Grob Viking T1 (BGA3048)	RAF No 614 VGS, Wethersfield
	ZE593	Grob Viking T1 (BGA3049)	RAF No 614 VGS, Wethersfield
	ZE594	Grob Viking T1 (BGA3050)	RAF No 662 VGS, Arbroath
	ZE595	Grob Viking T1 (BGA3051)	RAF No 625 VGS, South Cerney
	ZE600	Grob Viking T1 (BGA3052)	RAF No 626 VGS, Predannack
	ZE601	Grob Viking T1 (BGA3053)	RAF No 625 VGS, South Cerney
	ZE602	Grob Viking T1 (BGA3054)	RAF, stored Kemble
	ZE603	Grob Viking T1 (BGA3055)	RAF, stored Kemble
	ZE604	Grob Viking T1 (BGA3056)	RAF, stored Kemble
	ZE605	Grob Viking T1 (BGA3057)	RAF No 636 VGS, Swansea
	ZE606	Grob Viking T1 (BGA3058)	RAF No 626 VGS, Predannack
	ZE607	Grob Viking T1 (BGA3059)	RAF No 636 VGS, Swansea
	ZE608	Grob Viking T1 (BGA3060)	RAF No 625 VGS, South Cerney
	ZE609	Grob Viking T1 (BGA3061)	RAF No 626 VGS, Predannack
	ZE610	Grob Viking T1 (BGA3062)	RAF No 621 VGS, Weston-super-Mare
	ZE611	Grob Viking T1 (BGA3063)	RAF No 621 VGS, Weston-super-Mare
	ZE612	Grob Viking T1 (BGA3064)	RAF No 621 VGS, Weston-super-Mare
	ZE613	Grob Viking T1 (BGA3065)	RAF No 621 VGS, Weston-super-Mare
	ZE614	Grob Viking T1 (BGA3066)	RAF No 621 VGS, Weston-super-Mare
	ZE625	Grob Viking T1 (BGA3067)	RAF No 643 VGS, Scampton
	ZE626	Grob Viking T1 (BGA3068)	RAF, stored Kemble
	ZE627	Grob Viking T1 (BGA3069)	RAF No 7 AEF, Newton
	ZE628	Grob Viking T1 (BGA3070)	RAF No 643 VGS, Scampton
	ZE629	Grob Viking T1 (BGA3071)	RAF No 662 VGS, Arbroath
	ZE630	Grob Viking T1 (BGA3072)	RAF, stored Kemble
	ZE631	Grob Viking T1 (BGA3073)	RAF No 643 VGS, Scampton
	ZE632	Grob Viking T1 (BGA3074)	RAF, stored Kemble
	ZE633	Grob Viking T1 (BGA3075)	RAF, stored Kemble
	ZE634	Grob Viking T1 (BGA3076)	MoD(PE) Slingsby, Kirkbymoorside
	ZE635	Grob Viking T1 (BGA3077)	RAFC Cranwell Glider Flight
	ZE636	Grob Viking T1 (BGA3078)	RAF Halton Glider Flight
	ZE637	Grob Viking T1 (BGA3079)	RAF No 614 VGS, Wethersfield
	ZE650	Grob Viking T1 (BGA3080)	RAF, stored Kemble
	ZE651	Grob Viking T1 (BGA3081)	RAF, stored Kemble
	ZE652	Grob Viking T1 (BGA3082)	RAF ACCGS, Syerston
	ZE653	Grob Viking T1 (BGA3083)	RAF No 615 VGS, Kenley
	ZE654	Grob Viking T1 (BGA3084)	RAF No —
	ZE655	Grob Viking T1 (BGA3085)	RAF No —
	ZE656	Grob Viking T1 (BGA3086)	RAF No 617 VGS, Manston
	ZE657	Grob Viking T1 (BGA3087)	RAF No 617 VGS, Manston
	ZE658	Grob Viking T1 (BGA3088)	RAF, stored Kemble
	ZE659	Grob Viking T1 (BGA3089)	RAF No 615 VGS, Kenley
	ZE677	Grob Viking T1 (BGA3090)	RAF No 615 VGS, Kenley
	ZE678	Grob Viking T1 (BGA3091)	RAF No 615 VGS, Kenley
	ZE679	Grob Viking T1 (BGA3092)	RAF No 615 VGS, Kenley
	ZE680	Grob Viking T1 (BGA3093)	RAF No 617 VGS, Manston
	ZE681	Grob Viking T1 (BGA3094)	RAF No 615 VGS, Kenley
	ZE682	Grob Viking T1 (BGA3095)	RAF No 643 VGS, Scampton
	ZE683	Grob Viking T1 (BGA3096)	RAF No 617 VGS, Manston
	ZE684	Grob Viking T1 (BGA3097)	RAF No 617 VGS, Manston
	ZE685	Grob Viking T1 (BGA3098)	RAF No 617 VGS, Manston
	ZE686	Grob Viking T1 (BGA3099)	MoD(PE), Slingsby, Kirkbymoorside
	ZE690	BAe Sea Harrier FRS2	MoD(PE) for RN
	ZE691	BAe Sea Harrier FRS2	MoD(PE) for RN
	ZE692	BAe Sea Harrier FRS2	MoD(PE) for RN
	ZE693	BAe Sea Harrier FRS2	MoD(PE) for RN
	ZE694	BAe Sea Harrier FRS2	MoD(PE) for RN
	ZE695	BAe Sea Harrier FRS2	MoD(PE) for RN
	ZE696	BAe Sea Harrier FRS2	MoD(PE) for RN
	ZE697	BAe Sea Harrier FRS2	MoD(PE) for RN
	ZE698	BAe Sea Harrier FRS2	MoD(PE) for RN
	ZE700	BAe 146 CC2	RAF Queen's Flight, Benson
	ZE701	BAe 146 CC2	RAF Queen's Flight, Benson
	ZE704	Lockheed TriStar K2 (N508PA)	RAF No 216 Sqn, Brize Norton
	ZE705	Lockheed TriStar K2 (N509PA)	RAF No 216 Sqn, Brize Norton
	ZE706	Lockheed TriStar K2 (N503PA)	MoD(PE) Marshalls, Cambridge
	ZE728	Panavia Tornado F3T	MoD(PE), BAe Warton
	ZE729	Panavia Tornado F3	MoD(PE), BAe Warton
	ZE730	Panavia Tornado F3	MoD(PE), BAe Warton
	ZE731	Panavia Tornado F3	MoD(PE), BAe Warton
	ZE732	Panavia Tornado F3	MoD(PE), BAe Warton
	ZE733	Panavia Tornado F3	MoD(PE), BAe Warton

Serial	Type (alternative identity)	Owner, Operator or Location	Notes
ZE734	Panavia Tornado F3	MoD(PE), BAe Warton	
ZE735	Panavia Tornado F3T	MoD(PE), BAe Warton	
ZE736	Panavia Tornado F3	MoD(PE), BAe Warton	
ZE737	Panavia Tornado F3	MoD(PE), BAe Warton	
ZE755	Panavia Tornado F3	MoD(PE), BAe Warton	
ZE756	Panavia Tornado F3	MoD(PE), BAe Warton	
ZE757	Panavia Tornado F3	MoD(PE), BAe Warton	
ZE758	Panavia Tornado F3	MoD(PE), BAe Warton	
ZE759	Panavia Tornado F3T	MoD(PE), BAe Warton	
ZE760	Panavia Tornado F3	MoD(PE), BAe Warton	
ZE761	Panavia Tornado F3	MoD(PE), BAe Warton	
ZE762	Panavia Tornado F3	MoD(PE), BAe Warton	
ZE763	Panavia Tornado F3	MoD(PE), BAe Warton	
ZE764	Panavia Tornado F3	MoD(PE), BAe Warton	
ZE785	Panavia Tornado F3	MoD(PE), BAe Warton	
ZE786	Panavia Tornado F3T	MoD(PE), BAe Warton	
ZE787	Panavia Tornado F3	MoD(PE), BAe Warton	
ZE788	Panavia Tornado F3	MoD(PE), BAe Warton	
ZE789	Panavia Tornado F3	MoD(PE), BAe Warton	
ZE790	Panavia Tornado F3	MoD(PE), BAe Warton	
ZE791	Panavia Tornado F3	MoD(PE), BAe Warton	
ZE792	Panavia Tornado F3	MoD(PE), BAe Warton	
ZE793	Panavia Tornado F3T	MoD(PE), BAe Warton	
ZE794	Panavia Tornado F3	MoD(PE), BAe Warton	
ZE808	Panavia Tornado F3	MoD(PE), BAe Warton	
ZE809	Panavia Tornado F3	MoD(PE), BAe Warton	
ZE810	Panavia Tornado F3	MoD(PE), BAe Warton	
ZE811	Panavia Tornado F3	MoD(PE), BAe Warton	
ZE812	Panavia Tornado F3	MoD(PE), BAe Warton	
ZE830	Panavia Tornado F3T	MoD(PE), BAe Warton	
ZE831	Panavia Tornado F3	MoD(PE), BAe Warton	
ZE832	Panavia Tornado F3	MoD(PE), BAe Warton	
ZE833	Panavia Tornado F3	MoD(PE), BAe Warton	
ZE834	Panavia Tornado F3	MoD(PE), BAe Warton	
ZE835	Panavia Tornado F3	MoD(PE), BAe Warton	
ZE836	Panavia Tornado F3	MoD(PE), BAe Warton	
ZE837	Panavia Tornado F3T	MoD(PE), BAe Warton	
ZE838	Panavia Tornado F3	MoD(PE), BAe Warton	
ZE839	Panavia Tornado F3	MoD(PE), BAe Warton	
ZE858	Panavia Tornado F3	MoD(PE), BAe Warton	
ZE859	Panavia Tornado F3	MoD(PE), BAe Warton	
ZE860	Panavia Tornado F3	MoD(PE), BAe Warton	
ZE861	Panavia Tornado F3	MoD(PE), BAe Warton	
ZE862	Panavia Tornado F3T	MoD(PE), BAe Warton	
ZE882	Panavia Tornado F3	MoD(PE), BAe Warton	
ZE883	Panavia Tornado F3	MoD(PE), BAe Warton	
ZE884	Panavia Tornado F3	MoD(PE), BAe Warton	
ZE885	Panavia Tornado F3	MoD(PE), BAe Warton	
ZE886	Panavia Tornado F3	MoD(PE), BAe Warton	
ZE887	Panavia Tornado F3	MoD(PE), BAe Warton	
ZE888	Panavia Tornado F3T	MoD(PE), BAe Warton	
ZE889	Panavia Tornado F3	MoD(PE), BAe Warton	
ZE890	Panavia Tornado F3	MoD(PE), BAe Warton	
ZE891	Panavia Tornado F3	MoD(PE), BAe Warton	
ZE905	Panavia Tornado F3	MoD(PE), BAe Warton	
ZE906	Panavia Tornado F3	MoD(PE), BAe Warton	
ZE907	Panavia Tornado F3	MoD(PE), BAe Warton	
ZE908	Panavia Tornado F3T	MoD(PE), BAe Warton	
ZE909	Panavia Tornado F3	MoD(PE), BAe Warton	
ZE910	Panavia Tornado F3	MoD(PE), BAe Warton	
ZE911	Panavia Tornado F3	MoD(PE), BAe Warton	
ZE912	Panavia Tornado F3	MoD(PE), BAe Warton	
ZE913	Panavia Tornado F3	MoD(PE), BAe Warton	
ZE914	Panavia Tornado F3	MoD(PE), BAe Warton	
ZE934	Panavia Tornado F3T	MoD(PE), BAe Warton	
ZE935	Panavia Tornado F3	MoD(PE), BAe Warton	
ZE936	Panavia Tornado F3	MoD(PE), BAe Warton	
ZE937	Panavia Tornado F3	MoD(PE), BAe Warton	
ZE938	Panavia Tornado F3	MoD(PE), BAe Warton	
ZE939	Panavia Tornado F3	MoD(PE), BAe Warton	
ZE940	Panavia Tornado F3	MoD(PE), BAe Warton	
ZE941	Panavia Tornado F3T	MoD(PE), BAe Warton	
ZE942	Panavia Tornado F3	MoD(PE), BAe Warton	
ZE943	Panavia Tornado F3	MoD(PE), BAe Warton	

Notes	Serial	Type (alternative identity)	Owner, Operator or Location
	ZE960	Panavia Tornado F3	MoD(PE), BAe Warton
	ZE961	Panavia Tornado F3	MoD(PE), BAe Warton
	ZE962	Panavia Tornado F3	MoD(PE), BAe Warton
	ZE963	Panavia Tornado F3	MoD(PE), BAe Warton
	ZE964	Panavia Tornado F3T	MoD(PE), BAe Warton
	ZE965	Panavia Tornado F3	MoD(PE), BAe Warton
	ZE966	Panavia Tornado F3	MoD(PE), BAe Warton
	ZE967	Panavia Tornado F3	MoD(PE), BAe Warton
	ZE968	Panavia Tornado F3	MoD(PE), BAe Warton
	ZE969	Panavia Tornado F3	MoD(PE), BAe Warton
	ZE982	Panavia Tornado F3	MoD(PE), BAe Warton
	ZE983	Panavia Tornado F3	MoD(PE), BAe Warton
	ZF115	WS61 Sea King Mk 4	MoD(PE) A&AEE, Boscombe Down
	ZF116	WS61 Sea King HC4	RN NASU, Yeovilton
	ZF117	WS61 Sea King HC4 [I]	RN No 845 Sqn, Yeovilton
	ZF118	WS61 Sea King HC4 [H]	RN No 845 Sqn, Yeovilton
	ZF119	WS61 Sea King HC4 [VJ]	RN No 846 Sqn, Yeovilton
	ZF120	WS61 Sea King HC4	RN NASU, Yeovilton
	ZF121	WS61 Sea King HC4	RN NASU, Yeovilton
	ZF122	WS61 Sea King HC4	RN NASU, Yeovilton
	ZF123	WS61 Sea King HC4	RN NASU, Yeovilton
	ZF124	WS61 Sea King HC4	RN, stored Wroughton
	ZF130	BAe 125-600B (G-BLUW)	MoD(PE) BAe Woodford
	ZF135	Short Tucano T1	MoD(PE) A&AEE, Boscombe Down
	ZF136	Short Tucano T1	MoD(PE) A&AEE, Boscombe Down
	ZF137	Short Tucano T1	MoD(PE) A&AEE, Boscombe Down
	ZF138	Short Tucano T1	MoD(PE) Short Bros, Belfast
	ZF139	Short Tucano T1	MoD(PE) Short Bros, Belfast
	ZF140	Short Tucano T1	MoD(PE) Short Bros, Belfast
	ZF141	Short Tucano T1	MoD(PE) Short Bros, Belfast
	ZF142	Short Tucano T1	MoD(PE) Short Bros, Belfast
	ZF143	Short Tucano T1	MoD(PE) Short Bros, Belfast
	ZF144	Short Tucano T1	MoD(PE) Short Bros, Belfast
	ZF145	Short Tucano T1	MoD(PE) Short Bros, Belfast
	ZF444	BN2A Islander (G-WOTG)	RAF Parachute Association, Weston-on-the-Green
	ZF520	Piper PA-31 Navajo Chieftain (N35823/G-BLZK)	MoD(PE) RAE Farnborough
	ZF521	Piper PA-31 Navajo Chieftain (N27509)	MoD(PE) RAE Farnborough
	ZF522	Piper PA-31 Navajo Chieftain (N4261A/G-RNAV/N27728)	MoD(PE) RAE Farnborough
	ZF526	WS61 Sea King Mk 42B	To Indian Navy as IN513
	ZF527	WS61 Sea King Mk 42B	Westlands, ditched 23 July 1987 (IN514)
	ZF534	BAe EAP	BAe Warton
	ZF537	WS Lynx AH7	AAC, Wroughton
	ZF538	WS Lynx AH7	AAC, Wroughton
	ZF539	WS Lynx AH7	AAC, Wroughton
	ZF540	WS Lynx AH7	AAC, Wroughton
	ZF541	WS Lynx AH7	AAC, Wroughton
	ZF557	WS Lynx AH7	AAC
	ZF558	WS Lynx AH7	AAC
	ZF559	WS Lynx AH7	AAC
	ZF560	WS Lynx AH7	AAC
	ZF561	WS Lynx AH7	AAC
	ZF562	WS Lynx AH7	AAC
	ZF563	WS Lynx AH7	AAC
	ZF573	BN2T Islander (G-SRAY)	MoD(PE)
	ZF577	BAC Lightning F53	BAe, stored Warton
	ZF578	BAC Lightning F53	BAe, stored Warton
	ZF579	BAC Lightning F53	BAe, stored Warton
	ZF580	BAC Lightning F53	BAe, stored Warton
	ZF581	BAC Lightning F53	BAe, stored Warton
	ZF582	BAC Lightning F53	BAe, stored Warton
	ZF583	BAC Lightning F53	BAe, stored Warton
	ZF584	BAC Lightning F53	BAe, stored Warton
	ZF585	BAC Lightning F53	BAe, stored Warton
	ZF586	BAC Lightning F53	BAe, stored Warton
	ZF587	BAC Lightning F53	BAe, stored Warton
	ZF588	BAC Lightning F53	BAe, stored Warton
	ZF589	BAC Lightning F53	BAe, stored Warton
	ZF590	BAC Lightning F53	BAe, stored Warton
	ZF591	BAC Lightning F53	BAe, stored Warton

Serial	Type (alternative identity)	Owner, Operator or Location	Notes
ZF592	BAC Lightning F53	BAe, stored Warton	
ZF593	BAC Lightning F53	BAe, stored Warton	
ZF594	BAC Lightning F53	BAe, stored Warton	
ZF595	BAC Lightning T55	BAe, stored Warton	
ZF596	BAC Lightning T55	BAe, stored Warton	
ZF597	BAC Lightning T55	BAe, stored Warton	
ZF598	BAC Lightning T55	BAe, stored Warton	
ZF622	Piper Navajo Chieftain (N35487)	MoD(PE) A&AEE Boscombe Down	
ZF641	WS EH-101	MoD(PE) Westlands, Yeovil	
ZF644	WS EH-101	MoD(PE) Westlands, Yeovil	
ZF649	WS EH-101	MoD(PE) Westlands, Yeovil	
ZG468	WS70 Blackhawk	Westland Helicopters, Yeovil	
ZG601	WS61 Sea King Mk 42B [W]	*To Indian Navy IN515*	
ZG602	WS61 Sea King Mk 42B	*To Indian Navy IN514*	
ZG621	BAC 167 Strikemaster (G-BIDB)	BAe Warton	
ZG622	BAC 167 Strikemaster (G-BIHZ)	BAe Warton	
ZG623	BAC 167 Strikemaster	BAe Warton	
ZH200	BAe Hawk 200	MoD(PE), BAe Dunsfold	

RAF Maintenance Command/ Support Command 'M' number cross-reference

1764M/K4972
2365M/K6038
4354M/BL614
5377M/EP120
5405M/LF738
5466M/LF751
5690M/MK356
5718M/BM597
5758M/DG202
6457M/ML427
6490M/LA255
6944M/RW386
6946M/RW388
6948M/DE673
6960M/MT847
7000M/TE392
7001M/TE356
7008M/EE549
7014M/N6720
7015M/NL985
7060M/VF301
7090M/EE531
7118M/LA198
7119M/LA226
7150M/PK683
7151M/VT229
7154M/WB188
7174M/VX272
7175M/VV106
7200M/VT812
7241M/TE311
7243M/TE462
7244M/TB382
7245M/RW382
7246M/TD248
7256M/TB752
7257M/TB252
7279M/TB752
7281M/TB252
7285M/VV119
7288M/PK724
7293M/RW393
7323M/VV217
7325M/R5868
7362M/*475081* (VP546)
7416M/WN907
7421M/WT660
7422M/WT684
7428M/WK198
7432M/WZ724
7443M/WX853
7451M/TE476
7458M/WX905
7464M/XA564
7467M/WP978
7470M/XA553
7473M/XE946
7491M/WT569
7496M/WT612
7499M/WT555
7510M/WT694
7525M/WT619
7530M/WT648
7532M/WT651
7533M/WT680
7543M/WN901
7544M/WN904
7548M/PS915
7554M/FS890
7564M/XE982
7570M/XD674
7582M/*WP180* (WP190)
7583M/WP185
7602M/WE600
7604M/*XD429* (XD542)
7605M/WS692
7606M/WV562
7607M/TJ138
7615M/WV679
7616M/WW388
7618M/WW442
7621M/WV686
7622M/WV606
7625M/WD356
7630M/VZ304
7631M/VX185
7641M/XA634
7645M/WD293
7646M/VX461
7648M/XF785
7656M/WJ573
7663M/XA571
7673M/WV332
7688M/WW421
7693M/WV483
7696M/WV493
7697M/WV495
7698M/WV499
7700M/WV544
7703M/WG725
7704M/TW536
7705M/WL505
7706M/WB584
7709M/WT933
7711M/PS915
7712M/WK281
7715M/XK724
7716M/WS776
7717M/XA549
7718M/WA577
7719M/WK277
7722M/XA571
7729M/WB758
7734M/XD536
7736M/WZ559
7737M/XD602
7739M/XA801
7741M/VZ477
7750M/WL168
7751M/WL131
7755M/WG760
7758M/PM651
7759M/PK664
7761M/XH318
7762M/XE670
7770M/WT746
7796M/WJ676
7805M/TW117
7806M/TA639
7809M/XA699
7816M/WG763
7817M/TX214
7822M/XP248
7825M/WK991
7827M/XA917
7829M/XH992
7839M/WV781
7840M/XK482
7841M/WV703
7847M/WV276
7849M/XF319
7851M/WZ706
7852M/XG506
7854M/XM191
7855M/XK416
7859M/XP283
7860M/XL738
7862M/XR246
7864M/XP244
7865M/TX226
7866M/XH278
7867M/XH980
7868M/WZ736
7869M/WK935
7870M/XM556
7881M/WD413
7882M/XD525
7883M/XT150
7887M/XD375
7890M/XD453
7891M/XM693
7894M/XD818
7895M/WF784
7896M/XA900
7898M/XP854
7899M/XG540
7900M/WA576
7902M/WZ550
7906M/WH132
7917M/WA591
7920M/WL360
7923M/XT133
7928M/XE849
7930M/WH301
7931M/RD253
7932M/WZ744
7933M/XR220
7937M/WS843
7938M/XH903
7939M/XD596
7940M/XL764
7949M/XF974
7955M/XH767
7957M/XF545
7959M/WS774
7960M/WS726
7961M/WS739
7964M/WS760
7965M/WS792
7967M/*WS844* (WS788)
7969M/WS840
7970M/WP907
7971M/XK699
7972M/XH764
7973M/WS807
7976M/XK418
7979M/XM529
7980M/XM561
7982M/XH892
7983M/XD506
7984M/XN597
7986M/WG777
7988M/XL149
7990M/XD452
7997M/XG452
7998M/XD515
8005M/WG768
8007M/XF990
8009M/XG518
8010M/XG547
8011M/XV269
8012M/VS562
8017M/XL762
8018M/XN344
8019M/WZ869
8020M/WB847
8021M/XL824
8022M/XN341
8023M/XD463
8025M/XH124
8027M/XM555
8032M/XH837
8033M/XD382
8034M/XL703
8040M/XR493
8041M/XF690
8043M/XF836
8046M/XL770
8049M/WE168
8050M/XG329
8051M/XN929
8052M/WH166
8053M/WK968
8054AM/XM410
8054BM/XM417
8055AM/XM402
8055BM/XM404
8056M/XG337
8057M/XR243
8060M/WW397
8062M/XR669
8063M/WT536
8070M/EP120
8071M/TE476
8072M/PK624
8073M/TB252
8074M/TE392
8075M/RW382
8076M/XM386
8077M/XN594
8078M/XM351
8079M/XN492
8080M/XM480
8081M/XM468
8082M/XM409
8083M/XM367
8084M/XM369
8085M/XM467
8086M/TB752
8087M/XN925
8088M/XN602
8092M/WK654
8094M/WT520
8099M/WD355
8101M/WH984
8102M/WT486
8103M/WR985
8106M/WR982
8108M/WV703
8113M/WV753
8114M/WL798
8117M/WR974
8118M/*WZ475* (WZ549)
8119M/WR971
8122M/XD613
8128M/WH775
8130M/WH798
8131M/WT507
8133M/WT518
8139M/XJ582
8140M/XJ571
8141M/XN688
8142M/XJ560
8143M/XN691
8147M/XR526
8151M/WV795
8153M/WV903
8154M/WV908
8155M/WV797
8156M/XE339
8158M/XE369
8159M/XD528
8160M/XD622
8161M/XE993
8162M/WM913
8163M/XP919
8164M/*WN105* (WF299)
8165M/WH791
8169M/WH364
8171M/XJ607
8172M/XJ609
8173M/XN685
8174M/WZ576
8176M/WH791

8177M/WM224
8179M/XN928
8180M/XN930
8182M/XN953
8183M/XN962
8184M/WT520
8186M/WR977
8187M/WH791
8188M/XG327
8189M/WD646
8190M/XJ918
8192M/XR658
8194M/XK862
8196M/XE920
8197M/WT346
8198M/WT339
8203M/XD377
8205M/XN819
8206M/WG419
8207M/WD318
8208M/WG303
8209M/WG418
8210M/WG471
8211M/WK570
8212M/WK587
8213M/WK626
8215M/WP869
8216M/WP927
8217M/WZ866
8222M/XJ604
8224M/XN699
8226M/XP921
8229M/XM355
8230M/XM362
8231M/XM375
8232M/XM381
8233M/XM408
8234M/XN458
8235M/XN549
8236M/XP573
8237M/XS179
8238M/XS180
8239M/XS210
8344M/WH960
8345M/XG540
8346M/XN734
8350M/WH840
8352M/XN632
8354M/WF791
8355M/*KG374* (KN645)
8357M/WK576
8359M/WF825
8360M/WP863
8361M/WB670
8362M/WG477
8363M/WG463
8364M/WG464
8365M/XK421
8366M/XG454
8367M/XG474
8368M/XF926
8369M/WE139
8370M/N1671
8371M/XA847
8372M/K8042
8373M/P2617
8375M/NX611
8376M/RF398
8377M/R9125
8378M/*T9707*
8379M/DG590
8380M/Z7197
8382M/VR930
8383M/K9942
8384M/X4590
8385M/N5912
8386M/NV778
8387M/T6296
8388M/XL993
8389M/VX573
8390M/SL542
8392M/SL674
8393M/XK987
8394M/WG422
8395M/WF408
8396M/XK740
8398M/WR967
8399M/WR539
8401M/XP686
8402M/XN769
8403M/XK531
8406M/XP831
8407M/XP585
8408M/XS186
8409M/XS209
8410M/XR662
8412M/XM147
8413M/XM192
8414M/XM173
8415M/XM181
8416M/XM183
8417M/XM144
8418M/XM178
8422M/XM169
8427M/XM172
8428M/XH593
8429M/XH592
8431M/XR651
8434M/XM411
8435M/XN512
8436M/XN554
8437M/WG362
8438M/XP761
8439M/WZ846
8440M/WD935
8441M/XR107
8442M/XP411
8444M/XP400
8445M/XK968
8446M/XP748
8447M/XP359
8453M/XP745
8454M/XP442
8455M/XP444
8457M/XS871
8458M/XP672
8459M/XR650
8460M/XP680
8462M/XX477
8463M/XP355
8465M/W1048
8466M/L-866
8467M/WP912
8468M/BT474
8470M/PN999
8472M/VH513
8473M/*WP180* (WP190)
8475M/PJ876
8477M/DG200
8478M/RN228
8479M/AX772
8482M/VK893
8487M/J-1172
8488M/WL627
8489M/XN816
8490M/WH703
8491M/WJ880
8492M/WJ872
8493M/XR571
8494M/XP557
8495M/XR672
8498M/XR670
8499M/XP357
8501M/XP640
8502M/XP686
8503M/XS451
8505M/XL384
8506M/XR704
8507M/XS215
8508M/XS218
8509M/XT141
8510M/XP567
8511M/WT305
8513M/XN724
8514M/XS176
8515M/WH869
8516M/XR643
8517M/XA932
8531M/XS418
8532M/XS423
8533M/XS449
8534M/XS450
8535M/XS454
8538M/XN781
8546M/XN728
8548M/WT507
8549M/WT534
8550M/XT595
8551M/XN774
8554M/TG511
8556M/XN855
8558M/XP439
8559M/XN467
8560M/XR569
8561M/XS100
8562M/XS110
8564M/XN387
8565M/*XF979* (E-408)
8566M/XV279
8567M/WL738
8568M/XP503
8569M/XR535
8570M/XR954
8571M/XR984
8572M/XM706
8573M/XM708
8575M/XP542
8576M/XP502
8577M/XP532
8578M/XR534
8579M/XR140
8580M/XP516
8581M/WJ775
8582M/XE874
8584M/WH903
8585M/XE670
8586M/XE643
8587M/XP677
8588M/XR681
8589M/XR700
8590M/XM191
8591M/XA813
8592M/XM969
8595M/XH278
8598M/WP270
8602M/XR541
8603M/XR951
8604M/XS104
8606M/XP530
8607M/XP538
8608M/XP540
8609M/XR953
8610M/XL502
8611M/WF128
8612M/XD182
8613M/XJ724
8614M/XP515
8615M/XP532
8616M/XP541
8617M/XM709
8618M/XP504
8619M/XP511
8620M/XP534
8621M/XR538
8622M/XR980
8623M/XR998
8624M/XS102
8625M/XS105
8626M/XS109
8627M/XP558
8628M/XJ380
8630M/WG362
8631M/XR574
8632M/XP533
8634M/WP314
8635M/XP514
8637M/XR991
8638M/XS101
8639M/XS107
8640M/XR977
8641M/XR987
8642M/XR537
8643M/WJ867
8645M/XD163
8646M/XK969
8647M/XP338
8648M/XK526
8650M/XP333
8652M/WH794
8653M/XS120
8654M/XL898
8655M/XN126
8656M/XP405
8657M/VZ634
8660M/XW538
8661M/XJ727
8662M/XR458
8664M/WJ603
8665M/WL754
8667M/WP972
8668M/WJ821
8670M/XL384
8671M/XJ435
8672M/XP351
8673M/XD165
8674M/XP395
8676M/XL577
8677M/*XF519* (XJ695)
8678M/XE656
8679M/XF526
8680M/XF527
8681M/XG164
8682M/XP404
8683M/WJ870
8684M/XJ634
8685M/XF516
8686M/XG158
8687M/XJ639
8689M/WK144
8691M/WT518
8693M/WH863
8695M/WJ817
8696M/WH773
8697M/WJ825
8699M/ZD232
8700M/ZD234
8701M/XP352
8702M/XG196
8703M/VW453
8704M/XN643
8705M/XT281
8706M/XF383
8707M/XF386
8708M/XF509
8709M/XG209
8710M/XG274
8711M/XG290
8712M/XF439
8713M/XG225
8714M/XK149
8715M/*XF445* (XG264)
8716M/XV155
8718M/XX396
8719M/XT257
8721M/XP354
8722M/WJ640
8723M/XL567
8724M/XW923
8726M/XP299
8727M/XR486
8728M/WT532
8729M/WJ815
8730M/XD186
8731M/XP361
8732M/XJ729
8733M/XL318
8734M/XM657
8735M/WJ681
8736M/XF375
8738M/*XF519* (XJ695)
8739M/XH170
8740M/WE173
8741M/XW329
8743M/WD790
8745M/XL392
8746M/XH171
8747M/WJ629
8749M/XH537
8751M/XT255
8752M/XR509
8753M/WL795
8754M/XG882
8755M/*WH699* (WJ637)
8756M/XL427
8757M/XM656
8760M/XL386
8761M/WJ977
8762M/WH740
8763M/WH665
8764M/XP344
8766M/XJ782
8767M/XX635
8768M/A-522

RAF Maintenance cross-reference

8769M/A-528
8770M/XL623
8771M/XM602
8772M/WR960
8773M/XV156
8774M/XV338
8776M/XV152
8777M/XX914
8778M/XM598
8779M/XM607
8780M/WK102
8781M/WE982
8782M/XH136
8783M/XW272
8784M/VP976
8785M/XS642
8786M/XN495
8789M/XK970
8790M/XK986
8791M/XP329
8792M/XP345
8793M/XP346
8794M/XP398
8795M/VP958
8796M/XK943
8797M/XX947
8798M/XG151
8799M/WV787
8800M/XG226
8801M/XS650
8802M/XJ608
8805M/XT772
8806M/XP140
8807M/XL587
8808M/XP695
8810M/XJ825
8811M/XL445
8813M/VT260
8814M/XM927
8815M/XX118
8816M/XX734
8819M/XS479
8820M/VP952
8821M/XX115
8822M/VP957
8823M/VP965
8824M/VP971
8825M/WB530
8826M/XV638
8827M/XX300
8828M/XS587
8829M/XE653
8830M/XF515
8831M/XG160
8832M/XG172
8833M/XL569
8834M/XL572
8835M/XL576
8836M/XL592
8837M/XL617
8838M/429366
8839M/XG194
8840M/XG252
8844M/XJ676
8845M/XS572
8846M/XE673
8847M/XX344
8848M/XZ135
8850M/XV436
8851M/XT595
8852M/XV337
8853M/XT277
8854M/XV154
8855M/XT284
8856M/XT274
8857M/XW544
8858M/XW541
8859M/XW545
8860M/XW549
8861M/XW528
8862M/XN473
8863M/XG154
8864M/WJ678
8865M/XN641
8866M/XL609
8867M/XK532
8868M/WH775
8869M/WH957
8870M/WH964
8871M/WJ565
8873M/XR453
8874M/XE597
8875M/XE624
8876M/*VM791* (XA312)
8877M/XP159
8879M/XX948
8880M/XF435
8881M/XG254
8882M/XR396
8883M/XX946
8884M/VX275
8885M/XW922
8886M/XA243
8887M/WK162
8888M/XA231
8889M/XN239
8890M/WT532
8892M/XL618
8893M/WT745
8894M/XT669
8895M/XX746
8896M/XX821
8897M/XX969
8898M/XX119
8899M/XX756
8900M/XZ368
8901M/XZ383
8902M/XX739
8903M/XX747
8904M/XX966
8905M/XX975
8906M/XX976
8907M/XZ371
8908M/XZ382
8909M/XV784
8910M/XL160
8911M/XH673
8912M/XL189
8913M/XT857
8915M/XH132
8916M/XL163
8917M/XM372
8918M/XX109
8919M/XT486
8920M/XT469
8921M/XT466
8923M/XX819
8924M/XP701
8925M/XP706
8926M/XP749
8927M/XP750
8928M/XP751
8929M/XP764
8930M/XR720
8931M/XV779
8932M/XR718
8933M/XX297
8934M/XR749
8935M/XR713
8936M/WV701
8937M/
8938M/
8939M/
8940M/
8941M/
8942M/
8943M/
8944M/
8945M/
8946M/
8947M/
8948M/
8949M/
8950M/

RN Engineering 'A' airframe number cross-reference

A646/SX300
A680/DE373
A696/SX300
A2001/*W5984* (HS618)
A2054/SX300
A2055/SX336
A2127/DE373
A2439/WF219
A2472/XA508
A2483/WF259
A2503/WM994
A2509/*WN105* (WF299)
A2510/WM913
A2511/*XE364* (WM983)
A2517/WM961
A2522/WM993
A2525/XN334
A2526/WV911
A2527/XP107
A2530/WM969
A2531/WG718
A2532/WV826
A2534/XE368
A2538/XJ393
A2539/XG831
A2540/WN464
A2542/XA862
A2543/XA870
A2556/XE327
A2557/WV798
A2571/XG577
A2572/XJ402
A2574/XD332
A2575/XG574
A2576/WV198
A2577/XB480
A2579/XN332
A2580/XE369
A2581/XK532
A2597/XS509
A2598/XJ482
A2600/XN934
A2602/XN925
A2603/XK911
A2605/XN308
A2607/XK944
A2608/XA459
A2609/XM329
A2610/XN647
A2611/XJ575
A2612/XN650
A2614/XN314
A2615/XT256
A2616/XN651
A2618/XP116
A2619/XS695
A2620/XN650
A2621/XJ584
A2622/XJ602
A2623/XN697
A2624/XN692
A2625/XL846
A2626/XL847
A2627/XN967
A2628/XP558
A2629/XM667
A2630/XL853
A2632/WV903
A2633/XE369
A2635/XE339
A2637/WV797
A2639/XN650
A2640/XP155
A2642/XL836
A2643/*XN297* (XN311)
A2645/WF225
A2646/XK988
A2647/XS463
A2648/XS125
A2649/XS869
A2650/XP160
A2651/XG596
A2653/XK943
A2654/XN302
A2655/XN953
A2658/XP984
A2659/XV669
A2660/WV908
A2661/WV795
A2662/*WN105* (WF299)
A2663/XN309
A2664/XV644
A2666/XS872
A2667/XP226
A2668/XS885
A2669/XP149
A2670/XS128
A2671/XS867
A2672/XS537
A2673/WF122
A2674/WF125
A2675/XS881
A2676/XR572
A2678/XR955
A2679/XP535
A2680/XP157
A2682/XM845
A2683/XS878
A2684/XP151
A2685/XS886
A2686/XS873
A2687/XS877
A2688/XP158
A2689/XM874
A2690/XS887
A2691/XS868
A2692/XM917
A2693/XM843
A2694/XS865
A2695/XS876
A2696/XS882
A2697/XS870
A2699/XS570
A2700/XP930
A2701/XL500
A2702/XS545
A2703/XT441
A2705/XS866
A2706/XM868
A2707/XS122
A2708/XR540
A2709/XR991
A2710/
A2712/XN359
A2713/XN386
A2714/XL880
A2715/
A2716/
A2717/
A2718/
A2719/
A2720/
A2721/
A2722/XT757
A2723/XT487
A2724/
A2725/
A2726/
A2727/
A2728/

A2729/	A2734/	A2739/	A2744/	A2749/
A2730/	A2735/	A2740/	A2745/	A2750/
A2731/	A2736/	A2741/	A2746/	
A2732/	A2737/	A2742/	A2747/	
A2733/	A2738/	A2743/	A2748/	

RAF Gliding and Soaring Association Markings

Identity	Type, Previous Identity and Competition Number	Club and Location	Notes
R1	Schempp-Hirth Janus C (BGA 2723)	Cranwell GC, RAF Cranwell	
R2	Schempp-Hirth Janus C	RAFG&SA Centre, RAF Bicester	
R3	Schleicher ASK-13	RAFG&SA Centre, RAF Bicester	
R4	Schleicher ASK-13	Anglia GC, RAF Wattisham	
R5	Schleicher Ka-7	Four Counties GC, RAF Syerston	
R7	Schleicher ASK-13	Clevelands GC, RAF Dishforth	
R8	Grob G102 Astir CS (OY-XGE)	RAFG&SA Centre, RAF Bicester	
R9	Schempp-Hirth Janus B	Four Counties GC, RAF Syerston	
R10	Schempp-Hirth Discus B [R10]	RAFG&SA Centre, RAF Bicester	
R11	Schempp-Hirth Discus	Chilterns GC, RAF Halton	
R15	Schleicher Ka-7	RAFG&SA Centre, RAF Bicester	
R16	Schempp-Hirth Ventus [16]	Bannerdown GC, RAF Hullavington	
R18	Schleicher ASW-19 [R18]	Fenlands GC, RAF Marham	
R20	Schleicher ASK-21	Bannerdown GC, RAF Hullavington	
R21	Schleicher ASK-21	RAFG&SA Centre, RAF Bicester	
R22	Schleicher ASK-21	Wrekin GC, RAF Cosford	
R25	Schleicher ASK-21	Fulmar GC, RAF Kinloss	
R26	Schempp-Hirth Nimbus 3 [26]	RAFG&SA Centre, RAF Bicester	
R27	Schempp-Hirth Ventus [27]	RAFG&SA Centre, RAF Bicester	
R29	Schleicher Ka-7	Humber GC, RAF Scampton	
R30	Glaser-Dirks DG-300 [R30]	Humber GC, RAF Scampton	
R32	Schleicher ASK-18	Fulmar GC, RAF Kinloss	
R33	Schleicher ASK-18	RAFG&SA Centre, RAF Bicester	
R34	Schleicher ASK-21	Bannerdown GC, RAF Hullavington	
R36	Schleicher ASK-18	Four Counties GC, RAF Syerston	
R37	Schleicher ASK-13	Wrekin GC, RAF Cosford	
R40	Schleicher ASK-21	RAFG&SA Centre, RAF Bicester	
R41	Schleicher ASK-13	Chilterns GC, RAF Halton	
R42	Schleicher K-8b	Anglia GC, RAF Wattisham	
R43	Schleicher ASK-18	Wrekin GC, RAF Cosford	
R44	Schleicher K-8b	RAFG&SA Centre, RAF Bicester	
R45	Schleicher K-8b	Fulmar GC, RAF Kinloss	
R46	Schleicher ASK-13	Fenlands GC, RAF Marham	
R47	Schleicher K-8b	Cranwell GC, RAF Cranwell	
R49	Schleicher ASK-18	Bannerdown GC, RAF Hullavington	
R50	Grob G103 Acro	RAFG&SA Centre, RAF Bicester	
R57	Grob G102 Astir	Four Counties GC, RAF Syerston	
R58	Grob G103a Twin Astir Acro (BGA 2873)	Four Counties GC, RAF Syerston	
R60	Grob G102 Astir	Clevelands GC, RAF Dishforth	
R63	Grob G102 Astir	Humber GC, RAF Scampton	
R66	Grob G102 Astir	Cranwell GC, RAF Cranwell	
R67	Grob G102 Astir	Anglia GC, RAF Wattisham	
R68	Grob G102 Astir	Wrekin GC, RAF Cosford	
R69	Grob G102 Astir	Fenlands GC, RAF Marham	
R75	Schleicher K-8b	Fenlands GC, RAF Marham	
R77	Grob G102 Astir	RAFG&SA Centre, RAF Bicester	
R78	Grob G102 Astir	Bannerdown GC, RAF Hullavington	
R82	Grob G102 Astir	Fulmar GC, RAF Kinloss	
R84	Grob G102 Astir	Chilterns GC, RAF Halton	
R85	Schleicher K-8b	Fenlands GC, RAF Marham	
R86	Schleicher ASK-13	Fenlands GC, RAF Marham	
R87	Schempp-Hirth Ventus [87]	Four Counties GC, RAF Syerston	
R88	Schleicher ASK-13	Humber GC, RAF Scampton	
R95	Schleicher K-8b	Clevelands GC, RAF Dishforth	
R96	Schleicher K-8b	Chilterns GC, RAF Halton	
R98	Schleicher K-8b	Humber GC, RAF Scampton	
232	Rolladen-Schneider LS4 [232]	Cranwell GC, RAF Cranwell	

RN Gliding and Soaring Association Markings

Notes	Identity	Type, Previous Identity and Competition Number	Club and Location
	N1	Eiri PiK-20D (BGA 2537/786)	Portsmouth Naval GC, RNAS Lee-on-Solent
	N11	Schleicher K-8b (BGA 2142)	Portsmouth Naval GC, RNAS Lee-on-Solent
	N12	Grob G102 Astir II (BGA 2630)	Portsmouth Naval GC, RNAS Lee-on-Solent
	N14	Slingsby T50 Skylark 4 (BGA 1239/ 103)	Portsmouth Naval GC, RNAS Lee-on-Solent
	N21	Slingsby T21B Sedbergh (BGA 673)	Portsmouth Naval GC, RNAS Lee-on-Solent
	N22	Omnipol L-13 Blanik (BGA 2407)	Portsmouth Naval GC, RNAS Lee-on-Solent
	N23	Slingsby T49B Capstan (BGA 1196)	Portsmouth Naval GC, RNAS Lee-on-Solent
	N27	Schleicher Ka-7 (BGA 1157)	Portsmouth Naval GC, RNAS Lee-on-Solent
	N29	Schleicher ASK-13 (BGA 3254)	Portsmouth Naval GC, RNAS Lee-on-Solent
	N51	Centrair 101A Pegasus (BGA 2987/ EVM)	Seahawk GC, RNAS Culdrose
	N52	SZD-30 Pirat II (BGA 1551/CHG)	Seahawk GC, RNAS Culdrose
	N53	LET L-13 Blanik (BGA 2263/DPC)	Seahawk GC, RNAS Culdrose
	N54	Slingsby T.49B Capstan (BGA 1360/ BZG)	Seahawk GC, RNAS Culdrose
	N55	Slingsby T.49B Capstan (BGA 1118/ BPD)	Seahawk GC, RNAS Culdrose

Army Gliding and Soaring Association Markings

Notes	Identity	Type, Previous Identity and Competition Number	Club and Location
	AGA 1	Rolladen-Schneider LS4 [412]	Wyvern GC, RAF Upavon
	AGA 2	Schempp-Hirth HS7 Mini-Nimbus C (BGA2553/ EBK) [52]	Kestrel GC, RAF Odiham
	AGA 3	Schempp-Hirth Cirrus 75 [388] (BGA 2xxx)	Kestrel GC, RAF Odiham
	AGA 6	Grob G102 Astir CS [212]	Wyvern GC, RAF Upavon
	AGA 8	Schleicher ASK-21 [EKG]	Wyvern GC, RAF Upavon
	AGA 9	Schleicher ASK-23 [A6]	Wyvern GC, RAF Upavon
	AGA 11	Schleicher ASK-21 [A3]	Kestrel GC, RAF Odiham
	AGA 14	Schleicher ASK-13 [A2]	Wyvern GC, RAF Upavon
	AGA 15	Schleicher ASK-13 [A1]	Kestrel GC, RAF Odiham
	AGA 16	Schleicher ASK-18 [35]	Kestrel GC, RAF Odiham
	AGA 18	Schleicher ASK-23 [A5]	Kestrel GC, RAF Odiham
	AGA	Schempp-Hirth Discus [12]	Wyvern GC, RAF Upavon

RN Landing Platform and Shore Station Code-letters

Alpha-Numeric Sequence

Sqn code	*Deck letters*	*Name and Pennant Number*	*Type/task*	*Notes*
323	AB	HMS *Ambuscade* (F172)	Type 21	
430	AC	HMS *Achilles* (F12)	Leander	
455	AE	HMS *Ariadne* (F72)	Leander	
341	AG	HMS *Avenger* (F185)	Type 21	
327	AL	HMS *Alacrity* (F174)	Type 21	
472	AM	HMS *Andromeda* (F57)	Leander	
470	AP	HMS *Apollo* (F70)	Leander	
426	AR	HMS *Arethusa* (F38)	Leander	
	AS	RFA *Argus* (A135)	Aviation Training ship	
466	AT	HMS *Argonaut* (F56)	Leander	
322	AV	HMS *Active* (F171)	Type 21	
326	AW	HMS *Arrow* (F173)	Type 21	
320	AZ	HMS *Amazon* (F169)	Type 21	
328	BA	HMS *Brave* (F94)	Type 22	
—	BD	RFA *Sir Bedivere* (L3004)	Landing ship	
—	BE	RFA *Blue Rover* (A270)	Fleet tanker	
333	BM	HMS *Birmingham* (D86)	Type 42	
334	BS	HMS *Bristol* (D23)	Type 82	
342	BT	HMS *Brilliant* (F90)	Type 22	
—	BV	HMS *Black Rover* (A273)	Fleet tanker	
346/7	BW	HMS *Broadsword* (F88)	Type 22	
403	BX	HMS *Battleaxe* (F89)	Type 22	
330	BZ	HMS *Brazen* (F91)	Type 22	
335	CF	HMS *Cardiff* (D108)	Type 42	
—	CH	HMS *Challenger* (K07)	Seabed ops	
463	CP	HMS *Cleopatra* (F28)	Leander	
—	CU	RNAS Culdrose (HMS *Seahawk*)		
—	CW	HMS *Cornwall* (F99)	Type 22	
431	CY	HMS *Charybdis* (F75)	Leander	
—	DC	HMS *Dumbarton Castle* (P268)	Fishery protection	
—	DG	RFA *Diligence* (A132)	Maintenance	
464	DN	HMS *Danae* (F47)	Leander	
411	EB	HMS *Edinburgh* (D97)	Type 42	
434/5	ED	HMS *Endurance* (A171)	Ice Patrol	
—	EN	RFA *Engadine* (K08)	Helicopter support	
433	EU	HMS *Euryalus* (F15)	Leander	
420	EX	HMS *Exeter* (D89)	Type 42	
342	FA	RFA *Fort Austin* (A386)	Support ship	
343	FG	RFA *Fort Grange* (A385)	Support ship	
—	FL	RNAY Fleetlands		
—	FS	HMS *Fearless* (L10)	Assault	
410	GC	HMS *Gloucester* (D96)	Type 42	
—	GN	RFA *Green Rover* (A268)	Fleet tanker	
—	GR	RFA *Sir Geraint* (L3027)	Landing ship	
—	GV	RFA *Gold Rover* (A271)	Fleet tanker	
344	GW	HMS *Glasgow* (D88)	Type 42	
—	GY	RFA *Grey Rover* (A269)	Fleet tanker	
416	HL	HMS *Hecla* (A133)	Hecla	
414	HT	HMS *Hecate* (A137)	Hecla	
—	ID	HMS *Intrepid* (L11)	Assault	
465	JO	HMS *Juno* (F52)	Leander	
443	JP	HMS *Jupiter* (F60)	Leander	
—	L	HMS *Illustrious* (R06)	Carrier	
—	LC	HMS *Leeds Castle* (P258)	Fishery protection	
—	LN	RFA *Sir Lancelot* (L3029)	Landing ship	
405	LO	HMS *London* (F95)	Type 22	
332	LP	HMS *Liverpool* (D92)	Type 42	
—	LS	RNAS Lee-on-Solent (HMS *Daedalus*)		
360	MC	HMS *Manchester* (D95)	Type 42	
424	MV	HMS *Minerva* (F45)	Leander	
—	N	HMS *Invincible* (R05)	Carrier	

Notes	Sqn code	Deck letters	Name and Pennant Number	Type/task
	345	NC	HMS *Newcastle* (D87)	Type 42
	417	NM	HMS *Nottingham* (D91)	Type 42
	347	OD	RFA *Olmeda* (A124)	Fleet tanker
	347	ON	RFA *Olna* (A123)	Fleet tanker
	347	OW	RFA *Olwen* (A122)	Fleet tanker
	471	PB	HMS *Phoebe* (F42)	Leander
	445	PLY	HMS *Plymouth* (F126)	Type 12
	454	PN	HMS *Penelope* (F127)	Leander
	—	PO	RNAS Portland (HMS *Osprey*)	
	—	PV	RFA *Sir Percival* (L3036)	Landing ship
	—	PW	Prestwick Airport (HMS *Gannet*)	
	—	R	HMS *Ark Royal* (R09)	Carrier
	436	RG	RFA *Regent* (A486)	Support ship
	462	RO	HMS *Rothesay* (F107)	Type 12
	437	RS	RFA *Resource* (A480)	Support ship
	432	SC	HMS *Scylla* (F71)	Leander
	337	SD	HMS *Sheffield* (F96)	Type 23
	334	SN	HMS *Southampton* (D90)	Type 42
	450	SS	HMS *Sirius* (F40)	Leander
	—	TM	RFA *Sir Tristram* (L3505)	Landing ship
	347	TS	RFA *Tidespring* (A75)	Fleet tanker
	375	VB	HMS *Beaver* (F93)	Type 22
	—	VL	RNAS Yeovilton (HMS *Heron*)	
	—	WU	RNAY Wroughton	
	376	XB	HMS *Boxer* (F92)	Type 22
	407	YK	HMS *York* (D98)	Type 42
			HMS *Coventry* (F98)	Type 22
No pad			RFA *Oakleaf*	Fleet tanker
No pad			RFA *Orangeleaf*	Fleet tanker
			HMS *Norfolk*	Type 23
			HMS *Argyll*	Type 23
			HMS *Lancaster*	Type 23
			HMS *Marlborough*	Type 23
			HMS *Campbeltown* (F86)	Type 22
			HMS *Chatham* (F87)	Type 22
			RFA *Sir Galahad*	Landing ship

Ships' Numeric Code — Deck Letters Analysis

	0	1	2	3	4	5	6	7	8
32	AZ	GIB	AV	AB			AW	AL	BA
33	BZ		LP	BM	BS SN	CF		SD OD ON OW TS BW	—
34		AG	BT FA	FG	GW	NC	BW		
36	MC								
37						VB	XB		
40			BX	BX		LO		YK	
41	GC	EB			HT		HL	NM	PO
42	EX				MV		AR		
43	AC	CY	SC	EU	ED	ED	RG	RS	
44				JP		PLY			
45	SS				PN	AE			
46			RO	CP	DN	JO	AT		
47	AP	PB	AM						

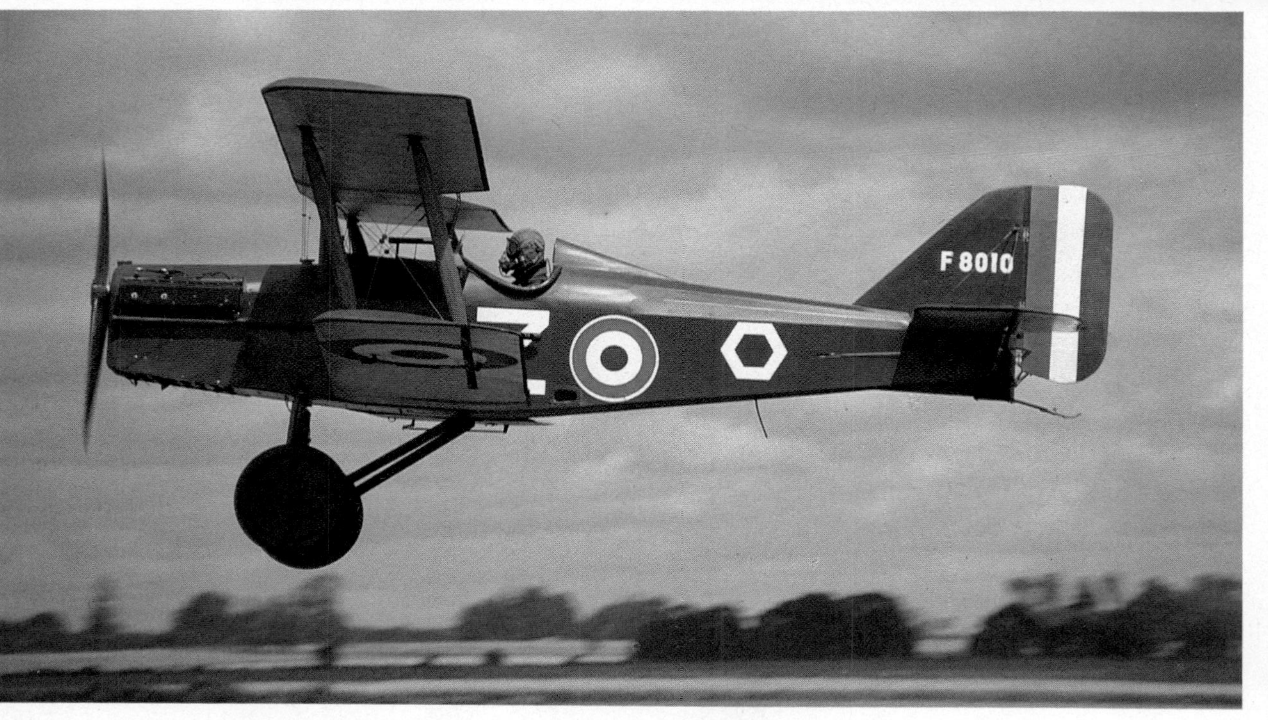

RAF SE5a Replica F8010 in the markings of No 85 Squadron, coded Z. *Peter R. March (PRM)*

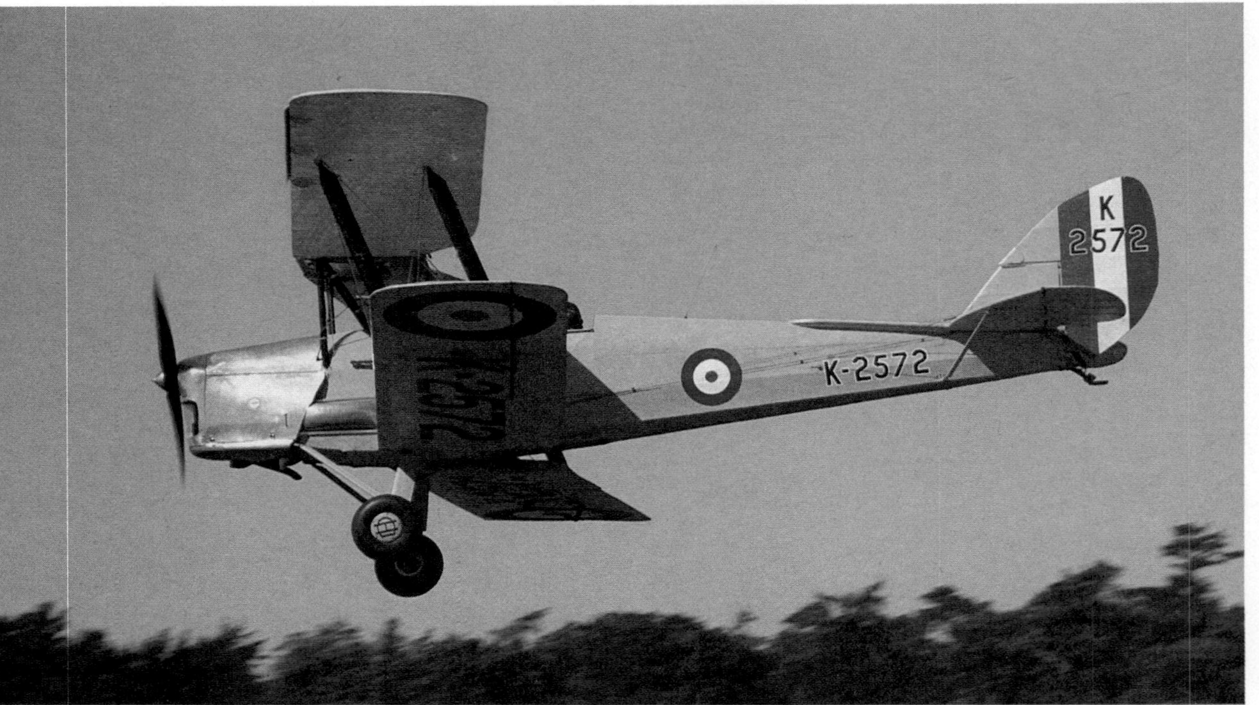

Tiger Moth G-AOZH in RAF Training Command colours as K2572. *PRM*

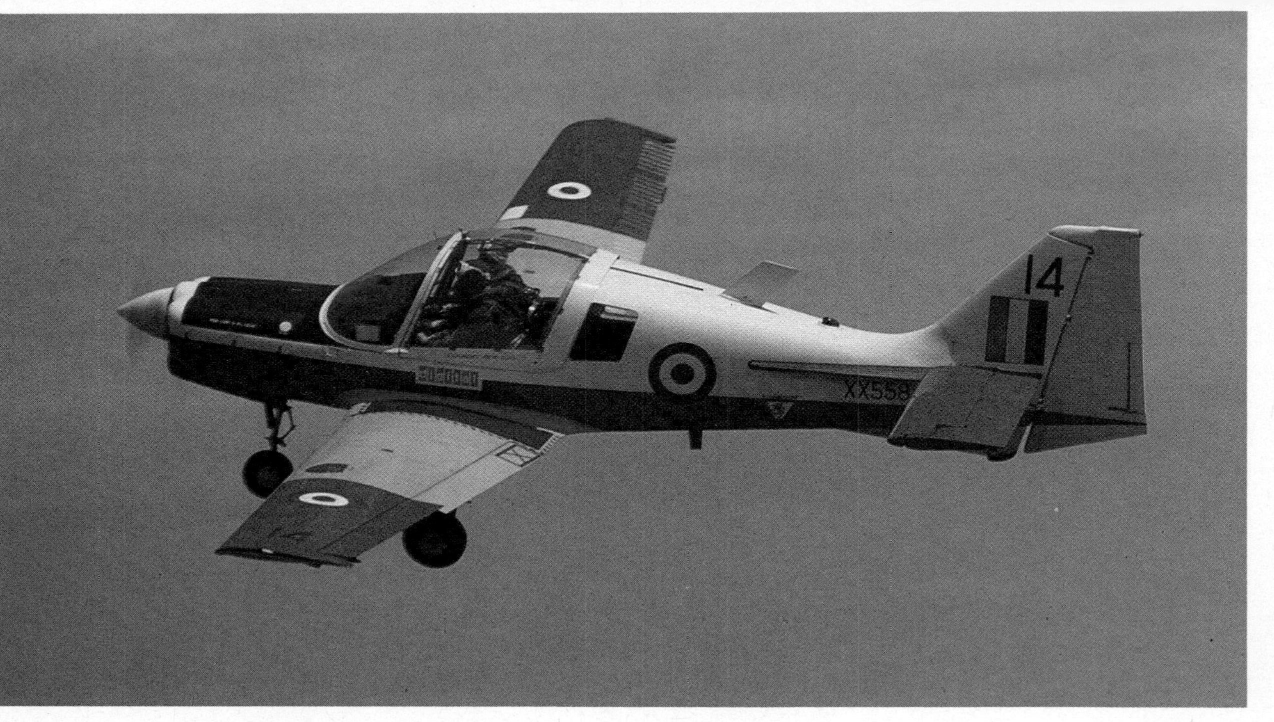

Cosford-based Bulldog T1 XX558 of the Birmingham University Air Squadron. *Andrew March*

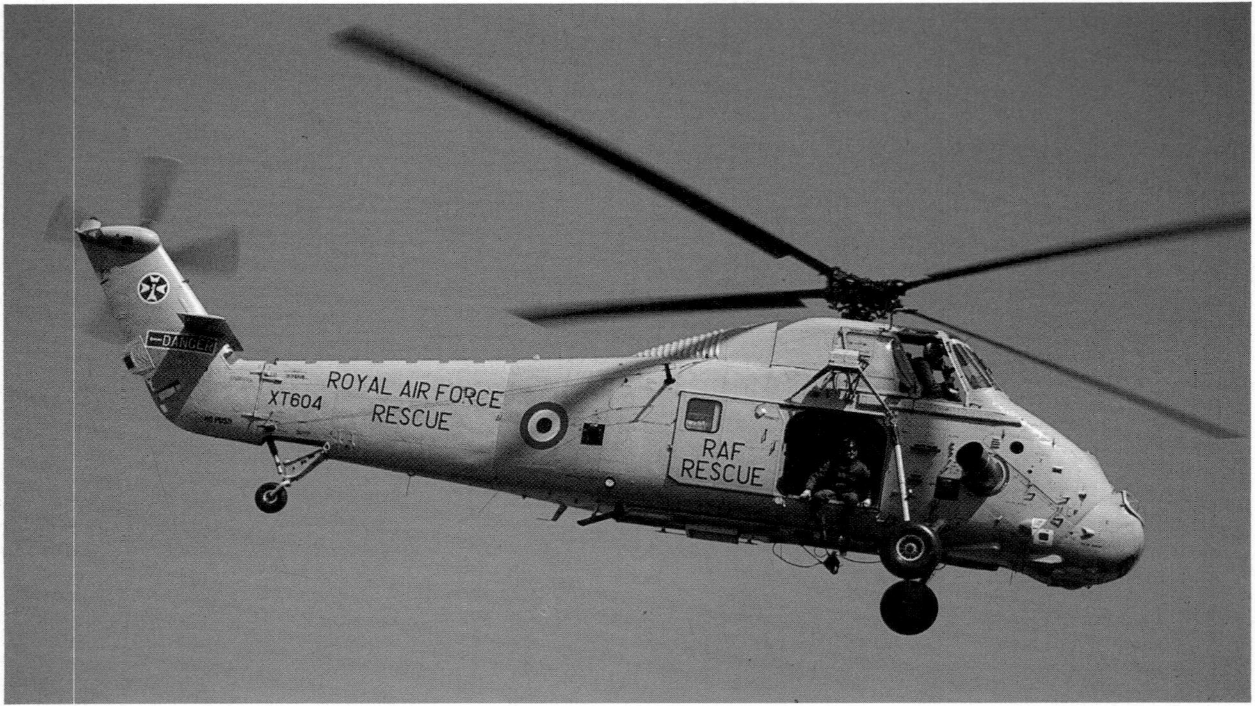

Westland Wessex HC2 XT604 operated by No 22 Squadron for SAR duties. *Andrew March*

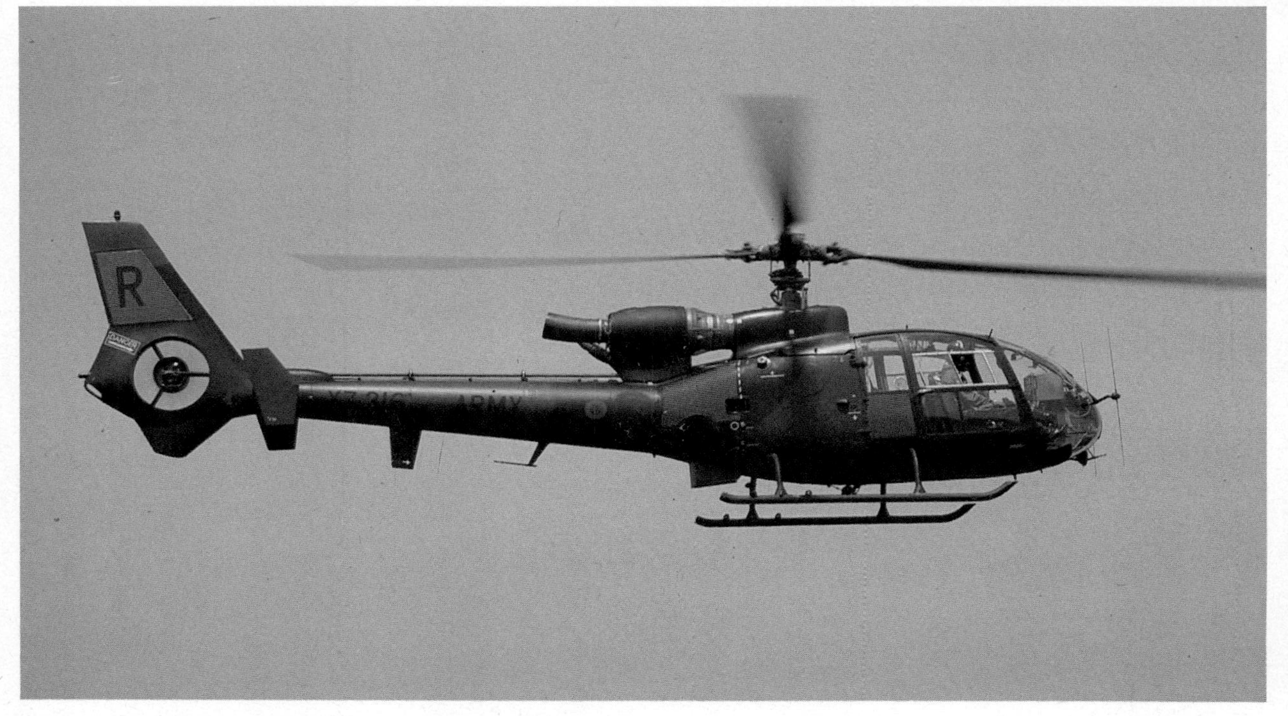

In AAC training colours, Gazelle AH1 XZ316 is based at Middle Wallop. *PRM*

RAF Germany Chinook HC1 ZA709 (BD) is with No 18 Squadron at RAF Gütersloh. *PRM*

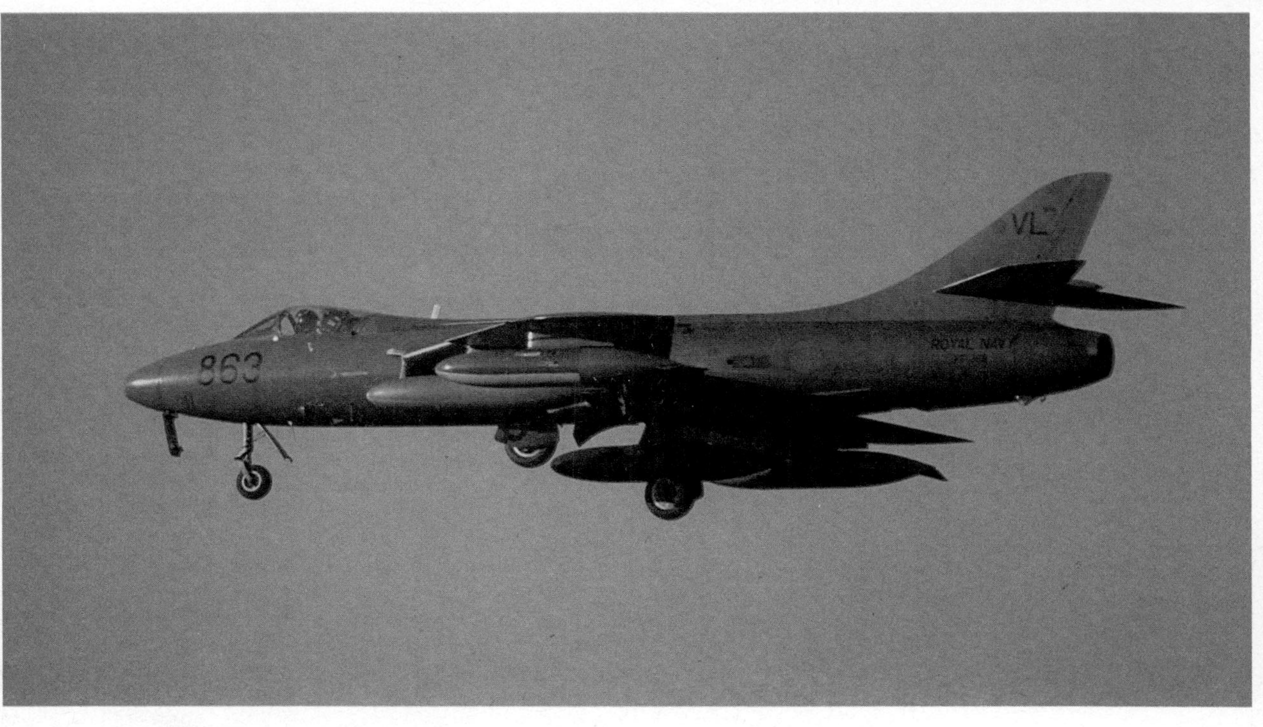

Hunter GA11 XF368 remains in service with FRADU at RNAS Yeovilton. *PRM*

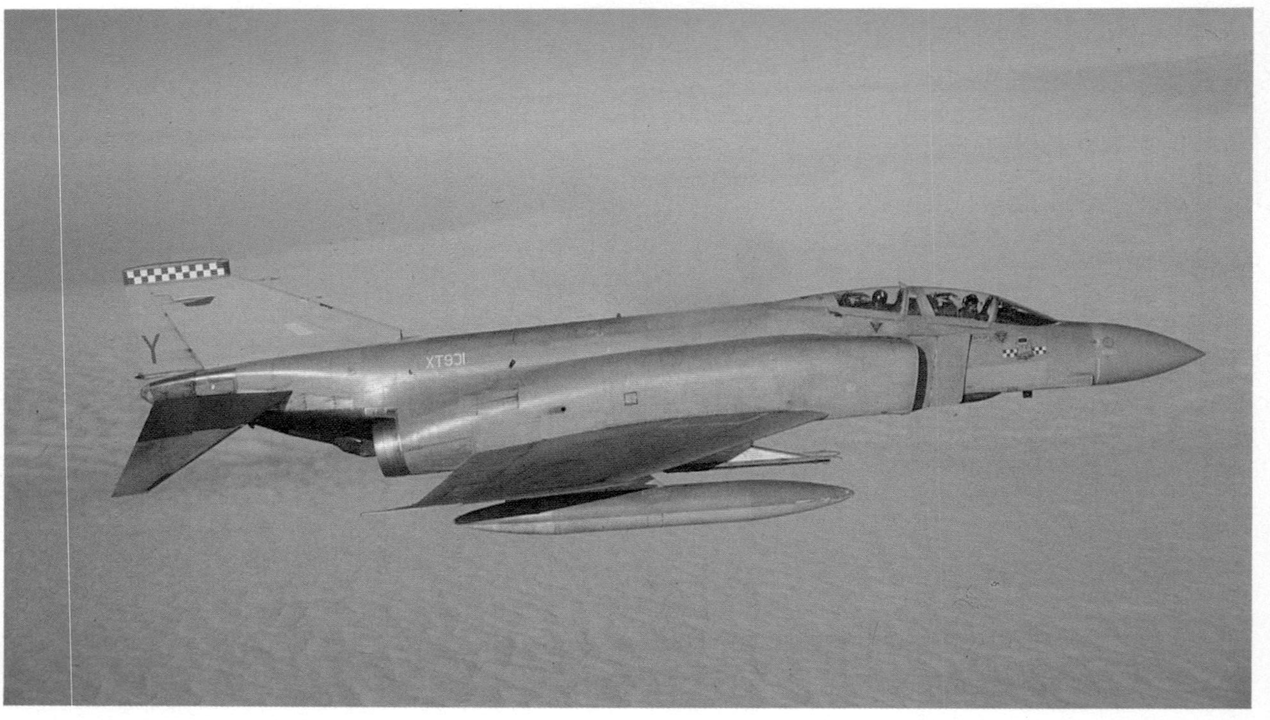

Phantom FGR2 XT901 in the colours of No 56 Squadron. *PRM*

No 216 Squadron at Brize Norton has this TriStar K1 ZD951 in service. *PRM*

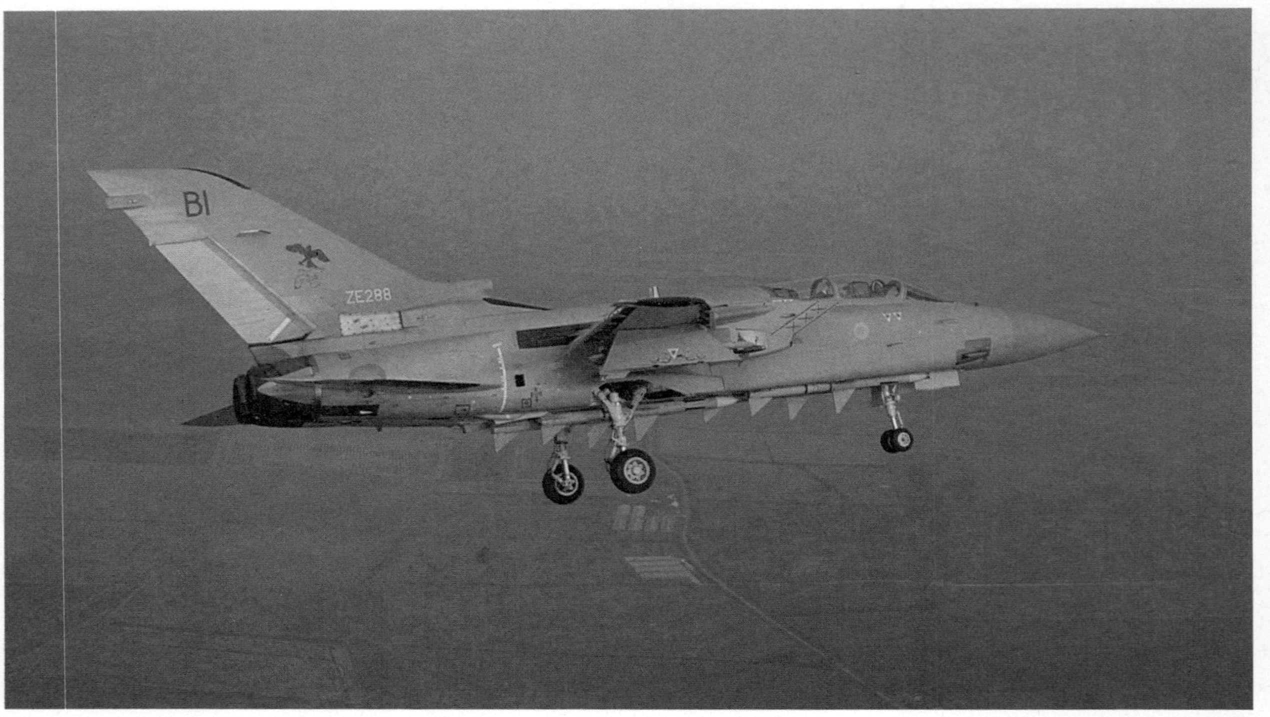

Tornado F3 ZE288 coded BI of No 29 Squadron. *Flt Lt Tony Paxton RAF*

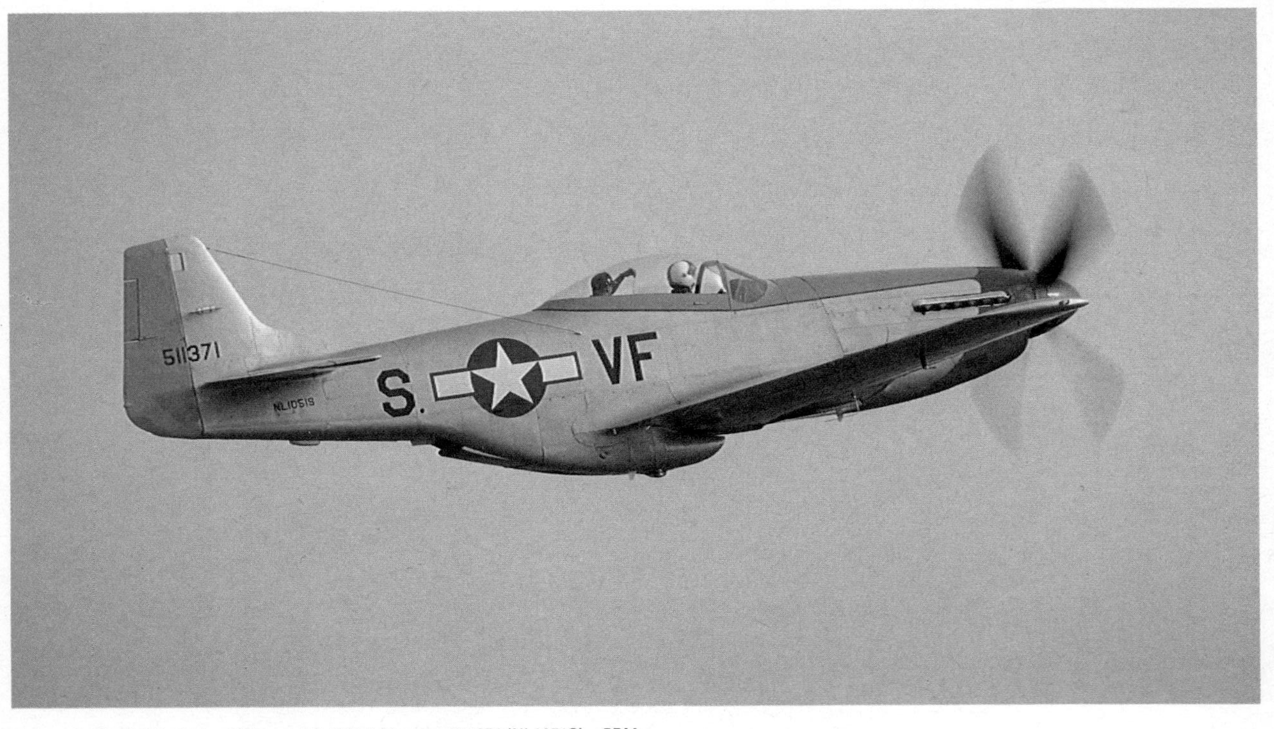

New arrival in Britain during 1987 was this P-51D Mustang 511371 (NL1051S). *PRM*

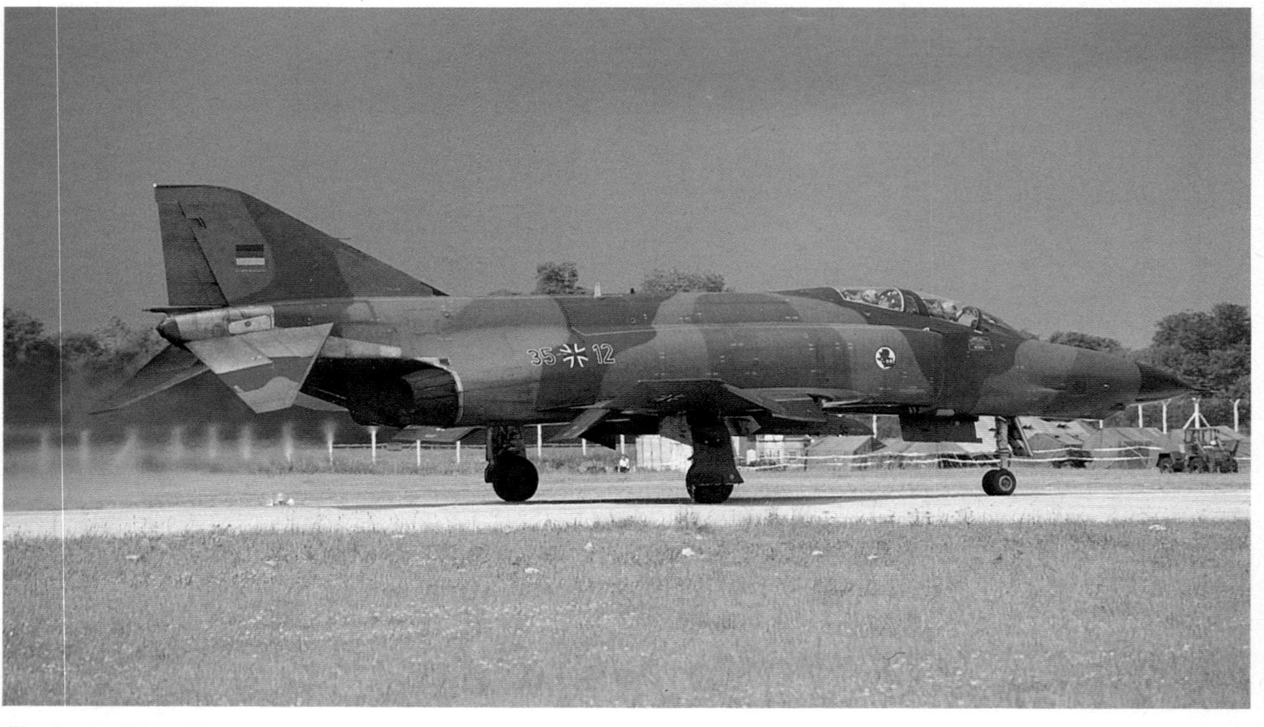

West German AF RF-4E Phantom 35+12 from AkG-51. *PRM*

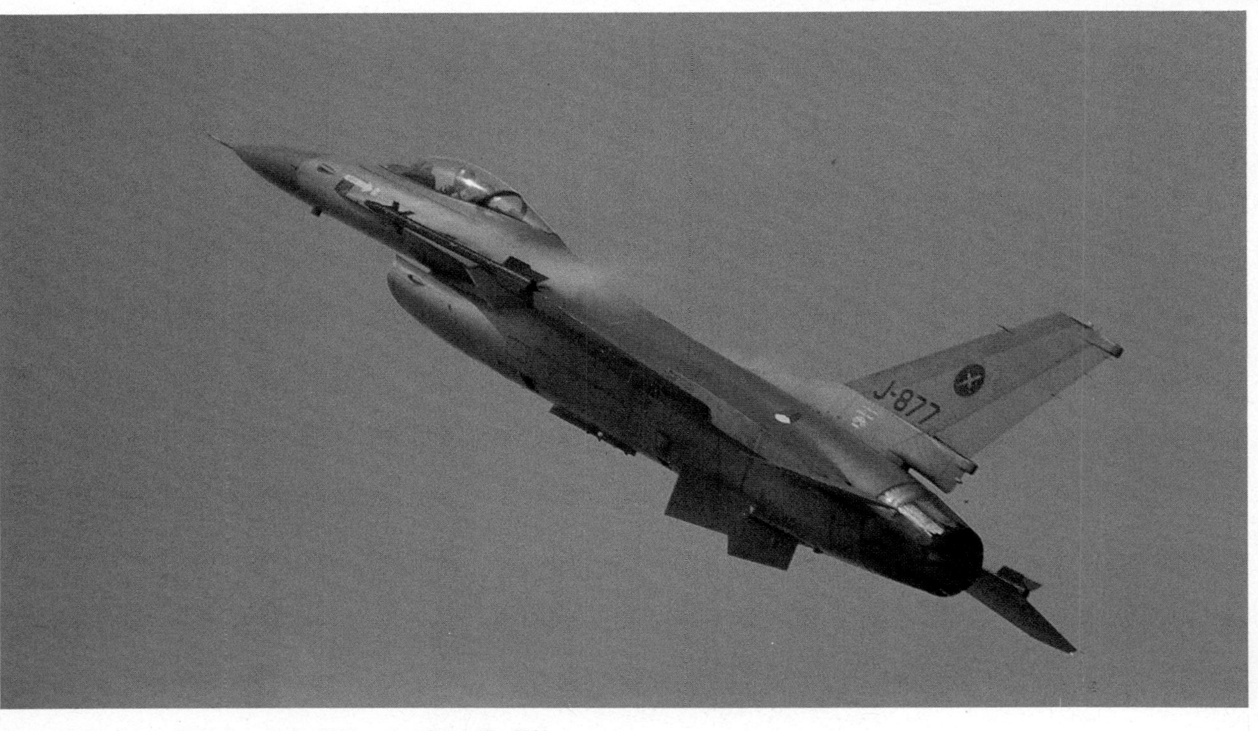

F-16A Fighting Falcon J877 is flown by No 312 Squadron RNethAF. *PRM*

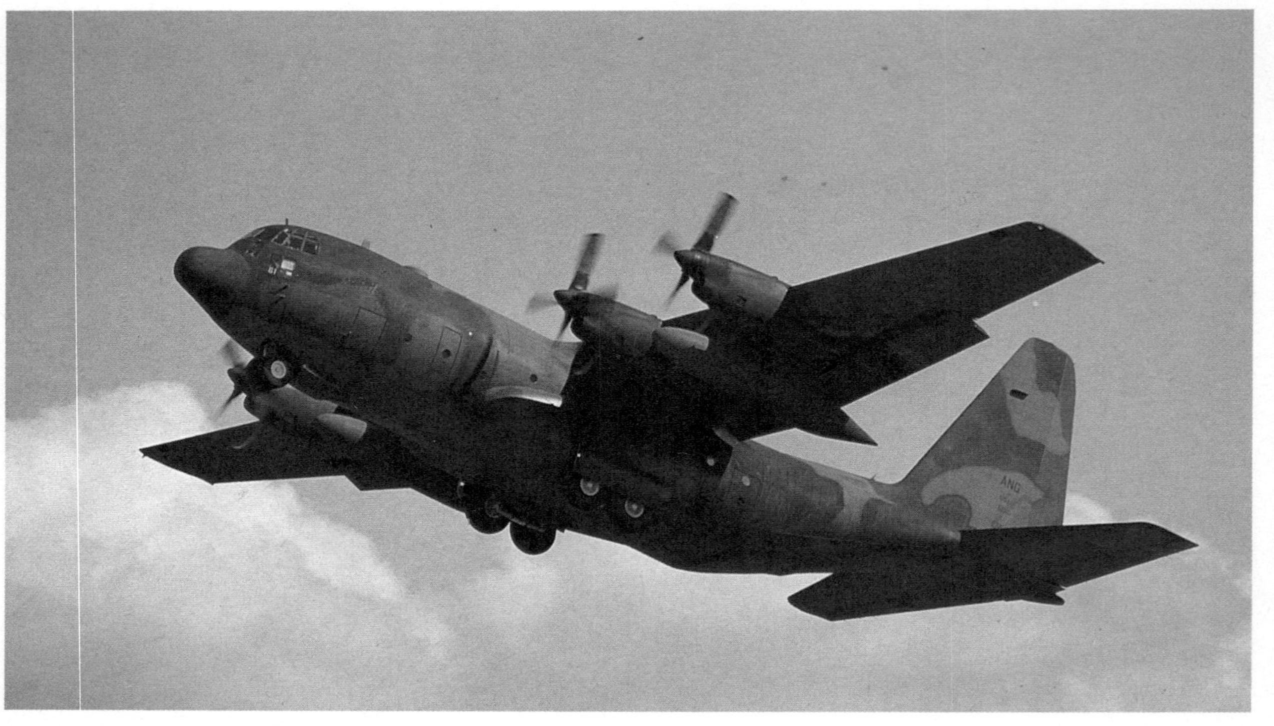

US Air National Guard C-130H Hercules 51361, flown by 181st TAS. *PRM*

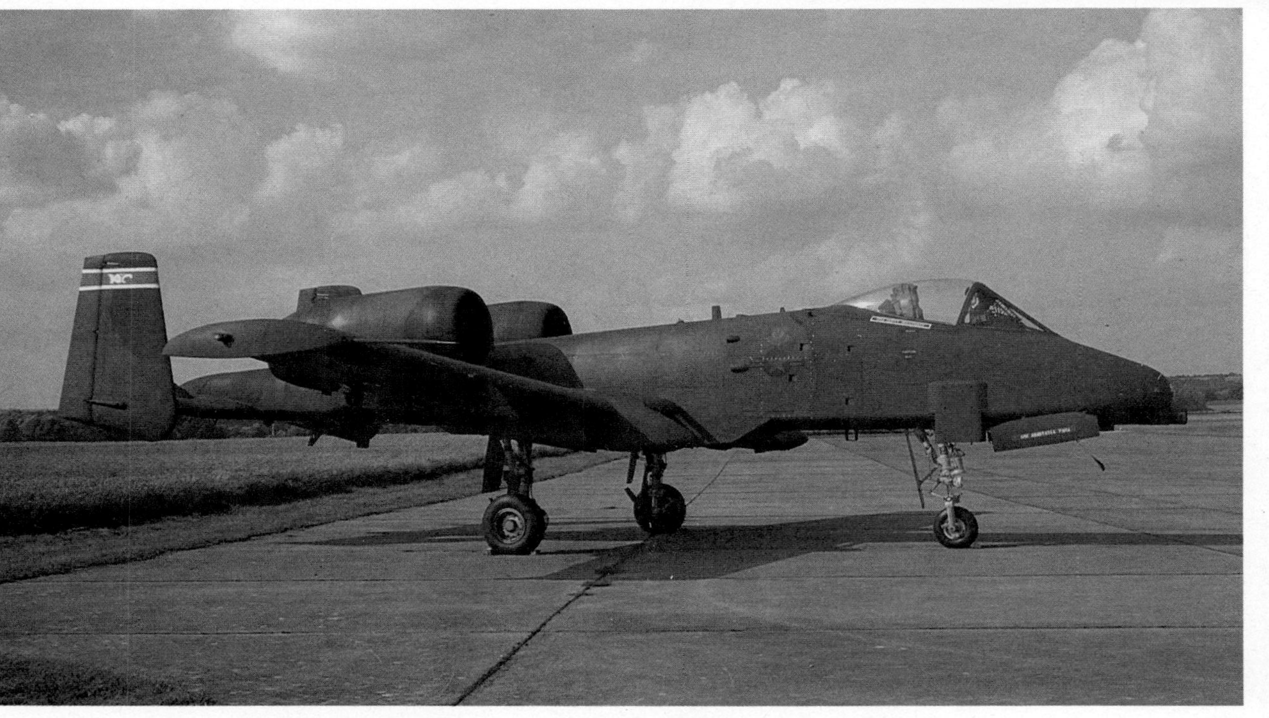

Purple tail marking identifies A-10A 81-988 from 510TFS/81TFW based at RAF Bentwaters. *PRM*

KC-10A Extender 40192, operated by 2BW of the USAF's Strategic Air Command. *PRM*

RN Code-Squadron-Base-Aircraft Cross-check

Code Numbers	*Deck/Base Letters*	*Unit*	*Location*	*Aircraft Type(s)*
000–005	R	801 Sqn	Yeovilton	Sea Harrier FRS1
010–020	R	820 Sqn	Culdrose	Sea King HAS5
122–128	L	800 Sqn	Yeovilton	Sea Harrier FRS1
130–139	—	826 Sqn	Culdrose	Sea King HAS5
180–187	—	849 Sqn	Culdrose	Sea King AEW2
251–254	—	824 Sqn	Prestwick	Sea King HAS5
264–274	L	814 Sqn	Culdrose	Sea King HAS5
300–306	PO	815 Sqn	Portland	Lynx HAS2/HAS3
320–479	*	815/829 Sqns	Portland	Lynx HAS2/HAS3/Wasp HAS1
500–510	—	810 Sqn	Culdrose	Sea King HAS5
538–559	CU	705 Sqn	Culdrose	Gazelle HT2
560–575	CU	750 Sqn	Culdrose	Jetstream T2
576–579	—	750 Sqn	Culdrose	Jetstream T3
584–598	—	706 Sqn	Culdrose	Sea King HAS5
600–605	PO	829 Sqn	Portland	Lynx HAS2/HAS3
606–612	PO	829 Sqn	Portland	Wasp HAS1
620–628	PO	772 Sqn	Portland	Wessex HU5
630–638	PO	702 Sqn	Portland	Lynx HAS2/HAS3
640–648	PO	702 Sqn	Portland	Lynx HAS2/HAS3
701–707	PW	819 Sqn	Prestwick	Sea King HAS5
710–716	VL	899 Sqn	Yeovilton	Sea Harrier FRS1
717-718, 723	VL	899 Sqn	Yeovilton	Harrier T4N
719–720	VL	899 Sqn	Yeovilton	Hunter T8M
721-722	VL	899 Sqn	Yeovilton	Sea Harrier FRS1
738-739	VL	Station Flt	Yeovilton	Chipmunk T10
816–817	—	771 Sqn	Culdrose	Chipmunk T10
820–826	CU	771 Sqn	Culdrose	Sea King HAR5/Wessex HU5
830–838	VL	FRADU	Yeovilton	Hunter GA11
840–848	VL	FRADU	Yeovilton	Canberra TT18
860–868	VL	FRADU	Yeovilton	Hunter GA11
869–880	VL	FRADU	Yeovilton	Hunter T7/T8
901–912	—	FGF	Plymouth	Chipmunk T10

*See foregoing separate ships' Deck Letter Analysis

British-based Historic Aircraft in Overseas Markings

Some 'Historic' aircraft carry the markings of overseas air arms and can be seen in the UK, mainly preserved in museums and collections or taking part in air shows.

Notes	*Serial*	*Type (alternative identity)*	*Owner, operator and location*
	Argentina		
	A-517	FMA IA58 Pucara (G-BLRP)	Privately owned, Headcorn
	A-522	FMA IA58 Pucara (8768M)	FAA Museum, RNAS Yeovilton
	A-528	FMA IA58 Pucara (8769M)	Museum of Army Flying, Middle Wallop
	A-533	FMA IA58 Pucara (ZD486)	Museum of Army Flying, Middle Wallop
	A-549	FMA IA58 Pucara (ZD487)	Imperial War Museum, Duxford
	AE-406	Bell UH-1H [656]	Museum of Army Flying, Middle Wallop
	AE-409	Bell UH-1H	Museum of Army Flying, Middle Wallop
	AE-422	Bell UH-1H	FAA Museum, RNAS Yeovilton
	AE-424	Bell UH-1H (G-BMLA)	Privately owned, Panshangar
	AE-520	Vertol CH-47C Chinook	RAF, stored Wroughton
	0729	Beech T-34C Turbo Mentor [1-A-411]	FAA Museum, RNAS Yeovilton
	0767	Macchi MB339AA [4-A-116]	FAA Museum, RNAS Yeovilton

Serial	Type (alternative identity)	Owner, operator and location	Notes
Australia			
A2-4	Supermarine Seagull V (VH-ALB)	Battle of Britain Museum, Hendon	
A16-199	Lockheed Hudson IV (G-BEOX) (FH174) [SF-R]	RAF Museum, Hendon	
Belgium			
FT-36	Lockheed T-33A	Dumfries & Galloway Aviation Museum, Tinwald Downs	
FT-37	Lockheed T 33A	RAF Alconbury	
HD-75	Hanriot HD1 (OO-APJ/G-AFDX/N75)	RAF Museum, Hendon	
Canada			
671	DHC Chipmunk T10 (G-BNZC)	Privately owned, Duxford	
920	VS Stranraer (CF-BXO) [Q-N]	RAF Museum, Hendon	
5481	Hawker Hurricane	Privately owned, Sandown	
5424	Hawker Hurricane II (G-HURI)	Privately owned, Coningsby	
9059	Bristol Bolingbroke IVT	Privately owned, Portsmouth	
9893	Bristol Bolingbroke IVT	Imperial War Museum store	
9940	Bristol Bolingbroke IVT	Royal Scottish Museum of Flight, East Fortune	
10201	Bristol Bolingbroke IVT	Strathallan Aircraft Collection	
18393	Avro Canada CF-100 (G-BCYK)	Imperial War Museum, Duxford	
20385	CCF AT-16 Harvard IV (G-BGPB)	Harvard Formation Team, North Weald	
Denmark			
E-402	Hawker Hunter F51	Lovaux, Hurn	
E-407	Hawker Hunter F51	Privately owned, Lutterworth	
E-419	Hawker Hunter F51	North East Aircraft Museum, Usworth	
E-421	Hawker Hunter F51	Brooklands College of Technology, Surrey	
E-423	Hawker Hunter F51	Second World War Aircraft Preservation Society, Lasham	
E-424	Hawker Hunter F51	Lincolnshire Aviation Museum, East Kirkby	
E-425	Hawker Hunter F51	Midland Air Museum, Coventry	
E-427	Hawker Hunter F51 (G-9-447)	BAe OTD, Brough	
E-430	Hawker Hunter F51	Privately owned, Charlwood, West Sussex	
ET-273	Hawker Hunter T7	Lovaux, Macclesfield	
L866	Consolidated Catalina (8466M)	RAF Cosford Aerospace Museum	
R-756	Lockheed F-104G	Midland Air Museum, Coventry	
Egypt			
097	Yak 18	Privately owned, Earls Colne	
Eire			
177	Percival Provost T1 (G-BLIW)	Privately owned, Shoreham	
178	Percival Provost T1 (G-BKOS)	Privately owned, Kingsclere	
Finland			
VI-3	Valtion Viima (G-BAAY)	Privately owned, White Waltham	
France			
9	Dassault Mystere IVA	RAF Bentwaters	
16	Dassault Mystere IVA	RAF Lakenheath	
19	Deperdussin Replica (BAPC136)	Leisure Sport, Thorpe Park	
25	Dassault Mystere IVA	RAF Woodbridge	
36	Dassault Mystere IVA [EABDR 9]	RAF Upper Heyford BDRT	
37	Nord 3400 [MAB]	Privately owned, Coventry	
39	Nord 3400 [MOC]	Privately owned, Coventry	
45	SNCAN Stampe SV4C (G-BHFG)	Privately owned, Enstone	
46	Dassault Mystere IVA [EABDR 8]	RAF Upper Heyford	
50	Dassault Mystere IVA	RAF Woodbridge	
57	Dassault Mystere IVA [8-MT]	Imperial War Museum, Duxford	
59	Dassault Mystere IVA [314-TH]	Wales Aircraft Museum, Cardiff	
60	Dassault Mystere IVA [12]	RAF Lakenheath Fire Section	
65	Nord 3202 (G-BMBF)	Privately owned, Breighton	
68	Nord 3400 [MHA]	Privately owned, Coventry	
70	Dassault Mystere IVA	Midland Air Museum, Coventry	
75	Dassault Mystere IVA [11]	RAF Lakenheath	
79	Dassault Mystere IVA [8-NB]	Norfolk & Suffolk Aviation Museum, Flixton	
83	Dassault Mystere IVA [8-MS]	Newark Air Museum, Winthorpe	
84	Dassault Mystere IVA	Lashenden Air Warfare Museum, Headcorn	

Notes	Serial	Type (alternative identity)	Owner, operator and location
	85	Dassault Mystere IVA	Privately owned, Bruntingthorpe
	92	MH Broussard (G-BJGW) [31-GW]	*see Morocco*
	97	Dassault Mystere IVA [4]	RAF Lakenheath
	99	Dassault Mystere IVA	RAF Lakenheath
	101	Dassault Mystere IVA [8-MN]	Bomber County Aviation Museum, Hemswell
	103	Nord Norecrin (G-BHXJ)	Privately owned, Popham
	104	Dassault Mystere IVA	RAF Bentwaters
	113	Dassault Mystere IVA	RAF Lakenheath
	120	Stampe SV4C (G-AZGC)	Privately owned, Booker
	121	Dassault Mystere IVA [8-MY]	City of Norwich Aviation Museum
	121	Nord 3400 [MJA]	Privately owned, Coventry
	124	Nord 3400 [MOO]	Privately owned, Coventry
	126	Dassault Mystere IVA	RAF Lakenheath
	127	Dassault Mystere IVA [EABDR 7]	RAF Upper Heyford
	129	Dassault Mystere IVA [EABDR 6]	RAF Upper Heyford
	133	Dassault Mystere IVA	RAF Woodbridge
	145	Dassault Mystere IVA	RAF Lakenheath
	146	Dassualt Mystere IVA [8-MC]	North East Aircraft Museum, Usworth
	217	MH Broussard (G-BKPU)	Privately owned, Shawdene
	241	Dassault Mystere IVA [2]	RAF Lakenheath
	276	Dassault Mystere IVA	RAF Woodbridge
	285	Dassault Mystere IVA	RAF Lakenheath
	300	Dassault Mystere IVA [5]	RAF Lakenheath
	309	Dassault Mystere IVA [8]	RAF Lakenheath
	318	Dassault Mystere IVA [8-NY]	Dumfries & Galloway Aviation Museum, Tinwald Downs
	319	Dassault Mystere IVA [8-ND]	Rebel Air Museum, Earls Colne
	1076	Morane MS230 (G-AVEB)	Privately owned, Booker
	3398	Spad XIII Replica (G-BFYO) [2]	FAA Museum, RNAS Yeovilton
	133722	Vought F4U-7 Corsair (NX1337A) [15F22]	Privately owned, Duxford/Sutton Bridge
	Germany		
	C19/18	Albatros Replica (BAPC 118)	Privately owned, North Weald
	D5397/17	Albatros D.VA Replica (G-BFXL)	FAA Museum, RNAS Yeovilton
	D2+600	CASA 352L (G-BFHG)	Aces High, North Weald
	N7+AA	CASA 352L (G-BFHF)	Privately owned, Coventry
	N8+AA	CASA 352L (G-BFHD)	Privately owned, North Weald
	A1+BT	CZL Super Aero (G-APRR)	Privately owned, Elstree
	475081	Fieseler Fi156C Storch (VP546/ 7362M)	RAF St Athan Historic Aircraft Collection
	28368	Flettner Fl282V Kolibri	Midland Air Museum, Coventry
	100143	Focke-Achgelis Fa330	Imperial War Museum, Duxford
	100502	Focke-Achgelis Fa330	Lincolnshire Aviation Museum, East Kirkby
	100509	Focke-Achgelis Fa330	Science Museum, stored South Kensington
	100545	Focke-Achgelis Fa330	Torbay Aircraft Museum, Paignton
	100549	Focke-Achgelis Fa330	Greater Manchester Museum of Science and Industry
	8	Focke Wulf FW190 Replica (G-WULF)	Privately owned, Elstree
	7334	Focke Wulf FW190 Replica (G-SYFW) [2+1]	Privately owned, Guernsey
	584219/38	Focke Wulf FW190F-8/UI (PN999/8470M)	RAF St Athan Historic Aircraft Collection
	733682	Focke Wulf FW190A-8/R6	Imperial War Museum, Duxford
	4253/18	Fokker D.VII (G-BFPL)	Privately owned, Lower Upham
	5125/18	Fokker D.VII Replica (BAPC 110)	Leisure Sport, Thorpe Park
	8417/18	Fokker D.VII	RAF Museum Restoration Centre, Cardington
	102/18	Fokker Dr.1 Dreidekker Replica (BAPC 88)	FAA Museum, RNAS Yeovilton
	150/17	Fokker Dr.1 Dreidekker Replica (BAPC 139)	Leisure Sport, Thorpe Park
	152/17	Fokker Dr.1 Dreidekker Replica (G-ATJM)	Privately owned, North Weald
	425/17	Fokker Dr.1 Dreidekker Replica (BAPC 133)	Torbay Aircraft Museum, Paignton
	425/17	Fokker Dr.1 Dreidekker Replica (G-BEFR)	Privately owned, St Athan
	422/15	Fokker EIII replica (G-AVJO)	Privately owned, Booker
	22912	Hansa Brandenburg W.29 Replica (BAPC 138)	Leisure Sport, Thorpe Park

Serial	Type (alternative identity)	Owner, operator and location	Notes
701152	Heinkel He111H-23 (8471M) [NT+SL]	Battle of Britain Museum, Hendon	
120227	Heinkel He162A Salamander (VH513/8472M) [2]	RAF St Athan Historic Aircraft Collection	
120235	Heinkel He162A Salamander	Imperial War Museum, Duxford	
14	Hispano HA1112 (C4K-235/G-BJZZ G-HUNN)	Privately owned, Winchester	
17+NK	Amiot AAC1 (6316)	Imperial War Museum, Duxford	
494083	Junkers Ju87D-3 (8474M) [RI+JK]	Battle of Britain Museum, Hendon	
360043	Junkers Ju88R-1 (PJ876/8475M) [D5+EV]	Battle of Britain Museum, Hendon	
22+57	Lockheed F104G	Bomber County Aviation Museum, Hemswell	
7198/18	LVG C.VI (G-AANJ)	Shuttleworth Collection, Old Warden	
6	Messerschmitt Bf109 Replica (BAPC74)	Torbay Aircraft Museum	
14	Messerschmitt Bf109 Replica (BAPC67)	Midland Air Museum, Coventry	
1190	Messerschmitt Bf109E-3	Privately owned, Hurn	
4101	Messerschmitt Bf109E-3 (DG200/8477M) [12]	Battle of Britain Museum, Hendon	
10639	Messerschmitt Bf109G-6 (RN228/8478M)	Privately owned, RAF Benson	
730301	Messerschmitt Bf110G-4 (AX772/8479M) [D5+RL]	Battle of Britain Museum, Hendon	
191316	Messerschmitt Me163B Komet	Science Museum, South Kensington	
191614	Messerschmitt Me163B Komet (8481M)	RAF Cosford Aerospace Museum	
191659	Messerschmitt Me163B Komet	Royal Scottish Museum of Flight, East Fortune	
191660	Messerschmitt Me163B Komet [3]	Imperial War Museum, Duxford	
191904	Messerschmitt Me163B Komet (8480M) [25]	RAF St Athan Historic Aircraft Collection	
112372	Messerschmitt Me262A-1 (VK893/8482M)	RAF St Athan Historic Aircraft Collection	
420430	Messerschmitt Me410A-1/U2 (8483M) [PD+VO]	RAF St Athan Historic Aircraft Collection	
ZA+WN	Morane-Saulnier MS500 (G-AZMH)	Privately owned, Chalmington	
FI+S	Morane-Saulnier MS505 (G-BIRW) Criquet	Royal Scottish Museum of Flight, East Fortune	
17	Nord 1002 (G-ATBG)	Privately owned, Sutton Bridge	
14	Pilatus P-2 (J-108/G-BJAX)	Privately owned, Duxford	
16+RF	Pilatus P-2 (U-110/G-PTWO)	Privately owned, Duxford	
1480	Bf109 Replica (BAPC66)	Hawkinge Aeronautical Trust	
Greece			
52-6541	Republic F-84F Thunderflash	North East Aircraft Museum, Usworth	
51-6151	Canadair F-86D Sabre	North East Aircraft Museum, Usworth	
India			
Q497	EE Canberra T4 (WH847)	Blackpool Airport Fire Service	
HS649	VS Spitfire XVIII	Privately owned, Chichester	
Iraq			
333	DH Vampire T55 (pod only)	Military Aircraft Preservation Group, Hadfield, Derbys	
Israel			
28	NA P-51D Mustang	Privately owned, Fowlmere, Cambs	
Italy			
MM5701	Fiat CR42 (BT474/8468M) [13-95]	Battle of Britain Museum, Hendon	
MM53211	Fiat G.46-4 (BAPC 79)	Privately owned, Lympne	
MM53432	NA T-6D [RM-11]	Privately owned, South Wales	
MM53795	CCF Harvard IV (G-BJST) [SC-66]	Privately owned, RAF Kemble	
MM53796	CCF Harvard IV [SC-52]	Privately owned, RAF Kemble	
MM54099	CCF T-6G Harvard [RR-56]	Privately owned, Duxford	
Morocco			
92	MH1521 Broussard (G-BJGW)	Privately owned, Duxford	
Netherlands			
E-15	Fokker S-11 Instructor (G-BIYU)	Privately owned, Denham	
R-163	Piper Super Cub (G-BIRH)	Privately owned, Lee-on-Solent	

Historic Aircraft

Notes	Serial	Type (alternative identity)	Owner, operator and location
	204/V	Lockheed SP-2H Neptune	RAF Cosford Aerospace Museum
	N-250	Hunter F6 (nose only) [G-9-185]	Science Museum, South Kensington
	Norway		
	56321	Saab Safir (G-BKPY)	Newark Air Museum, Winthorpe
	Poland		
	1120	MiG-15	RAF Museum, Hendon
	1420	MiG-15 (G-BMZF)	FAA Museum, RNAS Yeovilton
	Portugal		
	3460	Dornier 27 (G-BMFG)	Privately owned, Booker
	3497	Dornier 27 (G-BMFH)	Privately owned, Booker
	Russia		
	???	RP-63C Kingcobra (N62822/44-4393)	Privately owned, Duxford
	South Africa		
	6130	Lockheed Ventura II (AJ469)	RAF Museum Store, Henlow
	Spain		
	T2B-272	CASA C.352L	RAF Cosford Aerospace Museum
	HD5-1	Dornier Do24T-3 [58-1]	RAF Museum, Hendon
	T2-124	Bf-109K [FE-124]	Warbirds of GB, Bitteswell
	C5E-88	Bf-109E	Tangmere Military Aviation Museum
	Sweden		
	35075	Saab J-35J Draken [40]	Imperial War Museum, Duxford
	29640	Saab J-29F [08]	Midland Air Museum, Coventry
	Switzerland		
	U-125	Pilatus P-2 (G-BLKZ)	Privately owned, Goodwood
	U-142	Pilatus P-2 (G-BONE)	Privately owned, Southend
	U-143	Pilatus P-2 (G-CJCI)	Privately owned, Micheldever
	J-1008	DH Vampire FB6	Mosquito Aircraft Museum, London Colney
	J-1172	DH Vampire FB6 (8487M)	Greater Manchester Museum of Science and Industry
	J-1523	DH Venom FB50 (G-VENI)	Privately owned, Cranfield
	J-1601	DH Venom FB50 (G-VIDI)	Privately owned, Cranfield
	J-1605	DH Venom FB50 (G-BLID)	Privately owned, Duxford
	J-1614	DH Venom FB50 (G-BLIE)	Privately owned, Glasgow
	J-1632	DH Venom FB50 (G-VNOM)	Privately owned, Cranfield
	J-1704	DH Venom FB54	RAF Cosford Aerospace Museum
	USA		
	0-17899	Convair VT-29B	Imperial War Museum, Duxford
	100884	Douglas C-47A Dakota 3 (G-DAKS)	Privately owned, North Weald
	111989	Cessna L-19A Bird Dog (N33600)	Museum of Army Flying, Middle Wallop
	115042	NA T-6G Texan (G-BGHU) [TA-042]	Privately owned, Headcorn
	115302	Piper L-18C (G-BJTP)	Privately owned, Stoke Orchard, Glos
	121714	Grumman F8F-2B Bearcat (NX700H) [S/100]	Privately owned, Duxford
	13064	NA P-47D Thunderbolt	RAF Museum Restoration Centre, Cardington
	14060	Lockheed T-33A [LN]	RAF Lakenheath BDRT
	1411	Grumman Widgeon (N444M)	Privately owned, Biggin Hill
	14286	Lockheed T-33A [WK]	Imperial War Museum, Duxford
	14419	Lockheed T-33A [30-QC]	Midland Air Museum, Coventry
	140547	NA T-28C Trojan (N2800Q)	Privately owned, Duxford
	146289	NA T-28C Trojan (N99153)	Norfolk & Suffolk Aviation Museum, Flixton
	14700	NA T-6G Texan	Privately owned, Coventry
	150225	Westland Wessex (G-AYNC)	Privately owned, Hurn
	151632	NA TB-25N Mitchell (NL9494Z) (really 430925)	Privately owned, Coventry
	153008	McD F-4N Phantom	RAF Alconbury, BDRT
	155848	McD F-4S Phantom (WS-11/ VMFA-232]	FAA Museum, RNAS Yeovilton
	159233	AV-8A Harrier [CG-03]	FAA Museum, RNAS Yeovilton
	164	Beech D18S (G-BKGL) (really RCAF 5193)	British Aerial Museum, Duxford

Serial	*Type (alternative identity)*	*Owner, operator and location*	*Notes*
16718	Lockheed T-33A	City of Norwich Aviation Museum	
16769	Lockheed T-33A	RAF Mildenhall Fire Section	
17473	Lockheed T-33A	RAF Cosford Aerospace Museum	
17657	Douglas A-26K Invader (FY64) (nose only)	Privately owned, Canterbury	
181528	Piper J-3C-65 Cub	Privately owned, Southampton	
18-2001	Piper L-18 Super Cub (G-BIZV) (really 52-2401)	Privately owned, Poulton, Clwyd	
19252	Lockheed T-33A [314-UY]	Tangmere Military Aviation Museum	
226671	Republic P-47D Thunderbolt [MX-X] (NX47DD)	Privately owned, Duxford	
231983	Boeing B-17G (F-BDRS) [IY-GS] (really 44-83735)	Imperial War Museum, Duxford	
236800	Piper J-3C-65 Cub (G-BHPK) [A-44] (really 42-38410)	Privately owned, Sywell	
24198	Lockheed C-140B Jetstar	RAF Mildenhall, BDRT	
24535	Kaman HH-43F Huskie	Midland Air Museum, Coventry	
26	Boeing Stearman (G-BAVO)	Privately owned, Liverpool	
27767	Aeronca L-3A (G-BIHW)	Privately owned, Swansea	
2807	NA T-6G Texan (G-BHTH) [103]	Privately owned, Booker	
29963	Lockheed T-33A	Wales Aircraft Museum, Cardiff	
315509	Douglas C-47A (G-BHUB)	Imperial War Museum, Duxford	
329417	Piper J-3C-65 Cub (G-BDHK) (really 42-38400)	Privately owned, Coleford	
329601	Piper J-3C-65 Cub (G-AXHR) [D-44]	Privately owned, Nayland	
329934	Piper J-3C-65 Cub (G-BCPH) [72-B]	Privately owned, Booker	
330485	Piper J-3C-65 Cub (G-AJES) [44-C]	Privately owned, Dunkeswell	
37699	McD F-4C Phantom (FY63)	RAF Fairford BDRT	
413048	Piper J-3C-65 Cub (G-BCXJ) [39-E] (really 44-80752)	Privately owned, Compton Abbas	
41386	Thomas-Morse S4 Scout Replica (G-MJTD)	Privately owned, Hitchin	
42157	NA F-100D Super Sabre	North East Aviation Museum, Usworth	
42163	NA F-100D Super Sabre [11-YG]	Dumfries & Galloway Aviation Museum, Tinwald Downs	
42165	NA F-100D Super Sabre [11-ML]	Imperial War Museum, Duxford	
42174	NA F-100D Super Sabre [11-YE]	Midland Air Museum, Coventry	
42196	NA F-100D Super Sabre [LT]	Norfolk & Suffolk Aviation Museum, Flixton	
42204	NA F-100D Super Sabre [11-MQ]	RAF Alconbury	
42212	NA F-100D Super Sabre [LN]	RAF Sculthorpe	
42223	NA F-100D Super Sabre	Newark Air Museum, Winthorpe	
42239	NA F-100D Super Sabre [FW-239]	Privately owned, Bruntingthorpe	
429366	NA TB-25N Mitchell (N9115Z/ 8838M)	Bomber Command Museum, Hendon	
431171	NA B-25J Mitchell (N7614C)	Imperial War Museum, Duxford	
433318	Boeing B-25D	Privately owned, Duxford	
44	Piper L-18 Super Cub (G-BJLH) [K-33]	Privately owned, Little Snoring	
454537	Piper L-4J Cub (G-BFDL) [04-J]	Privately owned, Portmoak	
461748	Boeing B-29A Superfortress (G-BHDK) [Y]	Imperial War Museum, Duxford	
463221	NA P-51D Mustang (N51JJ) (really 473149) [G4-S]	Privately owned, Duxford	
472028	NA P-51D Mustang (41 IAF)	Privately owned, Teesside	
472216	NA P-51D Mustang (G-BIXL)	Privately owned, North Weald	
472258	NA P-51D Mustang (really 473979) [WZ-I]	Imperial War Museum, Duxford	
472773	NA P-51D Mustang [RL-F] (G-SUSY)	Privately owned, Micheldever	
473877	NA P-51D Mustang (N167F) [B6-S]	Privately owned, Duxford	
479609	Piper J-3C-65 Cub (G-BHXY) [PR]	Privately owned, Barton	
479766	Piper J-3C-65 Cub (G-BKHG)	Privately owned, Newport	
480015	Piper J-3C-65 Cub (G-AKIB)	Privately owned, White Waltham	
480133	Piper J-3C-65 Cub (G-BDCD) [44-B]	Privately owned, Slinfold	
480321	Piper J-3C-65 Cub (G-FRAN) [44-H]	Privately owned, Clacton	
480594	Piper J-3C-65 Cub (G-BEDJ)	Privately owned, Ashford Hill	
483009	NA AT-6D Texan (really 244450)	Epping Museum, North Weald	
483868	Boeing B-17G Fortress (N5237V) [A-N]	Bomber Command Museum, Hendon	
485784	Boeing B-17G (G-BEDF) [K-G]	Privately owned, Duxford	
511371	NA P-51D Mustang (NL1051S) [VF-S]	Privately owned, Southend	
51-15227	NA T-6G Harvard (G-BKRA) [10]	Privately owned, Shoreham	

Notes	Serial	Type (alternative identity)	Owner, operator and location
	540	Piper L-4 Cub (G-BCNX) (really 43-29877)	Privately owned, Monewden
	54137	NA T-6G Texan (G-CTKL)	Privately owned, Dunkeswell
	542265	NA F-100D Super Sabre [FW-2265]	RAF Wethersfield, at gate
	542447	Piper PA18-135 Super Cub (G-SCUB)	Privately owned, Anwick
	542457	Piper PA18-135 Super Cub (G-LION/R-167)	Privately owned, Orsett
	542474	Piper PA18-135 Super Cub (G-PCUB/R-184)	Privately owned, Redhill
	54433	Lockheed T-33A [WD]	Norfolk & Suffolk Aviation Museum, Flixton
	54439	Lockheed T-33A	North East Aviation Museum, Usworth
	5547	Lockheed T-33A (really 19036)	Newark Air Museum, Winthorpe
	599	NA P-51D Mustang (G-PSID) (really 4463788)	Privately owned, Duxford
	60312	McDonnell F-101F Voodoo [AR]	RAF Alconbury, BDRT
	60689	Boeing B-52D Stratofortress	Imperial War Museum, Duxford
	612414	Boeing CH47A Chinook	RAF Odiham, instructional use
	62-494	Republic F-105G Thunderchief [LN] (really 24434)	RAF Lakenheath, BDRT
	63000	NA F-100D Super Sabre (really 42160)	Wales Aircraft Museum, Cardiff
	63319	NA F-100D Super Sabre (really 42269) [319-FW]	RAF Lakenheath, at gate
	63-414	McD F-4C Phantom (37414)	RAF Woodbridge BDRT
	63-419	McD F-4C Phantom (37419)	RAF Alconbury BDRT
	63-428	Republic F-105G Thunderchief [JB] (really 24428)	RAF Upper Heyford
	63-449	McD F-4C Phantom (37449) [SA]	RAF Upper Heyford BDRT
	63-471	McD F-4C Phantom (37471) [LN]	RAF Lakenheath BDRT
	63-610	McD F-4C Phantom (37610)	RAF Lakenheath BDRT
	63935	NA F-100F Super Sabre [11-MN]	RAF Alconbury
	63938	NA F-100F Super Sabre [11-MU]	Lashenden Air Warfare Museum, Headcorn
	64-707	McD F-4C Phantom (40707)	RAF Mildenhall BDRT
	6771	Republic F-84F Thunderstreak (really 52-7133)	RAF Museum/RAeS Medway Branch, Rochester
	68-060	GD F111E (pod)	Dumfries & Galloway Aviation Museum, Tinwald Downs
	70270	McDonnell F-101B Voodoo	RAF Woodbridge
	7797	Aeronca L-16A (G-BFAF)	Privately owned, Finmere
	80260	McDonnell F-101B Voodoo	RAF Bentwaters
	82062	DHC U-6A Beaver	Midland Air Museum, Coventry
	88297	Goodyear FG-1D Corsair (N8297) [29]	Privately owned, Duxford
	897	Aeronca 11AC Chief (G-BJEV)	Privately owned, Little Gransden
	91007	Lockheed T-33A (G-TJET) (really 51-8566) [TR-007]	Privately owned, Cranfield
	Yugoslavia		
	13064	Republic P-47D Thunderbolt	RAF Museum Restoration Centre, Cardington

Isaacs Fury K3731 (G-RODI) is painted in the colours of No 43 Squadron. *PRM*

Piper Cub G-AJES is in USAAF colours as 330485. *PRM*

Both operated by the Battle of Britain Memorial Flight — Chipmunk T10 WK518 and Lancaster PA474. *PRM*

Jet Provost T5A XW323 operated by the RAF College, Cranwell. *PRM*

XX238 was one of two Hawks from RAF Valley painted in special markings for the 1987 display season. *PRM*

All of 750 Squadron's Jetstreams, like XX479, have been repainted in blue/white markings. *PRM*

Sea Harrier FRS1 ZD582 127/L of 800 Squadron. *PRM*

One of two airworthy Sea Vixen FAW2s, XS577 is flown by the RAE at Llanbedr. *PRM*

Operated by No 618 VGS, Schleicher Vanguard ZD650 is based at West Malling. *PRM*

A rare VIP C-141B Starlifter 70166 operated by 443MAW. *PRM*

Royal Swedish AF C-130E Hercules 84001 is flown by F7 from Satenas. *PRM*

This ex-Oregon ANG F-4C Phantom is used for Battle Damage Training at RAF Fairford. *PRM*

Irish Army Air Corps Military Aircraft Markings

Serial	*Type (alternative identity)*	*Owner, operator and location*	*Notes*
34	Miles Magister	Irish Aviation Museum Store, Castlemoate House, Dublin	
141	Avro Anson	Irish Aviation Museum Store, Castlemoate House, Dublin	
164	DH Chipmunk T20	Engineering Wing, Baldonnel (stored)	
168	DH Chipmunk T20	Training Wing, Gormanston	
172	DH Chipmunk T20	Engineering Wing, Baldonnel	
173	DH Chipmunk T20	South East Aviation Enthusiasts, Waterford	
176	DH Dove	South East Aviation Enthusiasts, Waterford	
181	Percival Provost T51	Baldonnel, stored	
183	Percival Provost T51	Irish Aviation Museum Store, Castlemoate House, Dublin	
184	Percival Provost T51	Baldonnel, stored	
187	DH Vampire T11	Aviation Society of Ireland, stored, Baldonnel	
189	Percival Provost T51	Baldonnel, stored	
191	DH Vampire T11	Irish Aviation Museum Store, Castlemoate House, Dublin	
192	DH Vampire T11	Institute of Technology, Bolton Street, Dublin, in store, Baldonnel	
193	DH Vampire T11	Baldonnel Fire Section	
195	Sud Alouette III	No 1 Support Wing, Baldonnel	
196	Sud Alouette III	No 1 Support Wing, Baldonnel	
197	Sud Alouette III	No 1 Support Wing, Baldonnel	
198	DH Vampire T11 (XE977)	On display, Baldonnel	
199	DH Chipmunk	Training Wing, Gormanston	
202	Sud Alouette III	No 1 Support Wing, Baldonnel	
203	Cessna FR172H	No 2 Support Wing, Gormanston	
205	Cessna FR172H	No 2 Support Wing, Gormanston	
206	Cessna FR172H	No 2 Support Wing, Gormanston	
207	Cessna FR172H	No 2 Support Wing, Gormanston	
208	Cessna FR172H	No 2 Support Wing, Gormanston	
209	Cessna FR172H	No 2 Support Wing, Gormanston	
210	Cessna FR172H	No 2 Support Wing, Gormanston	
211	Sud Alouette III	No 1 Support Wing, Baldonnel	
212	Sud Alouette III	No 1 Support Wing, Baldonnel	
213	Sud Alouette III	No 1 Support Wing, Baldonnel	
214	Sud Alouette III	No 1 Support Wing, Baldonnel	
215	Fouga Super Magister	No 1 Support Wing, Baldonnel	
216	Fouga Super Magister	No 1 Support Wing, Baldonnel	
217	Fouga Super Magister	No 1 Support Wing, Baldonnel	
218	Fouga Super Magister	No 1 Support Wing, Baldonnel	
219	Fouga Super Magister	No 1 Support Wing, Baldonnel	
220	Fouga Super Magister	No 1 Support Wing, Baldonnel	
221	Fouga Super Magister [3-KE]	Engineering Wing, Baldonnel	
222	SIAI SF-260W Warrior	Training Wing, Baldonnel	
223	SIAI SF-260W Warrior	Training Wing, Baldonnel	
225	SIAI SF-260W Warrior	Training Wing, Baldonnel	
226	SIAI SF-260W Warrior	Training Wing, Baldonnel	
227	SIAI SF-260W Warrior	Training Wing, Baldonnel	
228	SIAI SF-260W Warrior	Training Wing, Baldonnel	
229	SIAI SF-260W Warrior	Training Wing, Baldonnel	
230	SIAI SF-260W Warrior	Training Wing, Baldonnel	
231	SIAI SF-260W Warrior	Training Wing, Baldonnel	
232	Beech King Air 200 (EI-BCY)	Maritime Squadron, Baldonnel	
233	SIAI SF-260MC	Engineering Wing, Baldonnel (stored)	
234	Beech King Air 200 (EI-BFJ)	Maritime Squadron, Baldonnel	
235	SIAI SF-260W Warrior	Training Wing, Baldonnel	
237	Aerospatiale Gazelle	Advanced Flying Training School, Baldonnel	
238	HS125/700B	Transport Squadron, Baldonnel	

Notes	Serial	Type (alternative identity)	Owner, operator and location
	240	Beech King Air 200	Transport Squadron, Baldonnel
	241	Aerospatiale Gazelle	Advanced Flying Training School, Baldonnel
	243	Cessna FR172P	No 2 Support Wing, Gormanston
	244	SA365F Dauphin II	Naval Squadron, Baldonnel
	245	SA365F Dauphin II	Naval Squadron, Baldonnel
	246	SA365F Dauphin II	Naval Squadron, Baldonnel
	247	SA365F Dauphin II	Naval Squadron, Baldonnel
	248	SA365F Dauphin II	Naval Squadron, Baldonnel

Overseas Military Aircraft Markings

Aircraft included in this section are a selection of those likely to be seen visiting UK civil and military airfields on transport flights, exchange visits, exercises and for air shows. It is not a comprehensive list of *all* aircraft operated by the air arms concerned.

Serial

AUSTRALIA
Royal Australian Air Force
Boeing 707-338C
33 Sqn, Canberra
A20-623
A20-624
A20-627
A20-629
Lockheed
C-130H Hercules
36 Sqn, Richmond
A97-001
A97-002
A97-003
A97-004
A97-005
A97-006
A97-007
A97-008
A97-009
A97-010
A97-011
A97-012
Lockheed
C130E Hercules
37 Sqn, Richmond
A97-159
A97-160
A97-167
A97-168
A97-171
A97-172
A97-177
A97-178
A97-180
A97-181
A97-189
A97-190
Lockheed
P-3C Orion
Edinburgh, NSW
10 Sqn*
11 Sqn †
A9-656†
A9-657†
A9-658†
A9-659†
A9-660†
A9-661†
A9-662†
A9-663†
A9-664†
A9-665†
A9-751*
A9-752*
A9-753*
A9-754*
A9-755*
A9-756*
A9-757*
A9-758*
A9-759*
A9-760*

AUSTRIA
Oesterreichische Luftstreitkrafte
Saab 105ÖE (yellow)
I Staffel, Linz
1101/A
1102/B
1104/D
1105/E
1106/F
1107/G
1108/H
1109/I
1110/J
Saab 105ÖE (green)
II Staffel, Linz
1111/A
1112/B
1114/D
1116/F
1117/G
1119/I
1120/J
Saab 105ÖE (red)
II Staffel, Graz
1122/B
1123/C
1124/D
1125/E
1126/F
1127/G
1128/H
1129/I
1130/J
Saab 105ÖE (blue)
I Staffel, Zeltweg
1131/A
1132/B
1133/C
1134/D
1135/E
1136/F
1137/G
1139/I
1140/J
Short SC7
Skyvan 3M
Flachenstaffel, Tullin
5S-TA
5S-TB

BELGIUM
Force Aerienne Belge/
Belgische Luchtmacht
D-BD Alpha Jet
7/11 Smaldeel, Brustem VEC, Brustem
AT01
AT02
AT03
AT05
AT06
AT08
AT09
AT10
AT11
AT12
AT13
AT14
AT15
AT16
AT17
AT18
AT19
AT20
AT21
AT22

Serial

AT23
AT24
AT25
AT26
AT27
AT28
AT29
AT30
AT31
AT32
AT33

Dassault Mirage 5BA

1/8 Smaldeel, Bierset
2/42 Smaldeel, Florennes

BA01 2 Sm
BA03 8 Sm
BA04 1 Sm
BA05 1 Sm
BA08 1 Sm
BA10 1 Sm
BA11 2 Sm
BA15 8 Sm
BA16 1 Sm
BA17 2 Sm
BA18 8 Sm
BA20 2 Sm
BA21 2 Sm
BA22 1 Sm
BA23 2 Sm
BA26 1 Sm
BA27 8 Sm
BA30 2 Sm
BA31 1 Sm
BA33 1 Sm
BA37 1 Sm
BA39 1 Sm
BA42 8 Sm
BA43 1 Sm
BA44 1 Sm
BA45 8 Sm
BA46 2 Sm
BA48 8 Sm
BA50 2 Sm
BA52 8 Sm
BA53 2 Sm
BA54 8 Sm
BA56 2 Sm
BA57 2 Sm
BA59 2 Sm
BA60 8 Sm
BA62 1 Sm
BA63 8 Sm

Dassault Mirage 5BD

BD01 8 Sm
BD03 8 Sm
BD04 2 Sm
BD07 1 Sm
BD09 2 Sm
BD10 8 Sm
BD11 8 Sm
BD12 1 Sm
BD13 1 Sm
BD14 1 Sm
BD15 2 Sm

Dassault Mirage 5BR

BR03 42 Sm
BR04 42 Sm
BR07 42 Sm
BR08 42 Sm
BR09 42 Sm
BR10 42 Sm

Serial

BR12 42 Sm
BR13 42 Sm
BR14 42 Sm
BR15 42 Sm
BR16 42 Sm
BR17 42 Sm
BR19 42 Sm
BR21 42 Sm
BR22 42 Sm
BR23 42 Sm
BR24 42 Sm
BR25 42 Sm
BR26 42 Sm
BR27 42 Sm

Boeing 727-29C

21 Smaldeel, Melsbroek

CB01
CB02

Swearingen Merlin IIIA

21 Smaldeel, Melsbroek

CF01
CF02
CF04
CF05
CF06

Lockheed C-130H Hercules

20 Smaldeel, Melsbroek

CH01
CH02
CH03
CH04
CH05
CH06
CH07
CH08
CH09
CH10
CH11
CH12

Dassault Mystere 20

21 Smaldeel, Melsbroek

CM01
CM02

Hawker-Siddeley HS748 srs 2A

21 Smaldeel, Melsbroek

CS01
CS02
CS03

General Dynamics F-16A

349/350 Smaldeel, Bevekom (1 Wg);
OCS, Bevekom;
23/31 Smaldeel, Kleine Brogel (10 Wg)

FA01 349 Sm
FA02 350 Sm
FA03 349 Sm
FA04 350 Sm
FA05 349 Sm
FA09 349 Sm
FA10 349 Sm
FA12 350 Sm
FA15 350 Sm
FA16 349 Sm
FA17 349 Sm
FA18 350 Sm
FA19 OCS
FA20 OCS
FA21 349 Sm

Serial

FA22 OCS
FA23 350 Sm
FA25 349 Sm
FA26 OCS
FA27 349 Sm
FA28 350 Sm
FA30 350 Sm
FA31 349 Sm
FA32 350 Sm
FA34 349 Sm
FA36 350 Sm
FA37 OCS
FA38 350 Sm
FA39 350 Sm
FA40 OCS
FA43 349 Sm
FA44 350 Sm
FA45 OCS
FA46 OCS
FA47 OCS
FA48 350 Sm
FA49 349 Sm
FA50 350 Sm
FA51 350 Sm
FA53 350 Sm
FA54 OCS
FA55 350 Sm
FA56 31 Sm
FA57 23 Sm
FA58 31 Sm
FA60 31 Sm
FA61 23 Sm
FA62 31 Sm
FA64 31 Sm
FA65 23 Sm
FA66 31 Sm
FA67 23 Sm
FA68 31 Sm
FA69 23 Sm
FA70 31 Sm
FA71 23 Sm
FA72 31 Sm
FA73 23 Sm
FA74 31 Sm
FA75 23 Sm
FA76 31 Sm
FA77 23 Sm
FA78 31 Sm
FA80 31 Sm
FA81 23 Sm
FA82 31 Sm
FA83 23 Sm
FA84 31 Sm
FA85 23 Sm
FA86 31 Sm
FA87 23 Sm
FA88 31 Sm
FA89 23 Sm
FA90 31 Sm
FA91 23 Sm
FA92 31 Sm
FA93 23 Sm
FA94 31 Sm
FA95 23 Sm
FA96 31 Sm
FA97
FA98
FA99
FA100
FA101
FA102
FA103
FA104
FA105

Serial

FA106
FA107
FA108
FA109
FA110
FA111
FA112
FA113
FA114
FA115
FA116
FA117
FA118
FA119
FA120
FA121
FA122
FA123
FA124
FA125
FA126
FA127
FA128
FA129
FA130
FA131
FA132
FA133
FA134
FA135
FA136

General Dynamics F-16B
349/350 Smaldeel, Bevekom (1 Wg);
OCS, Bevekom;
23/31 Smaldeel, Kleine Brogel (10 Wg)
FB01 OCS
FB02 349 Sm
FB03 350 Sm
FB04 OCS
FB05 OCS
FB06 OCS
FB07 349 Sm
FB08 350 Sm
FB09 OCS
FB10 OCS
FB11 OCS
FB12 OCS
FB13 10 Wg
FB14 10 Wg
FB15 10 Wg
FB17 10 Wg
FB18 10 Wg
FB19 10 Wg
FB20 10 Wg
FB21
FB22
FB23
FB24

Westland Sea King Mk48
40 Smaldeel, Koksijde
RS01
RS02
RS03
RS04
RS05

Siai Marchetti SF.260MB
Ecole de Pilotage Elementaire, (5 Sm)
Gossoncourt
ST02
ST03
ST04
ST06
ST07
ST09
ST11
ST12
ST14
ST15
ST16
ST17
ST18
ST19
ST20
ST21
ST22
ST23
ST24
ST25
ST26
ST27
ST29
ST30
ST31
ST32
ST33
ST34
ST35
ST36

Belgische Landmacht

Britten-Norman BN-2A Islander
*15/16 Smaldeel, Brasschaat
†SvHLV, Brasschaat
B01/LA*
B02/LB*
B03/LC*
B04/LD†
B05/LE†
B06/LF†
B07/LG†
B08/LH†
B09/LI*
B10/LJ†
B11/LK†
B12/LL†

Sud Alouette II
16 Sm, Butzweilerhof
17 Sm, Werl
18 Sm, Merzbruck
†SvHLV, Brasschaat
A04 16 Sm
A05 †
A08 18 Sm
A09 17 Sm
A11 †
A12 17 Sm
A13 18 Sm
A14 16 Sm
A15 17 Sm
A16 17 Sm
A18 16 Sm
A20 18 Sm
A22 †
A23 18 Sm
A24 †
A25 16 Sm
A26 †
A27 18 Sm
A29 18 Sm
A30 17 Sm
A31 †
A32 18 Sm
A34 17 Sm
A35 16 Sm
A37 17 Sm
A38 17 Sm
A40 17Sm
A41 †
A42 18 Sm
A43 †
A44 †
A45 18 Sm
A46 17 Sm
A47 18 Sm
A48 17 Sm
A49 16 Sm
A50 16 Sm
A53 †
A54 †
A55 †
A56 16 Sm
A57 16 Sm
A59 17 Sm
A61 17 Sm
A62 17 Sm
A63 †
A64 16 Sm
A65 18 Sm
A66 †
A67 16 Sm
A68 17 Sm
A69 †
A70 18 Sm
A72 †
A73 †
A74 16 Sm
A75 18 Sm
A76 18 Sm
A77 †
A78 16 Sm
A79 16 Sm
A80 18 Sm
A81 †
A90 †
A92 †
A93 †
A94 †
A95 †

Belgische Zeemacht

Sud Alouette III
40 Smaldeel, Koksijde
M1 (OT-ZPA)
M2 (OT-ZPB)
M3 (OT-ZPC)

BRAZIL

Forca Aerea Brazileira

Lockheed C-130E Hercules
1 GT 2 Esq Afonsos
C-130 2451
C-130 2452
C-130 2454
C-130 2455
C-130 2456
C-130 2458
C-130 2460

Lockheed KC-130H Hercules
1 GT 1 Esq Afonsos
C-130 2461
C-130 2462

Serial

Lockheed C-130H Hercules
1 GT 1 Esq Afonsos
C-130 2463
C-130 2464
C-130 2465
C-130 2466
C-130 2467
C-130 2468

Lockheed RC-130E Hercules
6 GAV 1 Esq Recife
C-130 2459

CANADA
Canadian Armed Forces

McDonnell Douglas CF-18A Hornet
1st CAG, Sollingen
West Germany
188728
188729
188730
188731
188732
188733
188734
188735
188736
188738
188739
188740
188741
188742
188743
188744
188745
188746
188747
188748
188749
188750
188751
188752
188753
188754
188755
188756
188757
188758
188759
188760
188761
188762
188763
188765
188766
188767
188768
188769
188770

McDonnell Douglas CF-18B Hornet
1st CAG, Sollingen, West Germany
188918
188922
188923

Lockheed C-130E Hercules
426 Sqn, Trenton
429 Sqn, Winnipeg
435 Sqn, Edmonton
436 Sqn, Trenton
130305 426 Sqn
130306 426 Sqn
130307 429 Sqn
130308 426 Sqn
130309
130310 426 Sqn
130311
130313 435 Sqn
130314 436 Sqn
130315 436 Sqn
130316
130317 436 Sqn
130318
130319 435 Sqn
130320 436 Sqn
130321 436 Sqn
130322 436 Sqn
130323 436 Sqn
130324 436 Sqn
130325 436 Sqn
130326 436 Sqn
130327 436 Sqn
130328 436 Sqn

Lockheed C-130H Hercules
130332
130333
130334 435 Sqn
130335 435 Sqn
130336
130337

Canadair CT-133 Silver Star
1st CAG, Sollingen
West Germany
133052
133094
133345
133542

Bell CH-136 Kiowa
444 Sqn, Lahr, West Germany
136224
136225
136226
136227
136228
136229
136230
136232
136233
136234
136236
136237

Boeing CC-137 (B.707-374C)
437 Sqn, Ottawa
13701
13702
13703
13704
13705

Lockheed CP-140 Aurora
404/405/415 Sqns, Greenwood; 407 Sqn, Comox
140101 407 Sqn
140102 404 Sqn
140103 407 Sqn
140104 404 Sqn
140105 404 Sqn
140106 404 Sqn
140107 404 Sqn
140108 405 Sqn
140109 407 Sqn
140110 415 Sqn
140111 415 Sqn
140112 415 Sqn
140113 415 Sqn
140114 415 Sqn
140115 404 Sqn
140116 407 Sqn
140117 405 Sqn
140118 407 Sqn

DHC CC-142 Dash 8
412 Sqn, Lahr West Germany
142801
142802

Canadair CC-144 Challenger
412 Sqn, Lahr
West Germany
144601
144602
144605
144606
144608
144609
144610
144613
144614
144615
144616

CHILE
Fuerza Aérea de Chile

Lockheed C-130H Hercules
Grupo 10, Santiago
995
996

DENMARK
Kongelige Danske Flyvevaabnet

Saab A-35XD Draken
Eskadrille 725, Karup
A001
A002
A004
A005
A006
A007
A008
A009
A010
A011
A012
A014
A017
A018
A019
A020

Saab S-35XD Draken
Eskadrille 729, Karup
AR102

Serial

AR104
AR105
AR106
AR107
AR108
AR109
AR110
AR111
AR112
AR113
AR114
AR115
AR116
AR117
AR118
AR119
AR120

Saab Sk-35XD Draken
*Eskadrille 725, Karup
†Eskadrille 729, Karup
AT151†
AT152*
AT153†
AT154*
AT155†
AT156†
AT157*
AT158†
AT160*

Lockheed C-130H Hercules
Eskadrille 721, Vaerlose
B678
B679
B680

General Dynamics F-16A
Eskadrille 723, Aalborg;
Eskadrille 726, Aalborg;
Eskadrille 727, Skrydstrup;
Eskadrille 730, Skrydstrup
E004
E005
E006
E007
E008
E016
E017
E018
E174 Esk 730
E176 Esk 723
E177 Esk 730
E178 Esk 727
E180 Esk 726
E181 Esk 727
E182 Esk 730
E183 Esk 726
E184 Esk 723
E185 Esk 730
E187 Esk 727
E188 Esk 723
E189 Esk 726
E190 Esk 723
E191 Esk 730
E192 Esk 730
E193 Esk 726
E194 Esk 730
E195 Esk 723
E196 Esk 723
E197 Esk 726
E198 Esk 723
E199 Esk 727
E200 Esk 730
E201 Esk 727
E202 Esk 730
E203 Esk 723
E596 Esk 723
E597 Esk 730
E598 Esk 730
E599 Esk 726
E600 Esk 723
E601 Esk 727
E602 Esk 730
E603 Esk 730
E604 Esk 726
E605 Esk 730
E606 Esk 730
E607 Esk 726
E608 Esk 723
E609 Esk 730
E610 Esk 727
E611 Esk 727

General Dynamics F-16B
ET022
ET197
ET198
ET199
ET204 Esk 727
ET205 Esk 727
ET206 Esk 730
ET207 Esk 730
ET208 Esk 727
ET210 Esk 726
ET612 Esk 730
ET613 Esk 727
ET614 Esk 723
ET615 Esk 727

Grumman Gulfstream III
Eskadrille 721, Vaerlose
F249
F313
F330

Saab 17 Supporter
*Flyveskolen, Avno (FLSK);
†Haerens Flyvetjaeneste (Danish Army), Vandel;
‡Eskadrille 721, Vaerlose
T401 Aalborg Stn Flt
T402 Skystrup Stn Flt
T403 Karup Stn Flt
T404 Karup Stn Flt
T405 Karup Stn Flt
T407 Karup Stn Flt
T408‡
T409‡
T410†
T411†
T412†
T413†
T414†
T415 Aalborg Stn Flt
T417†
T418†
T419‡
T420*
T421*
T422*
T423*
T425*
T426*
T427*
T428*
T429 Aalborg Stn Flt
T430*
T431*
T432*

Sikorsky S-61A
Eskadrille 722, Vaerlose
U240
U275
U276
U277
U278
U279
U280
U481

Sovaernets Flyvetjaeneste (Navy)

Westland Lynx HAS80
Eskadrille 722, Vaerlose
S134
S142
S170
S175
S181
S191
S249
S256

Haerens Flyvetjaeneste (Army)

Hughes 500M
Vandel
H201
H202
H203
H205
H206
H207
H209
H210
H211
H212
H213
H244
H245
H246

ECUADOR

Lockheed C-130H Hercules
FAE-812
FAE-893

EGYPT

Al Quwwat al-Jawwiya Ilmisriya

Lockheed C-130H Hercules
16 Sqn, Cairo West
1271/SU-BAB
1272/SU-BAC
1273/SU-BAD
1274/SU-BAE
1275/SU-BAF
1277/SU-BAI
1278/SU-BAJ

Serial
1279/SU-BAK
1280/SU-BAL
1281/SU-BAM
1282/SU-BAN
1283/SU-BAP
1284/SU-BAQ
1285/SU-BAR
1286/SU-BAS
1287/SU-BAT
1288/SU-BAU
1289/SU-BAV
1290/SU-BEW
1291/SU-BEX
1292/SU-BEY

FRANCE
Armee de l'Air
Aerospatiale TB-30 Epsilon
CEAM, Mont de Marsan;
GE315, Cognac

Serial	
1	315-UA
2	315-UB (CEAM)
3	315-FZ
4	315-UC
5	315-UD
6	315-UE
7	315-UF
8	315-UG
9	315-UH
10	315-UI
11	315-UJ
12	315-UK
13	315-UL
14	315-UM
15	315-UN
16	315-UO
17	315-UP
18	315-UQ
19	315-UR
20	315-US
21	315-UT
22	315-UU
23	315-UV
24	315-UW
25	315-UX
26	315-UY
27	315-UZ
28	315-VA
29	315-VB
30	315-VC
31	315-VD
32	315-VE
33	315-VF
34	315-VG
35	315-VH
36	315-VI
37	315-VJ
38	315-VK
39	315-VL (CEV)
40	315-VM
41	315-VN
42	315-VO
43	315-VP
44	315-VQ
45	315-VR
46	315-VS
47	315-VT
48	315-VU
49	315-VV
50	315-VW
52	315-VX
53	315-VY
54	315-VZ
56	315-WA
58	315-WB
60	315-WC
61	315-WD
62	315-WE
63	315-WF
64	315-WG
65	315-WH
66	315-WI
67	315-WJ
68	315-WK
69	315-WL
70	315-WM
71	315-WN
72	315-WO
73	315-WP
74	315-WQ
75	315-WR
76	315-WS
77	315-WT
78	315-WU
79	315-WV
80	315-WW
81	315-WX
82	315-WY
83	315-WZ
84	315-XA
85	315-XB
86	315-XC
87	315-XD
88	315-XE
89	315-XF
90	315-XG
91	315-XH
92	315-XI
93	315-XJ
94	315-XK
95	315-XL
96	315-XM
97	315-XN
98	315-XO
99	315-XP
100	315-XQ
101	315-XR
102	315-XS
103	315-XT
104	315-XU
105	315-XV
106	315-XW
107	315-XX
108	315-XY
109	315-XZ
110	315-YA
111	315-YB
112	315-YC
113	315-YD
114	315-YE
115	315-YF
116	315-YG
117	315-YH
118	315-YI
119	315-YJ
120	315-YK
121	315-YL
122	315-YM
123	315-YN
124	315-YO
125	315-YP
126	315-YR

Boeing KC-135F/ *KC-135FR
ERV 93, Avord, Istres and Mont de Marsan

Serial
38470/CA*
38471/CB
38472/CC
38474/CE
38475/CF*
312735/93-CG*
312736/CH*
312737/CI*
312738/CJ
312739/CK*
312740/CL*

CAARP CAP-20
GI 312, Salon de Provence

Serial	
1	VU
02	VV
3	VW
4	VX
5	VY
6	VZ

Cessna 310
CEV

Serial	
045	AU
046	AV
185	AU
186	BI
0187	BJ
188	BK
190	BL
192	BM
193	BG
0194	BH
242	AW
244	AX
820	CL

Cessna 404

Serial	
692	DX
815	DY

Cessna 411
CEV

Serial	
6	AD
8	AE
185	AC
248	AB

D-BD Alpha Jet
*Patrouille de France
EC 1/8, EC 2/8 Cazaux;
GE 314, Tours; CEAM (330), Mont de Marsan

Serial		
01		
02	F-ZWRU	
E1	8-NP	2/8
E3	330-BR	
E4	314-LP	
E5	330-BU	
E6	8-NW	2/8
E7	314-LB	
E8		
E9		
E10	8-MM	1/8
E11	8-MP	1/8
E12	8-MC	1/8
E13	314-LH	
E14	F-TERD*(2)	
E15		
E17	8-MR	1/8
E18	314-LM	
E19	8-MK	1/8
E20		
E21	8-NR	2/8
E22	314-LQ	

Overseas Serials

Serial		
E23		
E24		
E25	314-LT	
E26	314-TI	
E27	8-MU	1/8
E28		
E29	314-LV	
E30	314-TP	
E31		
E32	314-LY	
E33	8-NL	2/8
E34	314-LZ	
E35	314-TH	
E36	314-TC	
E37		
E38		
E39	314-LP	
E40		
E41		
E42	314-TI	
E43	314-LI	
E44	(CEV)	
E45	314-TP	
E46	(CEV)	
E47	8-ND	2/8
E48	8-NZ	2/8
E49		
E50	314-LD	
E51	F-TERA* (6)	
E52	F-TERB* (3)	
E53	F-TERC* (8)	
E55	F-TERE* (4)	
E58	F-TERH* (9)	
E59	F-TERI*	
E60		
E61		
E63	F-TERL* (0)	
E64	314-TT	
E65	314-TU	
E66	314-TV	
E67	314-TW	
E68	8-NP	2/8
E69	8-NH	2/8
E70		
E72	314-LF	
E73	330-BT	
E74	8-ND	
E75	314-UF	
E76		
E77	8-NA	2/8
E79	8-NS	2/8
E80		
E81		
E82	8-NX	2/8
E83	8-MJ	1/8
E84	314-LL	
E85	314-LW	
E86	314-LN	
E87		
E88		
E89	314-TG	
E90		
E91		
E92	314-TB	
E93	8-NT	2/8
E94	314-TE	
E95	8-MO	1/8
E96	8-NN	2/8
E97	314-LE	
E98		
E99	8-MW	1/8
E100	(CEV)	

Serial		
E101	8-NG	2/8
E102	8-ME	1/8
E103	314-TO	
E104	314-LC	
E105	314-TF	
E106	314	
E107	F-TERK* (4)	
E108	314-UD	
E109	314-LK	
E110		
E112	8-NQ	2/8
E113		
E114		
E115		
E116	8-NV	2/8
E117	314-TZ	
E118		
E119	314-TR	
E120	314-TJ	
E121	8-NK	2/8
E122	314-UG	
E123	314-LJ	
E124	314-TE	
E125	314-TN	
E126	314-TQ	
E127	8-MY	1/8
E128	314-TX	
E129	8-NB	2/8
E130	8-MT	1/8
E131	314-TY	
E132	314-TL	
E133		
E134	8-NE	2/8
E135	314-TK	
E136	314-LO	
E137	8-MF	1/8
E138		
E139		
E140	314-UB	
E141	8-MQ	1/8
E142	8-MB	1/8
E143		
E144	314-LA	
E145	8-NM	2/8
E146	8-MG	1/8
E147		
E148	8-NJ	2/8
E149		
E150	8-NF	2/8
E151	314-LX	
E152	314-TA	
E153	314-TM	
E154	8-MA	1/8
E155	F-TERF* (5)	
E156		
E157	314-UC	
E158	314-LR	
E159	8-MD	1/8
E160		
E161	8-MN	1/8
E162	314-TA	
E163	314-LS	
E164	8-MS	
E165	314-UA	
E166		
E167	8-MV	1/8
E168		
E169	314-LG	
E170	F-TERM* (2)	
E171	F-TERN* (4)	
E172	F-TERO* (0)	
E173	F-TERP* (1)	

Serial		
E174	F-TERQ* (7)	
E175	314-LU	
E176	8-ML	1/8

Dassault Falcon 20C

CEV
EC.8, Cazaux
*ET.60, Villacoublay
†ET.65, Villacoublay
‡CIFAS 328, Bordeaux
CPIR-339, Luxeuil

1	CV (CEV)
22	CS (CEV)
49	(EC.8)
79	CT (CEV)
86	CG (CEV)
93	N*
104	CW (CEV)
115	339-WL
124	CC (CEV)
131	CD (CEV)
138	CR (CEV)
145	CU (CEV)
167	L*
182	JA‡
188	CX (CEV)
238	M*
260	†
263	(CEV)
268	†
291	P†
309	U*
422	L†
451	339-WN
463	339-WM
483	339-WO

Dassault Falcon 50

5	F-RAFI	EDT 60
147	F-RAFJ	EDT-60

Dassault Mirage IVA/IVP*

EB 1/91, Mont-de-Marsan;
EB 2/91, Cazaux;
EB 1/94 Istres;
EB 2/94, St Dizier; CIFAS 328
Bordeaux-Merignac

1	AP	
2	AA	
4	AC	
5	AD	
6	AE	
7	AF	
8/01*	AG	
9	AH	
11	AJ	328
12	AK	
13*	AL	
14	AM	
15	AN	
16	AO	
18	AQ	
19	AR	2/94
20	AS	
21	AT	
23	AV	
24	AW	2/94
25	AX	
26/02*	AY	
27	AZ	
29	BB	
31	BD	
32	BE	
33	BF	

Serial		
34	BG	2/94
36	BI	1/91
37	BJ	
39	BL	
42	BO	
43	BP	
44	BQ	2/94
45	BR	
46	BS	
47	BT	
48	BU	
49	BV	
51	BX	
52	BY	
53	BZ	
54	CA	1/91
55*	CB	
56	CC	
57	CD	2/94
59	CF	
61	CH	2/91
62	CI	2/91

Dassault Mirage F.1C

EC 5, Orange;
EC 12, Cambrai;
EC 30, Rheims; CEAM (330)
Mont de Marsan

Serial		
2	30-MC	2/30
3	30-MB	2/30
4	5-NJ	1/5
5		
8		
9	30-MR	2/30
10		
12		
14	30-MS	2/30
15	12-YA	1/12
16	30-SO	1/30
17		
18	30-ME	2/30
19		
20	30-FL	3/30
21	30-MI	2/30
22	12-ZD	2/12
23		
24		
25	12-ZC	2/12
26	30-FH	3/30
27		
29	30-FR	3/30
30	30-FA	3/30
31	12-ZA	2/12
32	12-KD	3/12
33	12-ZE	2/12
35		
36	12-ZB	2/12
37	12-YB	1/12
38	30-MG	2/30
39	12-KM	3/12
40		
41	30-SG	1/30
42	30-FK	3/30
43	12-YK	1/12
44	12-KB	3/12
47	12-KH	3/12
48		
49	12-ZF	2/12
50		
52	12-YG	1/12
54	30-SK	1/30
55		
60	12-KA	3/12
62	12-ZH	2/12
63	12-YJ	1/12
64	30-SP	1/30
67		
68	12-ZK	2/12
69	30-FJ	3/30
70	30-FO	3/30
71	12-KJ	3/12
72	30-MO	2/30
73	12-KP	3/12
74	12-ZJ	2/12
75		
76	30-MM	2/30
77	12-KF	3/12
78	30-SF	1/30
79	12-YM	1/12
80	30-FD	3/30
81	12-KK	3/12
82	30-FI	3/30
83	12-YE	1/12
84	12-YO	1/12
85		
87	30-SJ	1/30
90	12-YN	1/12
100	30-MQ	2/30
101	30-FE	3/30
102	30-SD	1/30
103	12-YC	1/12
201	330-AK	
202	5-NE	1/5
203	5-NC	1/5
204		
205		
206	5-OA	2/5
207	30-SM	1/30
208	5-NO	1/5
210	30-SE	1/30
211	5-NN	1/5
213	12-ZR	2/12
214	5-OG	2/5
216	5-OL	2/5
217	30-MK	2/30
218	5-OM	2/5
219	12-KI	3/12
220	5-OP	2/5
221	30-MP	2/30
223		
224	5-OI	2/5
225	330-AO	
226	5-OD	2/5
227	30-SI	1/30
228	5-OH	2/5
229	12-YD	1/12
230	330-AP	
231	12-YH	1/12
232	5-OC	2/5
233	5-NM	1/5
234	30-SN	1/30
235		
236		
237	5-ND	1/5
238	5-NR	1/5
239	30-FC	3/30
240	12-YP	1/12
241	30-SA	1/30
242	30-MF	2/30
243	12-KC	3/12
244	5-OQ	2/5
245	30-FB	3/30
246	5-OK	2/5
247	5-NI	1/5
248	12-ZQ	2/12
249	30-SQ	1/30
251	12-ZP	2/12
252	5-ON	2/5
253		
254	12-ZM	2/12
255	5-NQ	1/5
256	12-KO	3/12
257	12-YI	1/12
258	12-YL	1/12
259	30-SC	1/30
260	5-OB	2/5
261	12-ZI	2/12
262	30-MH	2/30
264	12-KN	3/12
265	5-NB	1/5
266	12-KG	3/12
267	5-NM	1/5
268	5-OO	2/5
270	12-KE	3/12
271	30-FM	3/30
272	5-NG	1/5
273	12-ZN	2/12
274	5-OF	2/5
275	5-NH	1/5
277		
278	5-OE	2/5
279	5-NK	1/5
280	5-NF	1/5
281	5-AU	3/5
282	5-AW	3/5
283	12-ZO	2/12

Dassault Mirage F.1CR

ER 33 Strasbourg CEAM
EAA601 Chateaudun (330),
Mont de Marsan; CEV, Istres

Serial		
601	(CEV)	
602	(CEV)	
603	33-NR	2/33
604	33-NK	2/33
605	33-NF	2/33
606	33-ND	2/33
607	33-CP	1/33
608	33-CN	1/33
609	33-CC	1/33
610	33-CH	1/33
611	33-CA	1/33
612	33-NJ	2/33
613	33-CE	1/33
614	33-CQ	1/33
615	33-NB	2/33
616	33-NG	2/33
617	33-NO	2/33
618	330-AA	
619	330-AC	
620	33-CJ	1/33
621		
622	33-CR	1/33
623	33-CM	1/33
624	33-NE	2/33
625	33-NH	2/33
626		
627	33-NI	2/33
628	33-CF	1/33
629	33-CG	1/33
630		
631	33-CB	
632	33-NM	2/33
633	33-NN	2/33
634		
635	33-NP	601
636	33-NQ	2/33

Serial		
637	330-AB	
638	330-AR	
639	33-NA	2/33
640	33-NB	601
641		
642		
643	33-CO	1/33
644		
645		
646	33-NH	2/33
647	33-NC	601
648		
649	33-CF	1/33
650	33-CG	1/33
651		1/33
652	33-CK	1/33
653		
654		
655		
656		
657		
658	33-NT	2/33
659		2/33
660	33-CI	1/33
661	33-CL	1/33
662		
663	33-NC	2/33
664	33-NS	2/33

Dassault Mirage 2000C
EC 1/2, ECT 2/2, EC 3/2, Dijon;
CEAM (330), Mont de Marsan

Serial		
01		
03		(CEV)
04		
1	2-EP	(CEV)
2		
3	330-AV	
4	330-AW	
5	330-AS	
6	330-AY	
8	2-EC	1/2
9	2-ED	1/2
10	2-EE	1/2
11	2-EF	1/2
12	2-EH	1/2
13	2-EI	1/2
14	2-EJ	1/2
15	2-EK	1/2
16	2-EL	1/2
17	2-EM	1/2
18	2-EN	1/2
19	2-LA	3/2
20	2-LE	3/2
21	2-LF	3/2
22	2-LG	3/2
23	2-LH	3/2
24	2-LI	3/2
25	2-LK	3/2
27	2-LM	3/2
28	2-LN	3/2
29	2-LO	3/2
30	2-EO	1/2
31	2-LP	3/2
32	2-EP	1/2
33	2-LQ	3/2
34	2-FL	2/2
35	2-FM	2/2
36	2-LB	3/2
37	2-LC	3/2
38	330-AT	
39		
40		
41		
42		
43		
44		
45		
46		
47		
48		
49		
50		

Dassault Mirage 2000B
CEAM, Mont de Marsan (330);
ECT 2/2, Dijon;
EC 3/2, Dijon

Serial		
501	2-EQ	(CEV)
502	330-AZ	
503	(CEAM)	
504	2-FA	2/2
505	2-FB	2/2
506	2-FC	2/2
507	2-LC	3/2
508	2-FE	2/2
509	2-FF	2/2
510	2-FG	2/2
511	2-FH	2/2
512	2-FI	2/2
513	2-FJ	2/2
514	2-FK	2/2
515		

Dassault Rafale

Serial	
01	AMD-BA

DHC6 Twin Otter
*ET 63 Toulouse;
ET 65 Villacoublay;
†GAM 56 Evreux

Serial	
292	OW†
296	OV
298	OY†
300	OZ†
603	65-CY‡
730	65-CA‡
742	65-CB‡
743	63-CZ*
745	63-VY*
786	63-VV*
790	63-VW*

Douglas DC8F
*EE.51 Evreux
†ET3/60 Charles de Galle

Serial	
45570	F-RAFE*
45819	F-RAFC†
45820	F-RAFA†
46013	F-RAFG†
46063	F-RAFD†
46130	F-RAFF†

Embraer Xingu
* GE 319 Avord;
† ETE 43 Bordeaux;
‡ETE 44 Aix-en-Provence

Serial	
054	YX
064	YY*
072	YA*
073	YB*
075	YC*
076	YD*
078	YE*
080	YF*
082	YG*
084	YH*
086	YI*
089	YJ*
091	YK*
092	YL*
095	YM*
096	YN*
098	YO*
099	YP*
101	YR†
102	YS†
103	YT*
105	YU*
107	YV*
108	YW‡
111	YQ*

Morane Saulnier Paris
ETE 41 Metz;
ETE 43 Bordeaux;
ETE 44 Aix-en-Provence;
ET 65 Villacoublay; CEAM (330) Mont de Marsan

Serial		
1	330-DB	
19	41-AR	
23	65-LA	
24		
25	41-AP	
26		
27	65-LZ	
29	43-BB	
30	65-LI	
34		
35	43-BC	
36	330-DO	
38	41-AT	
44	65-LD	
45		
51		
53	DD	
54	65-LK	
56	43-BD	
57	65-LP	
58	65-LB	
59	65-LV	
60	65-LQ	
61	65-LY	
62		
65	65-LF	
68	NB	(CEV)
70		
71	65-LZ	
73	41-AS	
75		
77	DE	(GE 314)
78	65-LU	
79	NL	(CEV)
80		
81	65-LL	
83	NC	(CEV)
91	65-LT	
92	330-DA	
93	65-LJ	
94	65-LH	
95		
97	43-BA	
100	NG	(CEV)
113	NI	(CEV)
114	NJ	(CEV)
115	OV	(CEV)
116	ON	(CEV)
117	AZ	(CEV)
118	NQ	(CEV)
119	NL	(CEV)

Serial

Nord 262 Fregate
†EdC 70 Chateaudun;
*ET 65 Villacoublay;
GE 316 Toulouse;
CEAM (330) Mont de Marsan;
CEV, Istres

Serial		
01	DM	(CEV)
3	OH	(CEV)
55	MH	(CEV)
58	MJ	(CEV)
64	AA*	
66	AB*	
67	MI	(CEV)
68	AC*	
76	316-DA	
77	AK*	
78	AF*	
80	AW*	
81	AH*	
83	316-DB	
86	316-DD	
87	316-DC	
88	AL*	
89	330-IR	
91	MB†	
92	316-DE	
93	AP*	
94	AU*	
95	AR*	
105	AE*	
106	MA†	
107	AX*	
108	AG*	
109	AM*	
110	AS*	(ETE 44)

Nord 2501 Noratlas
ET 63 Toulouse;
EE54: Metz*

Serial		
18	CR	(CEV)
28*		
41*		
66*		
114	316-FQ	
196	316-FO	
201	63-VJ	

Transall C-160
†Transall C-160 ELINT
ET 61 Orleans (C160A/F);
ET 64 Evreux (C160NG)

Serial		
A02	61-MI	
A04	61-BI	(CEV)
A06	61-ZB	
F1	61-MA	
F2	61-MB	
F3	61-MC	
F4	61-MD	
F5	61-ME	
F11	61-MF	
F12	61-MG	
F13	61-MH	
F14	61-MI	
F15	61-MJ	
F16	61-MK	
F17	61-ML	
F18	61-MM	
F42	61-MN	
F43	61-MO	
F44	61-MP	
F45	61-MQ	
F46	61-MR	
F47	61-MS	
F48	61-MT	
F49	61-MU	
F50	61-MV	
F51	61-MW	
F52	61-MX	
F53	61-MY	
F54	61-MZ	
F55	61-ZC	
F86	61-ZD	
F87	61-ZE	
F88	61-ZF	
F89	61-ZG	
F90	61-ZH	
F91	61-ZI	
F92	61-ZJ	
F93	61-ZK	
F94	61-ZL	
F95	61-ZM	
F96	61-ZN	
F97	61-ZO	
F98	61-ZP	
F99	61-ZQ	
F100	61-ZR	
F153	61-ZS	
F154	61-ZT	
F155	61-ZU	
F157	61-ZW	
F158	61-ZX	
F159	61-ZY	
F160	61-ZZ	
F201	64-GA	
F202	64-GB	
F203	64-GC	
F204	64-GD	
F205	64-GE	
F206	64-GF	
F207	64-GG	
F208	64-GH	
F210	64-GJ	
F211	64-GK	
F212	64-GL	
F213	64-GM	
F214	64-GN	
F215	64-GO	
F216†	F-ZJUP	
F217	64-GQ	
F218	64-GR	
F219	64-GS	
F220†	F-ZJUS	
F221†	F-ZJUU	
F222	64-GV	
F223	64-GW	
F224	64-GX	
(Command Post Prototype)		
F225	64-GY	
F226	64-GZ	
F227	64-GP	
F228†	F-ZJUY	
F229†	F-ZJUC	
F230†	F-ZJUA	
F231†	F-ZJUB	
F232†		

SEPECAT
Jaguar A
EC 3 Nancy; EC 1/7, 2/7, 3/7 St Dizier; EC 4/7 Istres;
EC 1/11, 2/11, 3/11 Toul;
EC 4/11 Bordeaux;
CEAM (330) Mont de Marsan

Serial		
A1		
A2	7-NK	4/7
A3		(CEV)
A5	3-XP	3/3
A7	3-XK	3/3
A8	3-XL	3/3
A9		
A10	3-XH	3/3
A11	3-XA	3/3
A12	11-YH	4/11
A13	3-XM	3/3
A14	11-MG	2/11
A15	7-IE	3/7
A16	3-XJ	3/3
A17	7-HE	1/7
A19	7-II	3/7
A20	7-NN	4/7
A21	7-IA	3/7
A22	7-HC	1/7
A23	7-HO	1/7
A24	7-HH	1/7
A25	7-IB	3/7
A26	7-HQ	1/7
A27	7-IQ	3/7
A28	3-XC	3/3
A29	7-HA	1/7
A31	7-NJ	4/7
A32	7-NL	4/7
A33	7-IH	3/7
A34		
A35	7-HG	1/7
A36		
A37	7-PA	2/7
A38	7-IC	3/7
A39	7-IP	3/7
A40	7-NF	4/7
A41	7-ND	4/7
A43	7-HD	1/7
A44	7-ID	3/7
A46	7-IM	3/7
A47	7-HP	1/7
A48	7-NH	4/7
A49	7-IM	3/7
A50	11-YM	4/11
A53	7-PG	2/7
A54	7-HM	1/7
A55	7-HN	1/77
A56	7-IK	3/7
A58	7-NM	4/7
A59	7-HB	1/7
A60	7-HF	1/7
A61	7-IF	3/7
A64	3-XB	3/3
A65	7-IO	3/7
A66	7-NC	4/7
A67	7-NB	4/7
A70	7-NI	4/7
A72	7-HJ	1/7
A73	7-PB	2/7
A74	7-NA	4/7
A75	3-XI	3/3
A76	7-HL	1/7
A79	7-NP	4/7
A80	7-IN	3/7
A82	11-YB	4/11
A83	11-YL	4/11
A84	11-YJ	4/11
A85		
A86		
A87	11-RX	3/11
A88	11-RQ	3/11
A89	11-MM	2/11
A90	11-MR	2/11
A91	11-YG	4/11
A92	11-RS	3/11
A93	11-MV	2/11
A94		
A95	11-MQ	2/11
A96	11-RC	3/11

Serial		
A97		
A98	11-MT	2/11
A99	11-EI	1/11
A100	11-YK	4/11
A101	11-RK	3/11
A103	11-EB	1/11
A104	11-MO	2/11
A107	11-YA	4/11
A108	11-EN	1/11
A110	11-MD	2/11
A112		
A113	11-MW	2/11
A115	11-RH	3/11
A117	11-MH	2/11
A118	11-YI	4/11
A119		
A120		
A121		
A122	11-EA	1/11
A123		
A124	11-YE	4/11
A126	11-YC	4/11
A127	11-EJ	1/11
A128	11-RI	3/11
A129		
A130	11-MC	2/11
A131		(CEV)
A133	11-EF	1/11
A135	11-RJ	3/11
A136		
A137	11-ES	1/11
A138	11-YF	4/11
A139	11-RW	3/11
A140	11-YO	4/11
A141	11-RN	3/11
A142		
A143		
A144		
A145	11-RG	3/11
A146	330-AI	
A148	11-YN	4/11
A149	11-EK	1/11
A150	11-YK	4/11
A151	11-YD	4/11
A152		
A153	11-EX	1/11
A154	11-RT	3/11
A155		
A156	11-EH	1/11
A157		
A158	11-EU	1/11
A159	11-EV	1/11
A160	(CEAM)	(CEV)

SEPECAT Jaguar E

Serial		
E1		(CEV)
E2	3-XO	3/3
E3	7-PN	2/7
E4	7-HK	1/7
E5	7-IJ	3/7
E6	11-ME	2/11
E7	7-PI	2/7
E8	7-PP	2/7
E9	7-PH	2/7
E10	11-YY	4/11
E11		
E12	7-IJ	3/7
E13	7-PD	2/7
E15	11-YZ	4/11
E16	7-HI	1/7
E17		(CEV)
E18	7-NG	4/7
E19	11-MB	2/11
E20	11-RV	3/11
E21	7-PO	2/7
E22	7-PC	2/7
E23		
E24	11-EM	1/11
E25	7-IL	3/7
E27	11-MA	2/11
E28	7-PK	2/7
E29		
E30		
E31	11-RF	3/11
E32	7-NE	4/7
E33		
E35	7-PF	2/7
E36		
E37	7-PQ	2/7
E38	7-PM	2/7
E39	11-YX	4/11
E40	11-EG	1/11

Aeronavale/Marine

Morane Saulnier Paris

ES 57, Landivisiau

32
33
40
41
42
46
47
48
85
87
88

Nord 262 Fregate

ES 2, Lann Bihoue;
ES 3, Hyeres;
ES 11, Le Bourget;
ES 55, Aspretto;
ES 56, Nimes-Garons

16 (2S)
28 (11S)
43
45
46 (56S)
51 (56S)
52 (56S)
53 (56S)
59 (2S)
60 (56S)
61 (3S)
62 (3S)
63 (2S)
65 (3S)
69 (56S)
70 (3S)
71 (56S)
72 (56S)
73 (56S)
75 (2S)
79 (3S)
100 (56S)
102 (4S)
104 (11S)

SA.321G Super Frelon

ES 27, Mururoa;
32 F, Lanveoc;
33 F, San Mandrier

101 (27S)
102 (32F)
105 (33F)
106 (27S)
118 (32F)
120 (32F)
122 (32F)
134 (32F)
137 (32F)
141 (32F)
144 (32F)
148 (33F)
149 (32F)
160 (32F)
162 (32F)
163 (33F)
164 (32F)
165 (32F)

Breguet 1050 Alizé

4F, Lann Bihoue;
6F, Nimes-Garons;
ES 20, Frejus;
ES 59, Hyeres

11 (4F)
12
17
22 (6F)
24
25 (4F)
26 (59S)
28
30 (6F)
31 (59S)
33
36 (6F)
41 (59S)
43 (6F)
44
45
47 (6F)
48 (4F)
50 (59S)
51 (4F)
52 (20S)
53
55 (59S)
56 (59S)
59 (6F)
60
64 (59S)
65 (6F)
68
73 (6F)
76 (4F)
87 (6F)

Breguet 1150 Atlantic

*21F/22F, Nimes-Garons;
†23F/24F, Lann Bihoue

01*
04*
1*
3*
5†
7*
9
11*
13*
15*
17*
21†
23†
24†

Serial
25
27*
31†
35*
38*
41*
44†
45*
47*
48
49*
50†
51
52*
53*
54*
55†
56
57*
61*
63†
65†
66†
67*
68
ANG.01
ANG.02
ANG.03
ANG.04

Dassault Etendard IVM
*16F, Landivisiau;
†ES 59, Hyeres

2*
3†
4*
5*
6*
7*
9*
11†
13†
14†
15†
16†
21*
22*
26†
29†
30*
32*
34†
36†
37†
40†
41†
42
52†
53†
56*
57†
59†
60*
62*
63*
66*

Dassault Etendard IVP
16F Landivisiau

101
107
108
109

Serial

114
115
117
118
120

Dassault Super Etendard
*11F, Landivisiau;
†14F, Landivisiau;
‡17F, Hyeres

1‡
2*
3‡
4
5
6†
7*
8†
9*
10*
11*
12*
13†
14‡
15†
16†
17†
18†
19
20
21
23‡
24†
25†
26‡*
27
28*
29‡
30
31†
32†
33‡
34
35*
37*
38*
39
40*
41†
42
43†
44†
45*
46‡
47*
48†
49‡
50†
51
52‡
53†
54†
55*
57‡
59‡
60*
61*
62‡
63†
64*
65‡
66†
68‡

Serial

69*
71*

Dassault Falcon 10(MER)
†ES3 Hyeres;
*ES 57 Landivisiau

32†
101*
129*
133*
143†
185†

Dassault Falcon Guardian
†ES 9 Noumea;
*ES 12 Papeete

48*
65†
72*
77†
80*

Embraer Xingu
ES 11, Le Bourget;
ES 20, Frejus;
ES 52, Lann Bihoue;
ERC, Cuers

55
65
66 (ERC)
67 (52S)
68 (52S)
69 (52S)
70 (52S)
71 (52S)
74 (52S)
77 (11S)
79 (52S)
81 (52S)
83 (52S)
85
87 (52S)
90 (52S)

LTV F-8E (FN) Crusader
12F, Landivisiau

1
2
3
4
5
6
7
8
10
11
12
17
18
19
23
25
27
28
29
33
34
35
37
39
40
41
42

Serial

Piper Navajo
ES 2, Lann Bihoue; ES 3, Hyeres
ES 11, Le Bourget
ES 20 Frejus
227 (2S)
232 (2S)
903 (3S)
904 (3S)
906 (3S)
912 (3S)
914 (3S)
916 (3S)
925 (2S)
927 (20S)
929 (2S)
931 (11S)

Westland Lynx HAS2 (FN)*; HAS4 (FN)†
31F, San Mandrier;
34F, Lanveoc;
35F, Lanveoc; ES 20 St Raphael
260* (20S)
262* (34F)
263* (34F)
264*
265*
266* (34F)
267*
268*
269 (34F)
270* (34F)
271* (34F)
272* (20S)
273*
274* (34F)
275* (34F)
276* (34F)
278* (34F)
621*
622* (34F)
623* (34F)
624*
625* (34F)
626* (34F)
627*
801† (20S)
802† (34F)
803†
804† (35F)
805†
806† (34F)
807† (34F)
808† (34F)
809†
810† (31F)
811†
812† (31F)
813†
814† (34F)

GREECE
Elliniki Aeroporia
Lockheed C-130H Hercules
356 Mira, Elefsis
741
742
743
744
745
746
747
748
749
750
751
752

ISRAEL
Heyl ha'avir
Lockheed C-130H Hercules
4X-FBA/102
4X-FBB/006
4X-FBC/305
Lockheed C-130E Hercules
4X-FBD/311
4X-FBE/304
4X-FBF/301
4X-FBG/310
4X-FBH/312
4X-FBI/314
4X-FBK/318
4X-FBL/313
4X-FBM/316
4X-FBN/307
4X-FBO/420
4X-FBP/208
Lockeed C-130H Hercules
4X-FBQ/420
4X-FBS/427
4X-FBT/435
4X-FBU/448
4X-FBW/436
4X-FBX/428
Lockheed KC-130H Hercules
4X-FBY/422
4X-FBZ/445

ITALY
Aeronautica Militare Italiano
Aeritalia G222
*46 Brigata Aerea, Pisa
†14°Stormo, Practica di Mare;
‡RSV, Practica di Mare
MM62101‡ RS-36
MM62102* 46-20
MM62104* 46-91
MM62105* 46-82
MM62107†
MM62108* 46-30
MM62109‡ 96
MM62110* 46-81
MM62111* 46-83
MM62112* 46-85
MM62113* 46-34
MM62114* 46-80
MM62115* 46-22
MM62116* 46-35
MM62117* 46-25
MM62118* 46-24
MM62119* 46-21
MM62120* 46-90
MM62121* 46-86
MM62122* 46-23
MM62123* 46-28
MM62124* 46-88
MM62125* 46-87
MM62126* 46-26
MM62127* 46-27
MM62128‡ RS-34
MM62129* RS-29
MM62130* 46-31
MM62132* 46-32
MM62133* 46-28
MM62134* 46-33
MM62143* 46-36
MM62144* 46-98

Aeritalia G222TCM
MM62103‡ RS-35
MM62135‡ RS-21
MM62136* 46-97
MM62137* 46-95
MM62138† 46

Aeritalia G222RM
14° Stormo, Practica di Mare
MM62139 14-20
MM62140 14-21
MM62141 14-22
MM62142

Aermacchi MB339
*Frecce Tricolori
† Brigata Aerea, Lecce; ‡14° Stormo, Practica di Mare
RSV, Practica di Mare

MM54438‡ 14-32
MM54439* 15
MM54440† 00
MM54441 61-71
MM54442 RS-45
MM54443† 50
MM54445 RS-49
MM54446 RS-50
MM54447† 61-02
MM54448† 61-03
MM54449† 04
MM54450‡ 14-30
MM54451‡ 61-86
MM54452‡
MM54453† 61-05
MM54454† 61-73
MM54455† 61-07
MM54456† 10
MM54457† 61-11
MM54458† 61-12
MM54459† 61-13
MM54460† 14
MM54461† 61-15
MM54462† 16
MM54463† 61-17
MM54464† 20
MM54465† 21
MM54467† 23
MM54468† 24
MM54469† 25
MM54470† 61-26
MM54471† 27
MM54472† 61-30
MM54473* 17
MM54474* 6
MM54475* 3
MM54476* 1
MM54477* 4
MM54478* 14
MM54479* 9
MM54480* 8
MM54481* 7
MM54482* 10

Serial	
MM54483*	12
MM54484*	2
MM54485*	1
MM54486*	5
MM54487‡	14-31
MM54488†	32
MM54489†	33
MM54490†	34
MM54491†	35
MM54492†	36
MM54493†	37
MM54494†	40
MM54495†	41
MM54496†	61-42
MM54497†	43
MM54498†	44
MM54499†	45
MM54500†	46
MM54501†	61-47
MM54503†	51
MM54504†	52
MM54505†	53
MM54506†	54
MM54507†	55
MM54508†	61-56
MM54509†	61-57
MM54510†	60
MM54511†	61
MM54512†	61-62
MM54513†	63
MM54514†	64
MM54515†	61-65
MM54516†	66
MM54517†	67
MM54518†	61-70
MM54532	61-71
MM54533†	61-72
MM54534†	61-73
MM54535†	74
MM54536*	9
MM54537*	0
MM54538†	61-75
MM54539†	61-76
MM54540†	61-77
MM54541‡	14-30
MM54542†	61-81
MM54543†	61-82
MM54544†	61-83
MM54545†	61-84
MM54546†	61-85
MM54547†	61-87
MM54548†	61-90
MM54549†	61-91
MM54550†	61-92
MM54551*	6
MM54552*	1

Dassault Falcon 50
31° Stormo, Roma Ciampino
MM62020
MM62021

Grumman Gulfstream III
31° Stormo, Roma Ciampino
MM62022
MM62025

Lockheed C-130H Hercules
46 Brigata Aerea, Pisa

Serial	
MM61988	46-02
MM61989	46-03
MM61990	46-04
MM61991	46-05
MM61992	46-06
MM61993	46-07
MM61994	46-08
MM61995	46-09
MM61997	46-11
MM61998	46-12
MM61999	46-13
MM62001	46-15

McDonnell Douglas DC9-32
31° Stormo, Roma Ciampino
MM62012
MM62013

Panavia Tornado
*TTTE RAF Cottesmore
6° Stormo, Ghedi
36° Stormo, Giola del Colle
RSV, Practica di Mare

Serial	
MM586	
MM7001	RS-01
MM7002*	I-92
MM7003*	I-93
MM7004*	I-90
MM7005*	I-91
MM7006	6-03
MM7007*	I-94
MM7008	6-02
MM7009	6-04
MM7010	6-06
MM7011	6-10
MM7012	6-11
MM7013	6-05
MM7014	6-12
MM7015	6-01
MM7016	6-23
MM7017	6-14
MM7018	6-24
MM7019	6-22
MM7020	6-21
MM7021	6-30
MM7022	6-26
MM7023	6-27
MM7024	6-32
MM7025	6-31
MM7026	6-33
MM7027	6-32
MM7028	6-34
MM7029	6-35
MM7030	6-36
MM7031	6-37
MM7033	6-42
MM7034	6-41
MM7035	36-30
MM7036	36-31
MM7037	
MM7038	36-33
MM7039	36-32
MM7040	36-35
MM7041	36-51
MM7042	36-50
MM7043	36-36
MM7044	36-42
MM7046	36-34
MM7047	36-37
MM7048	36-54
MM7049	36-40
MM7050	36-44
MM7051	36-43
MM7052	36-41
MM7053	36-45
MM7054	36-46
MM7055	36-47
MM7056	36-52
MM7057	
MM7058	
MM7059	36-53
MM7060	
MM7061	
MM7062	6-53
MM7063	6-52
MM7064	6-54
MM7065	6-55
MM7066	6-56
MM7067	RS-24
MM7068	6-60
MM7069	6-61
MM7070	6-62
MM7071	6-63
MM7072	6-64
MM7073	
MM7074	
MM7075	
MM7076	
MM7077	
MM7078	
MM7079	
MM7080	
MM7081	
MM7082	
MM7083	
MM7084	
MM7085	
MM7086	
MM7087	
MM7088	
MM55000*	I-42
MM55001*	I-40
MM55002*	I-41
MM55003*	I-43
MM55004*	I-44
MM55005	36-56
MM55006	6-15
MM55007	36-55
MM55008	6-20
MM55009	6-16
MM55010	6-50
MM55011	6-51

Piaggio-Douglas PD-808; †PD-808-GE; *PD-808-RM; ‡PD-808-TA
14° Gruppo, Treviso-San Angelo; 31° Stormo, Roma-Ciampino
RSV, Practica di Mare

Serial	
MM577‡	RS-08
MM578‡	RS-05
MM61948	(31)
MM61949	(31)
MM61950	(31)
MM61951	(31)
MM61952‡	(14)
MM61953‡	(31)
MM61954‡	14-52
MM61955†	(14)
MM61956‡	14-51
MM61957‡	14-57
MM61958†	(14)
MM61959†	(14)
MM61960†	(14)
MM61961†	(14)
MM61962†	(14)
MM61963†	(14)
MM62014*	14-53
MM62015*	14-54
MM62016*	14-55
MM62017*	14-56

Serial

JORDAN
Al Quwwat Al-Jawwiya
Alamalakiya Al-Urduniya
Lockheed
C-130B Hercules
3 Sqn, Amman
340
341
Lockheed
C-130H Hercules
3 Sqn, Amman
344
345
346
347

KUWAIT
Kuwait Air Force
McDonnell Douglas
DC9-32
KAF 320
KAF 321
Lockheed
L100-30 Hercules
KAF 322
KAF 323
KAF 324
KAF 325

LUXEMBOURG
NATO Boeing E-3A
NAEWF, Geilenkirchen
LX-N90442
LX-N90443
LX-N90444
LX-N90445
LX-N90446
LX-N90447
LX-N90448
LX-N90449
LX-N90450
LX-N90451
LX-N90452
LX-N90453
LX-N90454
LX-N90455
LX-N90456
LX-N90457
LX-N90458
LX-N90459
Boeing 707-329C
NAEWF, Geilenkirchen
LX-N19996
LX-N20198
LX-N20199

NETHERLANDS
Koninklijke Luchmacht
Fokker F-27-100
Friendship
334 Sqn, Soesterberg
C-1
C-2
C-3
Fokker F-27-300M
Troopship
334 Sqn, Soesterberg
C-4
C-5
C-6
C-7
C-8
C-9
C-10

Serial

C-11
C-12
F-27-200MPA
M-1
M-2
General Dynamics
F-16A/F16B*
306 Sqn, Volkel; 311 Sqn, Volkel; 312 Sqn, Volkel; 313 Sqn, Twente; 315 Sqn, Twente;
322 Sqn, Leeuwarden;
323 Sqn, Leeuwarden
J002
J003
J004
J005
J006
J007
J008
J013*
J014*
J015*
J016*
J017*
J018
J019
J020
J021
J022
J023
J024
J054
J055
J056
J057
J058
J059
J060
J061
J062
J063
J064
J065
J109*
J110*
J111*
J112*
J113*
J114
J115
J116
J117
J118
J119
J120
J135 315 Sqn
J136 315 Sqn
J137 315 Sqn
J138 315 Sqn
J139 315 Sqn
J140
J141
J142*
J143*
J144*
J145*
J146*
J192 311 Sqn
J193 311 Sqn
J194 311 Sqn
J195 315 Sqn
J196 311 Sqn
J197 311 Sqn

Serial

J198 315 Sqn
J199 315 Sqn
J200 315 Sqn
J201 315 Sqn
J202 315 Sqn
J203 315 Sqn
J204 315 Sqn
J205 315 Sqn
J206 315 Sqn
J207 315 Sqn
J208* 315 Sqn
J209* 315 Sqn
J210* 315 Sqn
J211* 315 Sqn
J212 323 Sqn
J213 323 Sqn
J214 323 Sqn
J215 322 Sqn
J218 322 Sqn
J219 322 Sqn
J220 322 Sqn
J221 322 Sqn
J222 322 Sqn
J223 322 Sqn
J226 322 Sqn
J228 322 Sqn
J229 322 Sqn
J230 322 Sqn
J231 323 Sqn
J232 323 Sqn
J234 323 Sqn
J235 323 Sqn
J236 323 Sqn
J238 322 Sqn
J239 322 Sqn
J240 322 Sqn
J241 322 Sqn
J242 322 Sqn
J243 322 Sqn
J245 323 Sqn
J246 323 Sqn
J247 323 Sqn
J248 323 Sqn
J249 323 Sqn
J250 323 Sqn
J251 322 Sqn
J253 323 Sqn
J254 323 Sqn
J255 323 Sqn
J256 323 Sqn
J257 322 Sqn
J258 311 Sqn
J259* 323 Sqn
J260* 322 Sqn
J261* 322 Sqn
J262* 323 Sqn
J263* 323 Sqn
J264* 322 Sqn
J265* 323 Sqn
J266* 323 Sqn
J267* 323 Sqn
J268* 323 Sqn
J269* 323 Sqn
J270* 323 Sqn
J358 315 Sqn
J359 315 Sqn
J360 315 Sqn
J361 315 Sqn
J362 315 Sqn
J363 315 Sqn
J364 315 Sqn
J365 315 Sqn
J366 315 Sqn
J367 315 Sqn

Serial	
J368*	315 Sqn
J369*	315 Sqn
J616	311 Sqn
J617	311 Sqn
J618	311 Sqn
J619	311 Sqn
J620	311 Sqn
J622	311 Sqn
J623	311 Sqn
J624	311 Sqn
J625	311 Sqn
J627	306 Sqn
J628	306 Sqn
J630	306 Sqn
J631	306 Sqn
J632	306 Sqn
J633	306 Sqn
J635	306 Sqn
J636	306 Sqn
J637	306 Sqn
J638	306 Sqn
J639	306 Sqn
J640	306 Sqn
J641	306 Sqn
J642	306 Sqn
J643	306 Sqn
J644	306 Sqn
J645	306 Sqn
J646	306 Sqn
J647	306 Sqn
J648	306 Sqn
J649*	306 Sqn
J650*	323 Sqn
J651*	311 Sqn
J652*	311 Sqn
J653*	306 Sqn
J654*	311 Sqn
J655*	306 Sqn
J656*	312 Sqn
J657*	311 Sqn
J819*	
J820*	
J821*	
J822*	
J823*	
J824	
J825	
J826	
J827	
J828	
J829	
J830	
J864	312 Sqn
J866	312 Sqn
J867	312 Sqn
J868	312 Sqn
J869	312 Sqn
J870	312 Sqn
J871	312 Sqn
J872	312 Sqn
J873	312 Sqn
J874	312 Sqn
J875	312 Sqn
J876	312 Sqn
J877	312 Sqn
J878	312 Sqn
J879	312 Sqn
J880	312 Sqn
J881	312 Sqn
J882*	312 Sqn
J884*	312 Sqn
J885*	315 Sqn
J901*	
J902*	

Serial	
J918*	
J919*	
J920*	
J921*	
J922*	
J923	
J924	
J925	
J926	
J927	
J928	
J929	

Northrop NF-5A
313 Sqn, Twente;
314 Sqn, Eindhoven;
316 Sqn, Gilze-Rijen

K3001	313 Sqn
K3004	313 Sqn
K3005	313 Sqn
K3008	314 Sqn
K3011	313 Sqn
K3012	313 Sqn
K3013	314 Sqn
K3014	313 Sqn
K3015	314 Sqn
K3016	316 Sqn
K3018	316 Sqn
K3021	314 Sqn
K3023	316 Sqn
K3024	313 Sqn
K3025	313 Sqn
K3027	316 Sqn
K3030	313 Sqn
K3031	316 Sqn
K3032	313 Sqn
K3033	314 Sqn
K3036	314 Sqn
K3039	313 Sqn
K3041	313 Sqn
K3042	313 Sqn
K3044	314 Sqn
K3045	313 Sqn
K3046	316 Sqn
K3047	316 Sqn
K3048	313 Sqn
K3049	314 Sqn
K3051	313 Sqn
K3052	316 Sqn
K3054	316 Sqn
K3055	314 Sqn
K3056	313 Sqn
K3058	313 Sqn
K3060	314 Sqn
K3061	314 Sqn
K3062	313 Sqn
K3063	316 Sqn
K3066	316 Sqn
K3067	314 Sqn
K3069	314 Sqn
K3070	314 Sqn
K3072	316 Sqn
K3073	314 Sqn

Northrop NF-5B
313 Sqn, Twente;
314 Sqn, Eindhoven;
316 Sqn, Gilze-Rijen

Serial	
K4001	313 Sqn
K4005	316 Sqn
K4006	316 Sqn
K4007	316 Sqn
K4009	316 Sqn
K4011	316 Sqn
K4012	316 Sqn
K4013	313 Sqn
K4014	316 Sqn
K4015	314 Sqn
K4016	313 Sqn
K4017	314 Sqn
K4019	314 Sqn
K4020	314 Sqn
K4021	314 Sqn
K4024	316 Sqn
K4025	316 Sqn
K4026	313 Sqn
K4027	316 Sqn
K4028	316 Sqn
K4029	316 Sqn

Sud Alouette III
*Grasshoppers
298 Sqn, Soesterberg;
300 Sqn, Deelen

A177
A208
A209
A217
A218
A226
A227
A235
A246
A247
A253
A254
A260
A261
A266
A267
A275
A281
A292
A293
A301
A302
A307
A319
A324
A336
A342
A343
A350
A351*
A366
A374
A383
A390*
A391
A398*
A399
A406
A407
A414
A451
A452
A453
A464
A465*
A470
A471
A482
A483
A488

Serial

A489
A494
A495
A499*
A500
A514
A515
A521
A522
A528
A529
A535
A536
A542
A549
A550

Marine Luchtvaart Dienst

Lockheed
P-3C Orion
320 Sqn, Valkenburg and Keflavik
300
301
302
303
304
305
306
307
308
309
310
311
312

Westland Lynx
*UH14A (7 Sqn)
†SH14B (860 Sqn)
‡SH14C (860 Sqn)
De Kooij
260* K
261* K
262* K
264* K
265* K
266† PH
267† K
268† K
270†
271† KN
272† K
273†
274†
276‡
277‡
278‡ K
279‡
280‡ EV
281‡ PH
282‡ PH
283‡

NEW ZEALAND

Royal New Zealand Air Force

Boeing 727-22C
40 Sqn, Whenuapai
NZ7271
NZ7272

Lockheed
C-130H Hercules
40 Sqn, Whenuapai
NZ7001
NZ7002
NZ7003

Serial

NZ7004
NZ7005

Lockheed
P-3K Orion
5 Sqn, Whenuapai
NZ4201
NZ4202
NZ4203
NZ4204
NZ4205
NZ4206

NIGERIA

Federal Nigerian Air Force

Lockheed
C-130H Hercules
Lagos
NAF-910
NAF-911
NAF-912
NAF-913
NAF-914
NAF-915
NAF-917
NAF-918†
NAF-918 (NAF 916)*
†camouflaged
*white/green

NORWAY

Kongelige Norske Luftforsvaret

Dassault
Falcon 20 ECM
335 Skv, Gardermoen
041
053
0125

General Dynamics
F-16A/*F-16B
331 Skv, Bodø; 332 Skv, Rygge; 334 Skv, Bodø; 338 Skv, Orland
272 332 Skv
273 332 Skv
274 332 Skv
275 332 Skv
276 332 Skv
277 332 Skv
278 332 Skv
279 332 Skv
281 332 Skv
282 332 Skv
284 332 Skv
285 332 Skv
286 332 Skv
287 338 Skv
288 338 Skv
289 338 Skv
290 338 Skv
291 338 Skv
292 338 Skv
293 338 Skv
294 338 Skv
295 332 Skv
296 338 Skv
297 338 Skv
298 338 Skv
299 332 Skv
300 334 Skv
302* 332 Skv
303* 332 Skv
304* 332 Skv

Serial

305* 332 Skv
306* 332 Skv
307* 338 Skv
658 334 Skv
659 334 Skv
660 334 Skv
661 334 Skv
662 334 Skv
663 334 Skv
664 334 Skv
665 334 Skv
666 334 Skv
667 334 Skv
668 334 Skv
669 334 Skv
670 334 Skv
671 334 Skv
672 334 Skv
673 334 Skv
674 331 Skv
675 331 Skv
676 331 Skv
677 332 Skv
678 331 Skv
679 331 Skv
680 331 Skv
681 331 Skv
682 331 Skv
683 331 Skv
685 331 Skv
687 331 Skv
3688 331 Skv
689* 331 Skv
690* 332 Skv
691* 334 Skv
692* 334 Skv
693* 331 Skv

Lockheed
C-130H Hercules
335 Skv, Gardermoen
952
953
954
955
956 UN
957

Lockheed
P-3B Orion
333 Skv, Andøya
576
583
599
600
601
602
603

Northrop F-5A
336 Skv, Rygge; 338 Skv, Orland
125 336 Skv
128 336 Skv
129 338 Skv
130 336 Skv
131 336 Skv
132 336 Skv
133 336 Skv
134 336 Skv
207 336 Skv
208 336 Skv
210 336 Skv
214 338 Skv
215 336 Skv
220 336 Skv

Serial	
222	336 Skv
225	336 Skv
369	336 Skv
370	338 Skv
372	338 Skv
373	338 Skv
374	336 Skv
375	338 Skv
563	338 Skv
565	336 Skv
568	338 Skv
571	338 Skv
573	338 Skv
575	336 Skv
895	336 Skv
896	336 Skv
897	336 Skv
898	336 Skv
901	338 Skv
902	336 Skv
904	338 Skv

Northrop F-5B
336 Skv, Rygge
135
136
241
242
243
244
387
594
595
906
907
908
909

Westland Sea King Mk43
330 Skv, Bodø
060
062
066
069
070
071
072
073
074
189

Westland Lynx Mk86
337 Skv
207
216
232
235
237

OMAN
Al Quwwat Al Jawwiya al Saltanat Oman

BAC 1-11 srs 485GD
4 Sqn, Seeb
551
552
553

Lockheed C-130H Hercules
4 Sqn, Seeb
501
502
503

Short Skyvan 3M Seavan*
2 Sqn, Seeb
901
902
903
904
906
907
908*
910
911
912
913
914
915
916

PORTUGAL
Forca Aerea Portuguesa

Cessna T-37C
*Asas de Portugal
102 Esq, Sintra
2401*
2402
2403
2404
2406*
2407
2410
2411
2412
2414
2415
2417
2418
2419
2420
2421*
2422
2423*
2424
2425
2426
2427
2428
2429*
2430*

Lockheed C-130H Hercules
501 Esq, Lisbon/Montijo
6801
6802
6803
6804
6805
6806

Falcon 20C
504 Esq, Lisbon/Montijo
8101
8102
8103

SAUDI ARABIA
Al Quwwat Al-Jawwiya as Sa' udiya

Grumman Gulfstream III
1 Sqn, Riyadh
103
107

Lockheed C-130 Hercules †1 Sqn, Riyadh
‡4 Sqn, Jeddah
*16 Sqn, Jeddah

Serial		
†	112	VC-130H
‡	451	C-130E
‡	452	C-130E
‡	455	C-130E
‡	456	KC-130H
‡	457	KC-130H
‡	458	KC-130H
‡	459	KC-130H
‡	460	C-130H
‡	461	C-130H
‡	462	C-130H
‡	463	C-130H
‡	464	C-130H
‡	465	C-130H
‡	466	C-130H
‡	467	C-130H
‡	468	C-130H
‡	469	C-130H
‡	470	C-130H
*	1601	C-130H
*	1602	C-130H
*	1603	C-130H
*	1604	C-130H
*	1605	C-130H
*	1606	C-130E
*	1607	C-130E
*	1608	C-130E
*	1609	C-130E
*	1610	C-130E
*	1611	C-130E
*	1612	C-130H
*	1614	C-130H
*	1615	C-130H
*	1616	KC-130H
*	1617	KC-130H
*	1618	C-130H
*	1619	C-130H
*	1621	KC-130H

Lockheed Jetstar
1 Sqn, Riyadh
101
102

SINGAPORE
Republic of Singapore Air Force

Lockheed C-130B Hercules
122 Sqn, Changi
720
721
724
725

Lockheed C-130H Hercules
122 Sqn, Changi
730
731
732
733

SPAIN
Ejercito del Aire

CASA 101 Aviojet
411/412 Esc, (Ala41) Matacan
793 Esc, (Ala 79), San Javier

E.25.01	79-01
XE.25-02	793-02
E.25-03	79-03
XE.25.04	793.04
E.25-05	79-05
E.25-06	79-06

Serial	
E.25-07	79-07
E.25-08	79-08
E.25-09	79-09
E.25-10	79-10
E.25-11	79-11
E.25-12	79-12
E.25-13	79-13
E.25-14	79-14
E.25-15	79-15
E.25-16	79-16
E.25-17	79-17
E.25-18	79-18
E.25-19	79-19
E.25-20	79-20
E.25-21	79-21
E.25-22	79-22
E.25-23	79-23
E.25-24	79-24
E.25-25	79-25
E.25-26	79-26
E.25-27	79-27
E.25-28	79-28
E.25-29	79-29
E.25-30	79-30
E.25-31	79-31
E.25-32	411-01
E.25-33	412-25
E.25-34	793-34
E.25-35	412-26
E.25-36	79-36
E.25-37	412-27
E.25-38	79-38
E.25-39	412-28
E.25-40	411-05
E.25-41	79-41
E.25-42	79-32
E.25-43	79-43
E.25-44	79-44
E.25-45	79-35
E.25-46	79-46
E.25-47	79-37
E.25-48	79-42
E.25-49	79-39
E.25-50	79-40
E.25-51	411-06
E.25-52	412-30
E.25-53	411-07
E.25-54	412-31
E.25-55	411-08
E.25-56	412-32
E.25-57	411-09
E.25-58	412-33
E.25-59	411-10
E.25-60	79-44
E.25-61	411-11
E.25-62	412-35
E.25-63	411-12
E.25-64	412-36
E.25-65	411-13
E.25-66	412-37
E.25-67	411-14
E.25-68	412-38
E.25-69	411-15
E.25-70	412-39
E.25-71	411-16
E.25-72	412-40
E.25-73	411-17
E.25-74	412-41
E.25-75	411-18
E.25-76	412-42
E.25-77	411-19
E.25-78	79-02
E.25-79	411-20
E.25-80	412-44
E.25-81	411-21
E.25-82	412-45
E.25-83	411-22
E.25-84	79-04
E.25-85	411-23
E.25-86	412-47
E.25-87	411-24
E.25-88	412-48

CASA 212 Aviocar
212 (XT.12),
212A (T.12B),
212B (TR.12A),
212D (TE.12B),
212E (T.12C).

351/352 Esc (Ala35), Getafe;
403 Esc Cuatro Vientos;
406 Esc Torrejon;
408 Esc, Getafe;
461 Esc Gando, Las Palmas;
721 Esc (Ala72), Alcantarilla;
744/745 Esc Matacan;
792 Esc (Ala79), San Javier.

Serial	
XT.12-1	406-10
TR.12A-3	403-11
TR.12A-4	403-02
TR.12A-5	403-13
TR.12A-6	403-04
TR.12A-7	403-05
TE.12B-8	792-3
TE.12B-9	792-5
TE.12B-10	792-1
T.12B-12	35-01
T.12B-13	745-13
T.12B-14	461-14
T.12B-15	351-15
T.12B-16	744-16
T.12B-17	35-03
T.12B-18	461-18
T.12B-19	461-19
T.12B-20	35-04
T.12B-21	35-05
T.12B-22	35-06
T.12B-23	72-01
T.12B-24	35-07
T.12B-25	744-25
T.12B-26	72-02
T.12B-27	461-27
T.12B-28	72-03
T.12B-29	352-29
T.12B-30	744-30
T.12B-31	461-31
T.12B-33	72-04
T.12B-34	744-34
T.12B-35	461-35
T.12B-36	35-09
T.12B-37	72-05
T.12B-38	35-10
T.12B-39	745-39
TE.12B-40	792-2
TE.12B-41	792-4
T.12C-42	792-6
T.12C-43	35-50
T.12B-44	33-50
T.12B-46	745-46
T.12B-47	721-47
T.12B-48	35-11
T.12B-49	461-49
T.12B-50	745-50
T.12B-51	744-51
T.12B-52	721-52
T.12B-53	35-12
T.12B-54	35-13
T.12B-55	461-55
T.12B-56	745-56
T.12B-57	72-08
T.12B-58	461-58
T.12B-59	352-59
T.12C-60	
T.12C-61	35-53
T.12B-63	351-63
T.12B-64	461-64
T.12B-65	745-65
T.12B-66	721-66
T.12B-67	745-67
T.12B-68	351-68
T.12B-69	351-69
T.12B-70	35-17
T.12B-71	351-71
TR.12D-72	408-01
TR.12D-73	408-02
TR.12D-74	408-03

Dassault Falcon 20
401 Esc (Ala45), Madrid
T.11-1/45-02
T.11-2/45-03
T.11-3/45-04
TM.11-4/45-05

Dassault Falcon 50
401 Esc (Ala45), Madrid
T.16-1/45-20

Douglas DC8-52
401 Esc (Ala 45), Madrid
T.15-1/45-01
T.15-2/45-07

Fokker F.27M Friendship 400MPA
802 Esc, Gando
D.2-01
D.2-02
D.2-03

Lockheed C-130H Hercules
311 Esc/312 Esc (Ala31), Zaragoza
T.10-2/31-02
T.10-3/31-03
T.10-4/31-04
T.10-8/31-05
T.10-9/31-06
T.10-10/31-07

Lockheed KC-130H Hercules
312 Esc (Ala31), Zaragosa
TK.10-5/31-50
TK.10-6/31-51
TK.10-7/31-52
TK.10-11/31-53
TK.10-12/31-54

SUDAN
Silakh Al Jawwiya as Sudaniya

Lockheed C-130H Hercules
1100
1101
1102
1103
1104
1105

Serial

SWEDEN
Kungliga Svenska Flygvapnet
Lockheed C-130E Hercules
F7, Satenäs
84001/841
84002/842
Lockheed C-130H Hercules
F7, Satenäs
84003/843
84004/844
84005/845
84006/846
84007/847
84008/848
Cessna 404
†F17, Ronneby
*F21, Lulea
87001/871*
87002/872*
87003/873†
Metro III
88002/882
88003/883
Vertol 107-II-4
*F15, Soderhamm
†F21, Lulea
04451/91*
04452/92*
04453/93
04454/94†
04455/95*
04456/96
04457/97
04458/98
04459/99
04460/90
Marine Flygtjanst Vertol 107-II-5
1HKP Div, Berga
04061/61
04063
04064/64
Kawasaki-Vertol KV.107-II
*1 HKPDiv, Berga
†2 HKPDiv, Säve
*04065/65
†04067/67
†04068/68
*04069/69
†04070/70
*04071/71
†04072/72

SWITZERLAND
Schweizerische Flugwaffe
Beech E-50 Twin Bonanza
Transport Corps, Dubendorf
A-711
A-712
A-713

THAILAND
Royal Thai Air Force
Douglas DC.8-62AF
60109
60110
60112 (HS-TGQ)

Serial

TURKEY
Turk Hava Kuvvetleri
Transall C.160D
221 Filo, Erkilet
019/12-019
020/12-020
021/12-021
022/12-022
023/12-023
024/12-024
026/12-026
027/12-027
028/12-028
029/12-029
030/12-030
031/12-031
032/12-032
033/12-033
034/12-034
035/12-035
036/12-036
037/12-037
038/12-038
039/12-039
040/12-040
Lockheed C-130E Hercules
222 Filo, Erkilet
00991/12-991
01468/12-468
01947/12-947
13186/12-186
13187/12-187
13188/12-188
13189/12-189
17949/12-949
Vickers V794 Viscount
224 Filo, Yesilkoy
430
431

UNITED ARAB EMIRATES
United Arab Emirates Air Force
Abu Dhabi
Lockheed C-130H Hercules
1211
1212
1213
1214
Lockheed C-130H Hercules
Dubai
311
312

WEST GERMANY
Luftwaffe
Boeing 707-307C
FBS-BMVg, Köln-Bonn
10+01
10+02
10+03
10+04
Canadair CL601 Challenger
FBS-BMVg, Köln-Bonn
12+01
12+02
12+03
12+04
12+05

Serial

12+06
12+07

HFB 320 Hansa Jet
*FBS-BMVg, Köln-Bonn;
†JBG32 Lechfeld;
‡WTD-61, Ingolstadt
16+01*
16+02*
16+03*
16+04‡
16+05*
16+07‡
16+21†
16+22
16+23†
16+24†
16+25†
16+26†
16+27†
16+28†

VFW 614
FBS-BMVg, Köln-Bonn
17+01
17+02
17+03

McD RF-4E Phantom
AKG 51, Bremgarten;
AKG 52, Leck;
TSLw 1, Kaufbeuren;
WTD 61, Ingolstadt

35+01	WTD 61
35+02	AKG 52
35+03	AKG 51
35+04	AKG 51
35+05	AKG 52
35+06	AKG 51
35+07	AKG 51
35+08	AKG 52
35+09	AKG 52
35+10	AKG 52
35+11	AKG 52
35+12	AKG 51
35+13	AKG 52
35+14	AKG 52
35+17	AKG 52
35+18	AKG 52
35+19	AKG 51
35+20	AKG 52
35+21	AKG 52
35+22	AKG 51
35+24	AKG 52
35+25	AKG 51
35+26	AKG 52
35+28	AKG 51
35+29	AKG 51
35+31	AKG 52
35+32	AKG 52
35+33	AKG 51
35+34	AKG 51
35+35	AKG 51
35+36	AKG 52
35+37	AKG 52
35+38	AKG 51
35+39	AKG 52
35+40	AKG 51
35+41	AKG 52
35+42	AKG 52
35+43	AKG 52
35+44	AKG 51
35+46	AKG 51

Serial	
35+48	AKG 51
35+49	AKG 51
35+50	AKG 51
35+51	AKG 51
35+52	AKG 52
35+53	AKG 52
35+54	AKG 52
35+56	AKG 51
35+57	AKG 51
35+58	AKG 51
35+59	AKG 51
35+60	AKG 52
35+61	AKG 51
35+62	TSLw 1
35+63	AKG 51
35+64	AKG 51
35+65	AKG 52
35+66	AKG 52
35+67	AKG 52
35+68	AKG 51
35+69	AKG 52
35+71	AKG 51
35+72	AKG 52
35+73	AKG 51
35+74	AKG 52
35+75	AKG 51
35+76	AKG 52
35+77	AKG 52
35+78	AKG 51
35+79	AKG 52
35+82	AKG 51
35+83	WTD 61
35+84	AKG 52
35+85	AKG 52
35+86	AKG 51
35+87	AKG 52
35+88	AKG 51

McD F-4F Phantom
JBG 35, Pferdsfeld;
JBG 36, Hopsten;
JG 71, Wittmundhaven;
JG 74, Neuburg;
TSLw 1, Kaufbeuren;
WTD 61, Ingolstadt

Serial	
37+01	JBG 36
37+03	JG 71
37+04	TSLw 1
37+05	JG 74
37+06	JG 71
37+07	JBG 36
37+08	JG 71
37+09	JBG 35
37+10	JG 71
37+11	JG 74
37+12	JBG 36
37+13	JBG 35
37+14	TSLw 1
37+15	WTD-61
37+16	WTD-61
37+17	JBG 36
37+18	JBG 35
37+19	JG 71
37+20	JG 74
37+21	JBG 36
37+22	JBG 35
37+23	JG 71
37+24	JG 74
37+25	JBG 36
37+26	JBG 35
37+28	JG 74
37+29	JBG 36
37+30	JBG 35
37+31	JG 71
37+32	JG 74
37+33	JBG 36
37+34	JBG 35
37+35	JG 71
37+36	JG 74
37+37	JBG 36
37+38	JBG 35
37+39	JG 71
37+40	JG 74
37+41	JBG 36
37+42	JBG 35
37+43	JG 71
37+44	JG 74
37+45	JBG 36
37+46	JBG 35
37+47	JG 71
37+48	JG 74
37+49	JBG 36
37+50	JBG 35
37+51	JG 71
37+52	JG 74
37+53	JBG 36
37+54	JBG 35
37+55	JG 71
37+56	JG 74
37+57	JBG 36
37+58	JBG 35
37+60	JG 74
37+61	JG 71
37+63	JG 71
37+64	JG 74
37+65	JBG 36
37+66	JBG 35
37+67	JG 71
37+69	JBG 36
37+70	JBG 35
37+71	JG 71
37+73	JBG 36
37+75	JG 71
37+76	JG 74
37+77	JBG 36
37+78	JBG 35
37+79	JBG 36
37+81	JBG 36
37+82	JBG 35
37+83	JG 71
37+84	JG 74
37+85	JBG 36
37+86	JG 71
37+88	JG 74
37+89	JBG 36
37+90	JBG 36
37+91	WTD 61
37+92	JG 74
37+93	JBG 36
37+94	JBG 35
37+96	JG 74
37+97	JBG 36
37+98	JBG 35
38+00	JG 74
38+01	JBG 36
38+02	JBG 35
38+03	JG 71
38+04	JG 74
38+05	JBG 36
38+06	JBG 35
38+07	JG 71
38+08	JG 74
38+09	JBG 36
38+10	JBG 35
38+11	JG 71
38+12	JG 74
38+13	JBG 36
38+14	JBG 35
38+16	JG 74
38+17	JBG 36
38+18	JBG 35
38+20	JG 74
38+21	JBG 36
38+24	JG 74
38+25	JBG 36
38+26	JBG 35
38+27	JG 71
38+28	JG 74
38+29	JBG 36
38+30	JBG 35
38+31	JG 71
38+32	JG 74
38+33	JG 36
38+34	JBG 35
38+36	JG 74
38+37	JBG 36
38+38	JBG 35
38+39	JG 71
38+40	JG 74
38+42	JBG 35
38+43	JG 71
38+44	JG 74
38+45	JBG 36
38+46	JBG 35
38+47	JG 71
38+48	JG 74
38+49	JBG 36
38+50	JBG 35
38+51	JG 71
38+52	JG 74
38+53	JBG 36
38+54	JBG 35
38+55	JBG 35
38+56	JG 74
38+57	JBG 36
38+58	JBG 35
38+59	JBG 36
38+60	JG 74
38+61	JG 71
38+62	JBG 35
38+63	JG 71
38+64	JG 74
38+66	JG 71
38+67	JG 71
38+68	JG 74
38+69	JBG 36
38+70	JBG 35
38+72	JG 74
38+73	JBG 36
38+74	JBG 35
38+75	JBG 35

D-BD Alpha Jet
JBG 41, Husum;
JBG 43, Oldenburg;
JBG 44, Beja (Portugal);
JBG 49, Fürstenfeldbruck;
WTD 61, Ingolstadt

Serial	
40+01	WTD 61
40+02	WTD 61
40+03	JBG 49
40+04	JBG 43
40+05	JBG 49
40+06	JBG 49
40+07	JBG 49
40+08	JBG 44
40+09	JBG 49

Serial	
40+11	JBG 43
40+12	JBG 49
40+13	JBG 43
40+14	JBG 43
40+15	JBG 41
40+16	JBG 41
40+17	JBG 49
40+18	JBG 49
40+20	JBG 43
40+21	JBG 41
40+22	JBG 41
40+23	JBG 49
40+24	JBG 43
40+25	JBG 49
40+26	JBG 41
40+27	JBG 43
40+28	JBG 41
40+29	JBG 49
40+30	JBG 49
40+31	JBG 43
40+32	JBG 43
40+33	JBG 49
40+34	JBG 41
40+35	JBG 49
40+36	JBG 43
40+37	JBG 49
40+38	JBG 43
40+39	JBG 41
40+40	JBG 49
40+41	JBG 41
40+42	JBG 49
40+43	JBG 43
40+44	JBG 43
40+45	JBG 41
40+46	JBG 43
40+47	JBG 49
40+48	JBG 43
40+49	JBG 49
40+50	JBG 43
40+51	JBG 41
40+52	JBG 44
40+53	JBG 44
40+54	JBG 43
40+56	JBG 49
40+57	JBG 43
40+58	JBG 43
40+59	JBG 49
40+60	JBG 41
40+61	JBG 43
40+62	JBG 41
40+63	JBG 41
40+64	JBG 49
40+65	JBG 49
40+66	JBG 44
40+67	JBG 49
40+68	JBG 41
40+69	JBG 43
40+70	JBG 41
40+71	JBG 44
40+72	JBG 49
40+73	JBG 49
40+74	JBG 41
40+75	JBG 43
40+76	JBG 49
40+77	JBG 49
40+78	JBG 43
40+79	JBG 43
40+80	JBG 43
40+81	JBG 41
40+82	JBG 49

Serial	
40+84	JBG 49
40+85	JBG 49
40+86	JBG 44
40+87	JBG 43
40+88	JBG 41
40+89	JBG 41
40+90	JBG 49
40+91	JBG 49
40+92	JBG 43
40+93	JBG 49
40+94	JBG 44
40+95	JBG 43
40+96	JBG 49
40+97	JBG 44
40+98	JBG 44
40+99	JBG 41
41+00	JBG 43
41+01	JBG 43
41+02	JBG 41
41+03	JBG 43
41+04	JBG 49
41+05	JBG 43
41+06	JBG 41
41+07	JBG 49
41+08	JBG 44
41+09	JBG 43
41+10	JBG 49
41+11	JBG 49
41+12	JBG 43
41+13	JBG 43
41+14	JBG 41
41+15	JBG 41
41+16	JBG 44
41+17	JBG 44
41+18	JBG 43
41+19	JBG 43
41+20	JBG 41
41+21	JBG 41
41+22	JBG 44
41+23	JBG 44
41+24	JBG 41
41+25	JBG 49
41+26	JBG 49
41+27	JBG 43
41+28	JBG 43
41+29	JBG 44
41+30	JBG 44
41+31	JBG 41
41+32	JBG 41
41+33	JBG 41
41+34	JBG 43
41+35	JBG 49
41+36	JBG 49
41+37	JBG 49
41+38	JBG 49
41+39	JBG 43
41+40	JBG 43
41+41	JBG 41
41+42	JBG 43
41+43	JBG 43
41+44	JBG 49
41+45	JBG 49
41+46	JBG 43
41+47	JBG 41
41+48	JBG 41
41+49	JBG 49
41+50	JBG 49
41+51	JBG 43
41+52	JBG 43
41+53	JBG 41

Serial	
41+54	JBG 41
41+55	JBG 49
41+56	JBG 49
41+57	JBG 43
41+58	JBG 43
41+59	JBG 41
41+60	JBG 41
41+61	JBG 44
41+62	JBG 49
41+63	JBG 41
41+64	JBG 43
41+65	JBG 41
41+66	JBG 41
41+67	JBG 49
41+68	JBG 49
41+70	JBG 43
41+71	JBG 41
41+72	JBG 41
41+73	JBG 41
41+74	JBG 41
41+75	JBG 41

Panavia Tornado Strike/Trainer*

†TTTE RAF Cottesmore;
JBG 31, Nörvenich;
JBG 32, Lechfeld;
JBG 34, Memmingen;
JBG 33, Büchel;
JBG 38, Jever;
MFG1, Schleswig;
MFG2, Eggebek;
TSLW1, Kaufbueren;
WTD61, Ingolstadt

Serial	
*43+01/G-20†	
*43+02/G-21†	
*43+03/G-22†	
*43+04/G-23†	
*43+05/G-24†	
*43+06/G-25†	
*43+07/G-26†	
*43+08/G-27†	
*43+09/G-28†	
*43+10/G-29†	
*43+11/G-30†	
43+12/G-70†	
43+13/G-71†	
43+14/G-72†	
*43+15/G-31†	
*43+16/G-32†	
*43+17/G-33†	
43+18/G-77†	
43+19/G-78†	
43+20/G-73†	
*43+22	JBG 38
*43+23/G-34†	
43+25/G-75†	
43+26/G-76†	
43+27	MFG 1
43+28	JBG 38
*43+29	JBG 31
43+30	JBG 38
*43+31/G-36†	
43+32	JBG 38
*43+33	JBG 38
43+34	JBG 38
*43+35/G-38†	

Overseas Serials

Serial	
43+36	JBG 38
*43+37/G-37†	
43+38	JBG 38
43+40	JBG 38
43+41	JBG 31
*43+42	MFG 1
*43+43	MFG 1
*43+44	MFG 1
*43+45	MFG 1
43+46	MFG 1
43+47	MFG 1
43+48	MFG 1
43+50	MFG 1
*43+51	MFG 1
43+52	MFG 1
43+53	MFG 1
43+54	MFG 1
43+55	MFG 1
43+56	MFG 1
43+57	MFG 1
43+58	MFG 1
43+59	MFG 1
43+60	MFG 1
43+61	MFG 1
43+62	MFG 1
43+63	MFG 1
43+64	MFG 1
43+65	MFG 1
43+67	MFG 1
43+68	MFG 1
43+69	MFG 1
43+70	MFG 1
43+71	MFG 1
43+72	MFG 1
43+73	MFG 1
43+74	MFG 1
43+75	MFG 1
43+76	MFG 1
43+77	MFG 1
43+78	MFG 1
43+79	MFG 1
43+80	MFG 1
43+81	MFG 1
43+82	MFG 1
43+83	MFG 1
43+84	MFG 1
43+85	MFG 1
43+86	TSLw1
43+87	MFG 1
43+88	MFG 1
43+89	MFG 1
*43+90	JBG 38
*43+91	JBG 38
*43+92	JBG 31
*43+94	JBG 31
43+95	JBG 32
43+96	JBG 31
*43+97	JBG 31
43+98	JBG 38
43+99	JBG 31
44+00	JBG 31
*44+01	JBG 38
44+02	JBG 31
44+03	JBG 31
44+04	JBG 31
*44+05	JBG 38
44+06	JBG 31
44+07	JBG 31
44+08	JBG 38
44+09	JBG 31
*44+10	JBG 38
44+11	JBG 38
44+12	JBG 31
44+13	JBG 38

Serial	
44+14	JBG 31
*44+15	JBG 38
44+16	JBG 31
44+17	JBG 38
44+18	JBG 31
44+19	JBG 31
*44+20	JBG 38
44+21	JBG 31
44+22	JBG 31
44+23	JBG 31
44+24	JBG 38
*44+25	JBG 38
44+26	JBG 31
44+27	JBG 31
44+28	JBG 31
44+29	JBG 31
44+30	JBG 31
44+31	JBG 31
44+32	JBG 31
44+33	JBG 31
44+34	JBG 31
44+35	JBG 31
*44+36	JBG 32
*44+37	JBG 32
*44+38	JBG 32
*44+39	JBG 32
44+40	JBG 33
44+41	JBG 31
44+42	JBG 32
44+43	JBG 32
44+44	JBG 31
44+46	JBG 32
44+48	JBG 31
44+49	JBG 31
44+50	JBG 32
44+51	JBG 32
44+52	JBG 31
44+53	JBG 32
44+54	JBG 32
44+55	JBG 32
44+56	JBG 32
44+57	JBG 32
44+58	JBG 32
44+59	JBG 32
44+60	JBG 32
44+61	JBG 32
44+62	JBG 32
44+63	JBG 32
44+64	JBG 32
44+65	TSLw 1
44+66	JBG 32
44+67	JBG 32
44+68	JBG 32
44+69	JBG 32
44+70	JBG 32
44+71	JBG 32
*44+72	JBG 33
*44+73	JBG 33
*44+74	JBG 33
*44+75	JBG 33
44+76	JBG 32
44+77	JBG 32
44+78	JBG 32
44+79	JBG 32
44+80	JBG 32
44+81	JBG 32
44+82	JBG 32
44+83	JBG 32
44+84	JBG 32
44+85	JBG 32
44+86	JBG 33
44+87	JBG 33
44+88	JBG 33
44+89	JBG 33

Serial	
44+90	
44+91	JBG 33
44+92	JBG 33
44+94	JBG 33
44+95	JBG 33
44+96	JBG 33
44+97	JBG 33
44+98	JBG 33
44+99	JBG 33
45+00	JBG 33
45+01	JBG 33
45+02	JBG 33
45+03	JBG 33
45+04	JBG 33
45+05	JBG 33
45+06	JBG 33
45+07	JBG 33
45+08	JBG 33
45+09	JBG 33
45+10	JBG 33
45+11	JBG 33
*45+12	MFG 2
*45+13	MFG 2
*45+14	MFG 2
*45+15	MFG 2
*45+16	MFG 2
45+17	JBG 33
45+18	JBG 33
45+19	JBG 33
45+20	JBG 33
45+21	JBG 33
45+22	JBG 33
45+23	JBG 33
45+24	JBG 33
45+25	JBG 33
45+26	MFG 2
45+27	MFG 2
45+28	MFG 2
45+29	MFG 2
45+30	MFG 2
45+31	MFG 2
45+32	MFG 2
45+33	MFG 2
45+34	MFG 2
45+35	MFG 2
45+36	MFG 2
45+37	MFG 2
45+38	MFG 2
45+39	MFG 2
45+40	MFG 2
45+41	MFG 2
45+42	MFG 2
45+43	
45+44	MFG 2
45+45	
45+46	MFG 2
45+47	MFG 2
45+48	MFG 2
45+49	MFG 2
45+50	MFG 2
45+51	MFG 2
45+52	MFG 2
45+53	MFG 2
45+54	MFG 2
45+55	MFG 2
45+56	MFG 2
45+57	MFG 2
45+58	
45+59	
*45+60	JBG 34
*45+61	JBG 34
*45+62	JBG 34
*45+63	JBG 34
45+64	

Serial
45+65
45+66
45+67
45+68
45+69
*45+70
45+71
45+72
*45+73
45+74
45+75
45+76
*45+77
45+78
45+79
45+80
45+81
45+82
45+83
45+84
45+85
45+86
45+87
45+88
45+89
45+90
45+91
45+92
45+93
45+94
45+95
45+96
45+97
45+98
45+99
*46+00
46+01
46+02
46+03
46+04
*46+05
*46+06
*46+07
46+08
46+09
46+10
46+11
46+12
46+13
46+14
46+15
46+16
46+17
46+18
46+19
46+20
46+21
46+22

Transall C-160

LTG 61, Landsberg; LTG 62, Wunstorf; LTG 63, Hohn WTD61 Ingolstadt

Serial	
50+06	LTG 63
50+07	LTG 61
50+08	LTG 61
50+09	LTG 62
50+10	LTG 62
50+17	LTG 62
50+29	LTG 62
50+33	LTG 63
50+34	LTG 62
50+35	LTG 62
50+36	LTG 62
50+37	LTG 62
50+38	LTG 62
50+39	LTG 62
50+40	LTG 61
50+41	LTG 63
50+42	LTG 63
50+43	LTG 61
50+44	LTG 61
50+45	LTG 63
50+46	LTG 62
50+47	LTG 61
50+48	
50+49	LTG 61
50+50	LTG 63
50+51	LTG 61
50+52	LTG 62
50+53	LTG 62
50+54	LTG 63
50+55	LTG 62
50+56	LTG 63
50+57	LTG 61
50+58	LTG 63
50+59	LTG 63
50+60	LTG 62
50+61	LTG 63
50+62	LTG 61
50+64	LTG 61
50+65	LTG 62
50+66	LTG 61
50+67	LTG 63
50+68	LTG 61
50+69	LTG 63
50+70	WTD 61
50+71	LTG 63
50+72	LTG 61
50+73	LTG 62
50+74	LTG 61
50+75	WTD 61
50+76	LTG 63
50+77	LTG 63
50+78	LTG 62
50+79	LTG 63
50+80	LTG 61
50+81	LTG 62
50+82	LTG 63
50+83	LTG 62
50+84	LTG 63
50+85	LTG 61
50+86	LTG 61
50+87	LTG 63
50+88	LTG 61
50+89	LTG 62
50+90	LTG 61
50+91	LTG 62
50+92	LTG 61
50+93	LTG 61
50+94	LTG 62
50+95	LTG 63
50+96	LTG 61
50+97	LTG 62
50+98	LTG 61
50+99	LTG 61
51+00	LTG 63
51+01	LTG 62
51+02	LTG 63
51+03	LTG 62
51+04	LTG 61
51+05	LTG 62
51+06	LTG 63
51+07	LTG 62
51+08	LTG 63
51+09	LTG 63
51+10	LTG 61
51+11	LTG 62
51+12	LTG 63
51+13	LTG 61
51+14	LTG 63
51+15	LTG 61

Dornier Do.28D-2 Skyservant

LTG61, Landsberg;
LTG 62, Wunstorf;
LTG 63, Hohn;
WTD 61, Ingolstadt;
FBS-BMVg, Köln-Bonn
MFG 5, Kiel-Holtenau

Serial	
58+05	WTD 61
58+08	LTG 62
58+09	LTG 62
58+14	LTG 62
58+15	JBG 31
58+18	LTG 63
58+20	JBG 31
58+23	LTG 62
58+26	LTG 63
58+28	JBG 35
58+29	LTG 61
58+30	LTG 62
58+32	JG 74
58+34	LTG 62
58+36	LTG 62
58+37	LTD 62
58+38	LTG 62
58+39	LTG 62
58+46	LTG 62
58+47	JG 74
58+49	JBG 49
58+50	JBG 31
58+52	LTG 62
58+53	JBG 32
58+54	AKG 51
58+55	JBG 32
58+58	JBG 33
58+59	JBG 34
58+60	AKG 52
58+61	JBG 34
58+62	JBG 36
58+65	JG 71
58+66	JBG 38
58+67	JBG 38
58+68	LTG 62
58+69	LTG 62
58+70	LTG 62
58+71	LTG 61
58+72	AKG 51
58+73	JBG 31
58+74	JBG 41
58+76	JBG 41
58+77	JBG 49
58+78	JBG 31
58+79	LTG 62
58+80	JBG 33
58+81	LTG 62
58+82	JBG 43
58+83	LTG 62
58+84	JBG 43
58+85	JBG 33
58+86	JBG 49
58+87	JBG 49
58+89	JBG 49
58+90	JBG 49
58+92	AKG 52
58+94	JBG 35
58+98	AKG 52
58+99	JG 71
59+00	FBS-BMVg
59+01	FBS-BMVg
59+02	FBS-BMVg
59+03	FBS-BMVg

Overseas Serials

Serial

59+04 FBS-BMVg
59+05 FBS-BMVg
59+06* MFG5
59+07* MFG5
59+08* MFG5
59+09* MFG5
59+10* MFG5
59+11* MFG5
59+12* MFG5
59+13* MFG5
59+14* MFG5
59+15* MFG5
59+16* MFG5
59+17* MFG5
59+18* MFG5
59+19* MFG5
59+20* MFG5
59+21* MFG5
59+22* MFG5
59+23* MFG5
59+24* MFG5
59+25* MFG5

Dornier Do228
FBS-BMVg, Köln-Bonn
98+78

Breguet
1151 Atlantic
MFG3 Nordholz
61+01
61+02
61+03
61+04
61+05
61+06
61+07
61+08
61+09
61+10
61+11
61+12
61+13
61+14
61+15
61+16
61+17
61+19
61+20

Westland
Lynx Mk88
MFG 3 Nordholz
83+01
83+02
83+03
83+04
83+05
83+06
83+07
83+08
83+09
83+10
83+11
83+12
83+13
83+14
83+15
83+16
83+17
83+18
83+19

Westland Sea
King HAS.41
MFG 5, Kiel-Holtenau
89+50
89+51

Serial

89+52*
89+53
89+54
89+55
89+56
89+57
89+58
89+59
89+60
89+61
89+62
89+63
89+65
89+66
89+67
89+68
89+69
89+70
89+71

English Electric Canberra
B2
MGA, Manching
99+34
99+35

Heeresfliegertruppe
Sikorsky/VFW CH-53G
HFlgRgt-15, Rheine-Bentlage
HFlgRgt-25, Laupheim
HFlgRgt-35, Mendig
HFWS, Bückeberg
WTD 61, Ingolstadt
84+01 WTD 61
84+02 WTD 61
84+03 15
84+04 35
84+05 35
84+06 35
84+07 HFWS
84+08 35
84+09 25
84+10 25
84+11 HFWS
84+12 15
84+13 HFWS
84+14 HFWS
84+15 25
84+16 HFWS
84+17 25
84+18 HFWS
84+19 HFWS
84+20 35
84+21 HFWS
84+22 35
84+23 35
84+24 35
84+25 35
84+26 35
84+27 35
84+28 35
84+29 35
84+30 35
84+31 35
84+32 35
84+33 35
84+34 35
84+35 35
84+36 35
84+37 35
84+38 35
84+39 35
84+40 25
84+41 HFWS
84+42 25
84+43 25

Serial

84+44 25
84+45 25
84+46 25
84+47 25
84+48 25
84+49 HFWS
84+50 25
84+51 25
84+52 25
84+53 25
84+54 25
84+55 25
84+56 25
84+57 25
84+58 25
84+59 25
84+60 25
84+62 25
84+63 25
84+64 25
84+65 35
84+66 35
84+67 35
84+68 15
84+69 15
84+70 15
84+71 15
84+72 15
84+73 15
84+74 15
84+75 15
84+76 15
84+77 15
84+78 15
84+79 15
84+80 15
84+82 15
84+83 15
84+84 15
84+85 15
84+86 15
84+87 15
84+88 15
84+89 15
84+90 15
84+91 15
84+92 35
84+93 35
84+94 35
84+95 25
84+96 25
84+97 25
84+98 25
84+99 15
85+00 15
85+01 35
85+02 35
85+03 35
85+04 25
85+05 25
85+06 25
85+07 15
85+08 15
85+09 15
85+10 35
85+11 25
85+12 15

US Military Aircraft Markings

All USAF aircraft have been allocated a fiscal year (FY) number since 1921. Individual aircraft are given a serial according to the fiscal year in which they are ordered. The numbers commence at 0001 and are prefixed with the year of allocation. For example F-111E 68-0001 was the first aircraft ordered in 1968. The fiscal year (FY) serial is carried on the technical bloc which is usually stencilled on the left-hand side of the aircraft just below the cockpit. The number displayed on the fin is a corruption of the FY serial. Most tactical aircraft carry the fiscal year in small figures followed by the last three digits of the serial in large figures. For example F-111F 70-2362 carries 70362 on its tail. An exception to this practice is the F-5E which carries the five digits of the production serial without the fiscal year. For example the FY serial of the F-5E which displays 01532 is 74-01532. Large transport and tanker aircraft such as C-130s and KC-135s usually display a five-figure number commencing with the last digit of the appropriate fiscal year and four figures of the production number. An example of this is EC-135H 61-0282 which displays 10282 on its fin. Aircraft of more than 10 years vintage which might duplicate a five-figure number of a more modern type in service, are prefixed 0-.

USN serials follow a straightforward numerical sequence which commenced, for the present series, with the allocation of 00001 to an SB2C Helldiver by the Bureau of Aeronautics in 1940. Numbers in the 163000 series are presently being issued. They are usually carried in full on the rear fuselage of the aircraft and displayed either as a four- or five-figure sequence or in full on the fin.

UK based USAF Aircraft

The following aircraft are normally based in the UK. They are listed in numerical order of type with individual aircraft in serial number order, as depicted on the aircraft. The number in brackets is either the alternative presentation of the five-figure number commencing with the last digit of the fiscal year, or the fiscal year where a five-figure serial is presented on the aircraft. Where it is possible to identify the allocation of aircraft to individual squadrons by means of colours carried on fin or cockpit edge, this is also provided.

Serial	*Notes*
Lockheed TR-1A/B*	
95RS/17RW, RAF Alconbury	
FY80	
01065*	
01068	
01069	
01070	
01077	
01078	
01079	
01081	
01083	
01084	
01085	
01086	

Serial	*Notes*
Northrop F-5E Tiger II	
527AS/10TFW, RAF Alconbury	
FY74	
01532	
01534	
01534 Replica at Alconbury gate	
01535	
01543	
01544	
01545	
01547	
01549	
01551	
01553	

Notes	Serial
	01554
	01556
	01559
	01560
	01563
	01566
	01568
	01569

Fairchild A-10A Thunderbolt II
WR: 81TFW:
78TFS red (r) Woodbridge
91TFS blue (bl) Woodbridge
92TFS yellow (y) Bentwaters
509TFS grey (gy) Bentwaters
510TFS purple (pr) Bentwaters
511TFS black (bk) Bentwaters

Notes	Serial
	79-217 (90217)
	79-218 (90218) y
	79-219 (90219) bk
	79-220 (90220) gy
	79-221 (90221) pr
	79-224 (90224) gy
	79-225 (90225) bl
	80-143 (00143) r
	80-144 (00144) gy
	80-145 (00145) y
	80-146 (00146) bk
	80-147 (00147) pr
	80-155 (00155) pr
	80-156 (00156) bk
	80-157 (00157) bk
	80-158 (00158) bl
	80-159 (00159) y
	80-160 (00160) pr
	80-167 (00167) bk
	80-168 (00168) y
	80-169 (00169) pr
	80-170 (00170) gy
	80-171 (00171) bl
	80-172 (00172) bk
	80-179 (00179) r
	80-180 (00180) bl
	80 181 (00181) y
	80-183 (00183) pr
	80-184 (00184) bk
	80-192 (00192) y
	80-194 (00194) gy
	80-195 (00195) pr
	80-196 (00196) bk
	80-203 (00203) r
	80-204 (00204) bl
	80-205 (00205) bl
	80-206 (00206) y
	80-207 (00207) y
	80-208 (00208) gy
	80-215 (00215) pr
	80-216 (00216) pr
	80-217 (00217) y
	80-218 (00218) gy
	80-219 (00219) gy
	80-220 (00220) bl
	80-227 (00227) gy
	80-228 (00228) pr
	80-229 (00229) bk
	80-230 (00230) bk
	80-231 (00231) gy
	80-232 (00232) bl
	80-233 (00233) r
	80-234 (00234) bl
	80-235 (00235) r
	80-236 (00236) r
	80-237 (00237) bk
	80-270 (00270) r
	80-271 (00271) bl
	80-272 (00272) y
	80-273 (00273) gy
	80-274 (00274) pr
	80-275 (00275) bk
	80-276 (00276) y
	80-277 (00277) bk
	80-278 (00278) r
	80-279 (00279) gy
	80-280 (00280) bl
	80-281 (00281) y
	81-939 (10939) gy
	81-940 (10940) bk
	81-941 (10941) r
	81-942 (10942) bl
	81-943 (10943) y
	81-944 (10944) pr
	81-947 (10947) gy
	81-948 (10948) gy
	81-949 (10949) bk
	81-950 (10950) r
	81-951 (10951) bl
	81-952 (10952) pr
	81-953 (10953) gy
	81-954 (10954) y
	81-955 (10955) bk
	81-956 (10956) bl
	81-957 (10957) y
	81-960 (10960) r
	81-961 (10961) r
	81-962 (10962) bl
	81-963 (10963) y
	81-964 (10964) gy
	81-965 (10965) pr
	81-966 (10966) pr
	81-967 (10967) bk
	81-976 (10976) bl
	81-977 (10977) y
	81-978 (10978) r
	81-979 (10979) multi
	81-980 (10980) pr
	819-81 (10981) multi
	81-982 (10982) bl
	81-983 (10983) bl
	81-984 (10984) r
	81-985 (10985) y
	81-986 (10986) bk
	81-987 (10987) gy
	81-988 (10988) pr
	81-990 (10990) gy
	819-91 (10991) bl
	81-992 (10992) y
	82-646 (20646) pr
	82-647 (20647) bk
	82-649 (20649) bl
	82-650 (20650) pr
	82-654 (20654) r
	82-655 (20655) bl
	82-656 (20656) y
	82-657 (20657) gy
	82-658 (20658) r
	82-659 (20659) bk

Sikorsky HH-53C
67 ARRS, RAF Woodbridge

Notes	Serial
	5784 (FY69)
	5796 (FY69)
	5797 (FY69)
	8284 (FY68)

Serial	Notes

General Dynamics EF-111A Raven
UH: RAF Upper Heyford
66ECIO/42ECS grey

66-030 (60030)
66-033 (60033)
66-037 (60037)
66-039 (60039)
66-041 (60041)
660-42 (70034)
66-055 (60055)
66-056 (60056)
66-057 (60057)
67-032 (70032)
67-035 (70035)
67-041 (70041)
67-052 (70052)

General Dynamics F-111E
UH: 20TFW, RAF Upper Heyford
55TFS blue/white (bl)
77TFS red (r)
79TFS yellow/black (y)

67-119 (70119) bl
67-120 (70120) y
67-121 (70121) bl
67-122 (70122) y
67-123 (70123) y
68-001 (80001) r
68-002 (80002) y
68-004 (80004) bl
68-005 (80005) bl
68-006 (80006) bl
68-007 (80007) r
68-009 (80009) r
68-010 (80010) y
68-011 (80011) r
68-013 (80013) y
68-014 (80014) bl
68-015 (80015) bl
68-016 (80016) bl
68-017 (80017) r
680-20 TFW (80020) multi
68-021 (80021) r
68-022 (80022) y
68-023 (80023) y
68-025 (80025) bl
68-026 (80026) bl
68-027 (80027) r
68-028 (80028) r
68-029 (80029) r
68-030 (80030) y
68-031 (80031) r
68-032 (80032) y
68-033 (80033) y
68-034 (80034) bl
68-035 (80035) bl
68-036 (80036) bl
68-037 (80037) r
68-038 (80038) r
68-039 (80039) r
68-040 (80040) y
68-041 (80041) r
68-043 (80043) y
68-044 (80044) bl
68-046 (80046) bl
68-047 (80047) r
68-048 (80048) r
68-049 (80049) r
68-050 (80050) y
68-051 (80051) r
68-052 (80052) y
68-053 (80053) y
68-054 (80054) bl
680-55 (80055) bl
68-056 (80056) bl
68-059 (80059) r
68-061 (80061) r
68-062 (80062) y
68-063 (80063) y
68-064 (80064) bl
68-065 (80065) bl
68-066 (80066) bl
68-067 (80067) r
68-068 (80068) r
68-069 (80069) r
68-071 (80071) r
68-072 (80072) y
68-073 (80073) y
68-074 (80074) bl
68-075 (80075) bl
68-076 (80076) bl
68-077 (80077) r
68-078 (80078) r
68-079 (80079) y
68-080 (80080) y
68-082 (80082) y
68-083 (80083) y
68-084 (80084) bl

General Dynamics F-111F
LN: 48TFW, RAF Lakenheath
492 TFS blue (bl)
493 TFS yellow (y)
494 TFS red (r)
495 TFS green (gn)

70-362 (02362) gn
70-363 (02363) gn
70-364 (02364) gn
70-365 (02365) bl
70-368 (02368) bl
70-369 (02369) gn
70-370 (02370) bl
70-371 (02371) y
70-372 (02372) gn
70-373 (02373) bl
70-374 (02374) y
70-375 (02375) y
70-376 (02376) r
70-378 (02378) r
70-379 (02379) bl
70-381 (02381) r
70-382 (02382) y
70-383 (02383) bl
70-384 (02384) r
70-385 (02385) y
70-386 (02386) y
70-387 (02387) gn
70-390 (02390) gn
70-391 (02391) gn
70-392 (02392) gn
70-394 (02394) bl
70-396 (02396) y
70-397 (02397) r
70-398 (02398) gn
70-399 (02399) bl
70-401 (02401) r
70-402 (02402) gn
70-403 (02403) bl
70-404 (02404) y
70-405 (02405) r
70-406 (02406) bl
70-408 (02408) r
70-409 (02409) r

Notes	Serial	Notes	Serial
	70-411 (02411) bl 70-412 (02412) gn 70-413 (02413) r 70-414 (02414) gn 70-415 (02415) y 70-416 (02416) r 70-417 (02417) r 70-419 (02419) gn 71-883 (10883) y 71-884 (10884) gn 71-885 (10885) gn 71-886 (10886) bl 71-887 (10887) y 71-888 (10888) bl 71-889 (10889) y 71-890 (10890) y 71-891 (10891) y 71-892 (10892) y 71-893 (10893) bl 71-894 (10894) gn 72-442 (21442) bl 72-443 (21443) r 72-444 (21444) r 72-445 (21445) bl 72-446 (21446) gn 72-448 (21448) multi 72-449 (21449) y 72-450 (21450) y 72-451 (21451) y 72-452 (21452) y 73-707 (30707) r 73-708 (30708) gn		73-710 (30710) r 73-711 (30711) r 73-712 (30712) r 73-713 (30713) gn 73-715 (30715) r 74-177 (40177) bl 74-178 (40178) gn 74-180 (40180) bl 74-181 (40181) bl 74-182 (40182) y 74-183 (40183) gn 74-184 (40184) r 74-185 (40185) r **Lockheed C-130 Hercules** 67ARRS/39 ARRW, RAF Woodbridge 60220 (FY66) HC-130P 95820 (FY69) HC-130N 95823 (FY69) HC-130N 95826 (FY69) HC-130N 95827 (FY69) HC-130N 95831 (FY69) HC-130N **Boeing EC-135H** 513ACCW/10 ACCS, RAF Mildenhall *FY61* 10282 EC-135H 10285 EC-135H 10286 EC-135H

UK based US Navy Aircraft

Notes	Serial	Notes	Serial
	Beech UC-12B Super King Air **8G:** Naval Air Facility, RAF Mildenhall 1322/8D (161322) 1501/8A (161501) 1503/8G (161503)		

European based USAF Aircraft

These aircraft are normally based in Western Europe with the USAFE. They are shown in numerical order of type designation, with individual aircraft in serial number order as carried on the aircraft. An alternative five-figure presentation of the serial is shown in brackets where appropriate. Fiscal year (FY) details are also provided if necessary. The unit allocation and operating bases are given for most aircraft.

Serial	Serial	Serial
Bell UH-1N 58 MAS Ramstein* 67ARRS Det 9 Zaragoza†	*FY69* 96603† 96606* 96607*	96608* 96611† 96615* 96630†

Serial	

McDonnell Douglas RF-4C Phantom
ZR: 26TRW/38TRS
Zweibrucken green/white

66-400 (60400)
67-443 (70443)
67-451 (70451)
68-554 (80554)
68-555 (80555)
68-557 (80557)
68-561 (80561)
68-563 (80563)
68-565 (80565)
68-567 (80567)
68-569 (80569)
68-577 (80577)
68-580 (80580)
68-583 (80583)
68-587 (80587)
68-590 (80590)
69-358 (90358)
69-360 (90360)
69-361 (90361)
69-365 (90365)
69-367 (90367)
69-368 (90368)
69-369 (90369)
69-370 (90370)
69-371 (90371)
69-372 (90372)
69-374 (90374)
69-381 (90381)
69-382 (90382)
69-383 (90383)
71-249 (10249)
71-251 (10251)
71-254 (10254)
71-259 (10259)
72-152 (20152)
72-153 (20153)

McDonnell Douglas F-4E Phantom
SP: 52TFW
Spangdahlem
23 TFS blue/white (bl)
81 TFS yellow/black (y)
480 TFS red/white (r)

Serial	
7-1247 (10247)	y
71-079 (11079)	r
72-160 (20160)	bl
72-166 (20166)	y
72-167 (20167)	r
72-407 (21407)	bl
72-477 (21477)	y
74-044 (41044)	bl
74-045 (41045)	y
740-480 (41048)	r
74-050 (41050)	y
740-52 (41052)	r
74-053 (41053)	y
74-055 (41055)	bl
74-057 (41057)	y
74-059 (41059)	bl
74-060 (41060)	bl
74-622 (41622)	y
74-628 (41628)	r
74-634 (41634)	y
74-635 (41635)	y
74-636 (41636)	r
74-638 (41638)	y
74-639 (41639)	y
74-641 (41641)	bl
74-642 (41642)	y
74-644 (41644)	bl
74-645 (41645)	r
74-648 (41648)	y
74-650 (40650)	bl
74-650 (41650)	y
74-651 (41651)	bl
74-652 (§)	
74-652 (§)	
74-653 (40653)	r
74-653 (41653)	bl
74-654 (40654)	bl
74-662 (40662)	bl
74-663 (40663)	y
74-664 (40664)	bl

McDonnell Douglas F-4G Phantom
SP: 52TFW
Spangdahlem
23 TFS blue/white (bl)
81 TFS yellow/black (y)
480 TFS red/white (r)

Serial	
69-202 (97202)	y
69-209 (97209)	y
69-210 (97210)	r
69-212 (97212)	bl
69-228 (97228)	bl
69-232 (97232)	r
69-234 (97234)	r
69-236 (97236)	r
69-237 (90237)	y
69-241 (90241)	bl
69-242 (90242)	bl
69-245 (90245)	bl
69-247 (90247)	y
69-248 (90248) [480TFS]	r
69-250 (90250)	r
69-253 (90253)	r
69-255 (90255)	bl
69-258 (90258)	y
69-259 (90259)	bl
69-262 (97262)	bl
69-263 (97263)	y
69-268 (97286)	r
69-269 (90269)	r
69-270 (90270)	bl
69-270 (97270)	r
69-274 (90274)	r
69-286 (90286)	y
69-291 (97291)	bl
69-293 (97293)	y
69-295 (97295)	y
69-546 (97546)	bl
69-556 (97556)	y
69-558 (97558)	r
69-566 (97566)	bl
69-571 (97571)	bl
69-579 (97579)	r
69-582 (97582)	y
69-587 (97587)	y

McDonnell Douglas C-9A Nightingale *VIP
435TAW/55AAS Rhein Main
(†Chievres)

FY71
10875
10876*†
10878*
10879
10881
10882*

Fairchild A-10A Thunderbolt II
WR: 81 TFW: RAF Woodbridge/Bentwaters, Forward Operating Locations (FOL) in West Germany

Det 1 Sembach AB
Det 2 WGAF Leipheim
Det 3 WGAF Ahlhorn
Det 4 WGAF Norvenich

At each, eight aircraft on rotation from the six UK-based Squadrons at RAF Woodbridge/Bentwaters — see USAF/UK-based section.

Beech C-12
(*58 MAS Ramstein
†7005ABS Stuttgart
‡JUSMG Torrejon
**MAAG Athens
§ MAAG, Ankara
‡‡JUSMG Turkey)

Serial	
22549 (FY76)†	C-12A
22550 (FY76)†	C-12A
31212 (FY83)‡	C-12A
31216 (FY73)§	C-12A
31218 (FY73)**	C-12A
40161 (FY84)*	C-12F
40162 (FY84)*	C-12F
40163 (FY84)*	C-12F
40164 (FY84)*	C-12F
40165 (FY84)*	C-12F
40166 (FY84)*	C-12F
60173 (FY70)§	C-12A

McDonnell Douglas F-15C/‡F-15D Eagle
CR: 32TFS Soesterberg
green/orange (gn)
orange/green (or)
BT: 36TFW Bitburg
22TFS red (r)
53TFS yellow/black (y)
525TFS blue (bl)
IS: 57FIS Keflavik
black/white (bk)

Serial		
78-549 (80549)	BT	bl
78-550 (80550)	BT	bl
79-004 (90004)‡	CR	or
79-005 (90005)‡	CR	or
79-006 (90006)‡	BT	bl
79-007 (90007)‡	BT	y
79-008 (90008)‡	BT	bl
79-009 (90009)‡	BT	y
79-010 (90010)‡	BT	y
79-011 (90011)‡	BT	r
79-012 (90012)‡	BT	r
79-015 (90015)	CR	or
79-016 (90016)	CR	or
79-017 (90017)	CR	or
79-018 (90018)	CR	or
79-019 (90019)	CR	or
79-020 (90020)	CR	or
79-021 (90021)	CR	or
79-022 (90022)	BT	r
79-023 (90023)	CR	or
79-024 (90024)	CR	or

USAF (EUR based)

Serial		
79-025 (90025)	BT	bl
79-026 (90026)	CR	or
79-027 (90027)	CR	or
79-028 (90028)	CR	or
79-029 (90029)	CR	or
79-030 (90030)	CR	gn
79-031 (90031)	CR	gn
79-032 (90032)	CR	or
79-033 (90033)	CR	or
79-034 (90034)	CR	or
79-035 (90035)	BT	bl
79-036 (90036)	BT	bl
79-037 (90037)	BT	bl
79-038 (90038)	BT	bl
79-039 (90039)	BT	bl
79-042 (90042)	BT	bl
79-043 (90043)	BT	bl
79-045 (90045)	BT	bl
79-046 (90046)	BT	bl
79-047 (90047)	BT	bl
79-048 (90048)	BT	y
79-049 (90049)	BT	r
79-050 (90050)	BT	bl
79-051 (90051)	BT	r
79-052 (90052)	BT	r
790-53 (90053)	BT	y
79-054 (90054)	BT	r
79-055 (90055)	BT	bl
79-056 (90056)	BT	r
79-057 (90057)	BT	r
79-058 (90058)	BT	bl
79-059 (90059)	BT	r
79-060 (90060)	BT	r
79-062 (90062)	BT	bl
79-063 (90063)	BT	r
79-064 (90064)	BT	r
79-065 (90065)	BT	r
79-066 (90066)	BT	y
79-067 (90067)	BT	y
79-068 (90068)	BT	y
79-069 (90069)	BT	y
79-070 (90070)	BT	y
79-072 (90072)	BT	y
79-073 (90073)	BT	y
79-074 (90074)	BT	y
79-075 (90075)	BT	y
79-076 (90076)	BT	y
79-077 (90077)	BT	bl
79-078 (90078)	BT	y
79-079 (90079)	BT	r
79-080 (90080)	BT	y
79-081 (90081)	BT	y
80-002 (00002)	BT	bl
80-003 (00003)	BT	r
80-004 (00004)	BT	r
80-005 (00005)	BT	r
80-006 (00006)	BT	r
80-009 (00009)	BT	r
80-010 (00010)	BT	r
80-011 (00011)	BT	y
80-012 (00012)	BT	bl
80-013 (00013)	BT	y
80-014 (00014)	BT	y
80-015 (00015)	BT	y
80-016 (00016)	BT	r
80-017 (00017)	BT	bl
80-018 (00018)	BT	bl
80-019 (00019)	BT	bl
80-020 (00020)	BT	bl
80-021 (00021)	BT	r
80-022 (00022)	BT	r

Serial		
80-023 (00023)	BT	r
80-024 (00024)	BT	bl
80-026 (00026)	BT	r
80-027 (00027)	CR	or
80-028 (00028)	BT	y
80-029 (00029)	BT	bl
80-031 (00031)	BT	r
80-033 (00033)	IS	
80-034 (00034)	IS	
80-035 (00035)	IS	bk
80-038 (00038)	IS	bk
80-039 (00039)	IS	
80-040 (00040)	IS	
80-041 (00041)	IS	bk
80-042 (00042)	IS	bk
80-043 (00043)	IS	bk
80-044 (00044)	IS	bk
80-045 (00045)	IS	
80-046 (00046)	IS	bk
80-047 (00047)	IS	
80-048 (00048)	IS	
80-049 (00049)	IS	bk
80-050 (00050)	IS	
80-051 (00051)	IS	
80-052 (00052)	IS	bk
80-056 (00056)‡	IS	
80-057 (00057)‡	IS	
81-045 (10045)	CR	or
81-046 (10046)	CR	or
81-047 (10047)	CR	or
81-048 (10048)	CR	gn
81-049 (10049)	CR	gn
81-065 (10065)‡	CR	or
84-001 (40001)	BT	y
84-003 (40003)	BT	y
84-007 (40007)	BT	
84-008 (40008)	BT	
84-009 (40009)	BT	
84-010 (40010)	BT	
84-013 (40013)	BT	
84-014 (40014)	BT	
84-020 (40020)	BT	
84-021 (40021)	BT	
84-023 (40023)	BT	
84-026 (40026)	BT	
84-043 (40043)‡	BT	y
84-044 (40044)‡	BT	y
85-096 (50096)	BT	
85-099 (50099)	BT	
85-100 (50100)	BT	
85-104 (50104)	BT	
85-105 (50105)	BT	
85-115 (50115)	BT	
85-132 (50132)‡	BT	
85-133 (50133)‡	BT	

General Dynamics F-16A/‡F-16B

TJ: 401TFW Torrejon
612TFS blue/white (bl)
613TFS yellow/black (y)
614TFS red/black (r)

Serial		
81-788 (10788)	TJ	bl
81-790 (10790)	TJ	bl
81-792 (10792)	TJ	bl
81-794 (10794)	TJ	bl
81-796 (10796)	TJ	bl
81-798 (10798)	TJ	bl
81-800 (10800)	TJ	r
81-802 (10802)	TJ	r
81-804 (10804)	TJ	r
81-806 (10806)	TJ	r
81-810 (10810)	TJ	r
81-821 (10821)‡	TJ	r
81-822 (10822)‡	TJ	r
82-002 (21002)	TJ	m
82-004 (21004)	TJ	r
82-007 (21007)	TJ	r
82-009 (21009)	TJ	r
82-011 (21011)	TJ	r
82-013 (21013)	TJ	bl
82-015 (21015)	TJ	bl
82-018 (21018)	TJ	y
82-020 (21020)	TJ	y
82-022 (21022)	TJ	bl
82-024 (21024)	TJ	bl
82-025 (21025)	TJ	bl
82-047 (21047)‡	TJ	r
82-900 (20900)	TJ	r
82-902 (20902)	TJ	r
82-904 (20904)	TJ	r
82-906 (20906)	TJ	r
82-908 (20908)	TJ	r
82-911 (20911)	TJ	r
82-914 (20914)	TJ	m
82-918 (20918)	TJ	r
82-920 (20920)	TJ	r
82-922 (20922)	TJ	m
82-924 (20924)	TJ	r
82-927 (20927)	TJ	r
82-928 (20928)	TJ	bl
82-931 (20931)	TJ	bl
82-933 (20933)	TJ	y
82-936 (20936)	TJ	y
82-938 (20938)	TJ	y
82-941 (20941)	TJ	y
82-943 (20943)	TJ	y
82-944 (20944)	TJ	y
82-946 (20946)	TJ	y
82-948 (20948)	TJ	y
82-949 (20949)	TJ	y
82-952 (20952)	TJ	y
82-954 (20954)	TJ	y
82-957 (20957)	TJ	y
82-962 (20962)	TJ	y
82-964 (20964)	TJ	y
82-965 (20965)	TJ	y
82-968 (20968)	TJ	y
82-970 (20970)	TJ	y
82-975 (20975)	TJ	y
82-977 (20977)	TJ	spcl
82-980 (20980)	TJ	y
82-981 (20981)	TJ	y
82-982 (20982)	TJ	bl
82-986 (20986)	TJ	bl
82-988 (20988)	TJ	bl
82-991 (20991)	TJ	bl
82-993 (20993)	TJ	bl
82-996 (20996)	TJ	bl
82-998 (20998)	TJ	bl
82-999 (20999)	TJ	r
83-066 (31066)	TJ	bl
83-067 (31067)	TJ	bl
83-068 (31068)	TJ	bl
83-069 (31069)	TJ	bl
83-071 (31071)	TJ	y
83-074 (31074)	TJ	bl
83-079 (31079)	TJ	y
83-087 (31087)	TJ	r
83-166 (31166)‡	TJ	y
83-167 (31167)‡	TJ	y
83-168 (31168)‡	TJ	bl
83-169 (31169)‡	TJ	bl

General Dynamics F-16C/‡F-16D

HR: 50TFW Hahn
10TFS blue/yellow (bl)
313TFS orange (or)
496TFS yellow (y)
RS: 86TFW Ramstein
512TFS green/black (gn)
526TFS red/black (r)
SP: 52TFW Spangdahlem
23TFS blue/white (bl)
81TFS yellow/black (y)
480TFS red/white (r)

Serial		
84-250 (41250)	HR	m
84-263 (41263)	HR	y
84-264 (41264)	HR	y
84-266 (41266)	HR	y
84-274 (41274)	HR	bl
84-275 (41275)	HR	y
84-278 (41278)	HR	bl
84-279 (41279)	HR	or
84-282 (41282)	HR	bl
84-283 (41283)	HR	or
84-284 (41284)	HR	y
84-287 (41287)	HR	or
84-288 (41288)	HR	or
84-289 (41289)	HR	y
84-290 (41290)	HR	bl
84-291 (41291)	HR	y
84-292 (41292)	HR	or
84-293 (41293)	HR	y
84-294 (41294)	HR	or
84-295 (41295)	HR	bl
84-296 (41296)	HR	y
84-297 (41297)	HR	y
84-298 (41298)	HR	y
84-299 (41299)	HR	y
84-300 (41300)	HR	bl
84-301 (41301)	HR	or
84-302 (41302)	HR	or
84-303 (41303)	HR	or
84-304 (41304)	HR	y
84-305 (41305)	HR	y
84-306 (41306)	HR	m
84-307 (41307)	HR	y
84-308 (41308)	HR	y
84-309 (41309)	HR	or
843-10 (41310)	HR	m
84-311 (41311)	HR	or
84-313 (41313)	HR	m
84-315 (41315)	HR	y
84-316 (41316)	HR	or
84-317 (41317)	HR	y
84-318 (41318)	HR	y
84-324 (41324)‡	HR	or
84-325 (41325)‡	HR	y
84-326 (41326)‡	HR	y
84-327 (41327)‡	HR	or
84-328 (41328)‡	HR	bl
84-374 (41374)	HR	bl
84-375 (41375)	HR	or
84-376 (41376)	HR	bl
84-382 (41382)	HR	bl
84-383 (41383)	HR	or
84-384 (41384)	HR	or
84-385 (41385)	HR	bl
84-386 (41386)	HR	y
84-387 (41387)	HR	bl
84-388 (41388)	HR	bl
84-389 (41389)	HR	bl
84-390 (41390)	HR	bl
84-391 (41391)	HR	y
84-392 (41392)	HR	bl
84-393 (41393)	HR	bl
84-394 (41394)	HR	m
84-395 (41395)	HR	or
85-398 (51398)	RS	r
85-399 (51399)	HR	bl
85-400 (51400)	RS	gn
85-401 (51401)	HR	or
85-402 (51402)	RS	r
85-403 (51403)	HR	bl
85-404 (51404)	HR	y
85-405 (51405)	HR	y
85-406 (51406)	HR	y
85-407 (51407)	HR	bl
85-408 (51408)	RS	r
85-409 (51409)	HR	bl
85-410 (51410)	RS	r
85-411 (51411)	HR	bl
85-412 (51412)	[512 TFS]	
85-413 (51413)	HR	m
85-415 (51415)	HR	bl
85-416 (51416)	HR	bl
85-417 (51417)	HR	or
85-418 (51418)	HR	bl
85-422 (51422)	RS	r
85-426 (51426)	[526 TFS]	
85-428 (51428)	RS	gn
85-434 (51434)	RS	r
85-436 (51436)	RS	gn
85-438 (51438)	RS	gn
85-440 (51440)	RS	gn
85-442 (51442)	RS	r
85-444 (51444)	RS	r
85-446 (51446)	RS	r
85-448 (51448)	RS	r
85-449 (51449)	RS	r
85-450 (51450)	RS	r
85-451 (51451)	RS	r
85-453 (51453)	RS	r
85-454 (51454)	RS	gn
85-455 (51455)	RS	gn
85-457 (51457)	RS	gn
85-458 (51458)	RS	gn
85-459 (51459)	RS	gn
85-460 (51460)	RS	r
85-461 (51461)	RS	r
85-462 (51462)	RS	r
85-464 (51464)	[86 TFW]	
85-465 (51465)	RS	r
85-466 (51466)	RS	gn
85-467 (51467)	RS	gn
85-468 (51468)	RS	gn
85-469 (51469)	RS	gn
85-470 (51470)	RS	gn
85-471 (51471)	RS	gn
85-472 (51472)	RS	gn
85-473 (51473)	RS	gn
85-474 (51474)	RS	r
85-475 (51475)	RS	r
85-476 (51476)	RS	r
85-477 (51477)	RS	r
85-478 (51478)	RS	r
85-479 (51479)	RS	gn
85-480 (51480)	SP	r
85-481 (51481)	RS	gn
854-86 (51486)	RS	m
85-509 (51509)‡	RS	gn
85-511 (51511)‡	RS	r
85-546 (51546)	SP	r
855-52 (51552)	SP	r
85-572 (51572)‡	SP	m
86-043 (60043)‡	SP	multi
86-209 (60209)	SP	r
86-216 (60216)	SP	r
86-219 (60219)	SP	r
86-222 (60222)	SP	r
86-223 (60223)	SP	bl
86-224 (60224)	SP	r
86-225 (60225)	SP	r
86-226 (60226)	SP	r
86-227 (60227)	SP	r
86-228 (60228)	SP	r
86-229 (60229)	SP	bl
86-230 (60230)	SP	y
86-231 (60231)	SP	bl
86-232 (60232)	SP	r
86-243 (60243)	SP	bl
86-244 (60244)	SP	bl
86-255 (60255)	SP	bl
86-260 (60260)	SP	y
86-263 (60263)	SP	y

Grumman C-20A Gulfstream III

58 MAS, Ramstein

FY83
30500
30501
30502

Gates C-21A Learjet

*58MAS Ramstein
†7005ABS Stuttgart

FY84
40081†
40082†
40083†
40084*
40085*
40086*

Shorts C-23A Sherpa

322MAW/10MAS Zweibrucken

FY83
30512 *Zweibrucken*
30513 *Ramstein*

FY84
40458 *Sembach*
40459 *Spangdahlem*
40460 *Hahn*
40461 *Rhein Main*
40462 *Mildenhall/Lakenheath*
40463 *Bitburg*
40464 *Zaragosa*
40465 *Alconbury*
40466 *Bentwaters/Woodbridge*
40467 *Upper Heyford*
40468 *Greenham Common*
40469 *Soesterberg*
40470 *Torrejon*
40471 *Wiesbaden*
40472 *Incirlik*
40473 *Florennes*

North American T-39A

1868FCS Rhein Main
24453 (FY62)

USAF (EUR based)

Serial

Cessna T-41 Mescalero

FY65
55186 (N5186F)
Spangdahlem
55187 (N5187F) Torrejon
55188 (N5188F) Ramstein

Sikorsky CH-53C
601TCW/601 TASS Sembach
01625 (FY70)
01626 (FY70)
01630 (FY70)
10924 (FY68)
10928 (FY68)
10930 (FY68)
10932 (FY68)

Lockheed C-130E Hercules
435TAW Rhein Main: 37TAS;
*7405 OS
01260 (FY70)
01264 (FY70)
01271 (FY70)
01274 (FY70)
10935 (FY68)
10938 (FY68)
10943 (FY68)
10947 (FY68)
17681 (FY64)
18240 (FY64)
21819 (FY62)*
21822 (FY62)*
21828 (FY62)*
37885 (FY63)
40502 (FY64)
40527 (FY64)
40550 (FY64)
96566 (FY69)
96582 (FY69)
96583 (FY69)

Lockheed EC-130H Hercules
SB: 66ECW/43 ECS, Sembach

FY73
31583 (FY73)
31585 (FY73)
31594 (FY73)
31595 (FY73)

Lockheed MC-130E Hercules
7SOS Rhein Main
40523 (FY64)
40555 (FY64)
40561 (FY64)
40566 (FY64)

Lockheed VC-140B Jetstar
58MAS Ramstein
24200 (FY62)

European based US Army Aircraft

Serial

Bell AH-1S (FM) Cobra
2nd Armoured Cavalry Regiment: Feucht
11th Armoured Cavalry Regiment: Fulda
3rd Aviation Battalion (Combat), 'B' Co: Giebelstadt
3rd Aviation Battalion (Combat), 'C' Co: Schweinfurt
8th Aviation Battalion (Combat), 'B' Co: Mainz-Finthen
8th Aviation Battalion (Combat), 'C' Co: Mainz-Finthen
308th Attack Helicopter Battalion, Hanau
501st Aviation Battalion (Combat), 'B' Co: Ansbach
501st Aviation Battalion (Combat), 'C' Co: Illesheim
503rd Aviation Battalion (Combat), 'B' Co: Hanau
503rd Aviation Battalion (Combat), 'C' Co: Hanau

FY68
15007 8 B Co
15015 3 C Co
15036 503 C Co
15038 501 B Co
15046 501 B Co
15057 10 AHB
15069 501 B Co
15084 503 B Co
15085 2 ACR
15092 503 B Co
15093 8 B Co
15104 308 AHB
15105 2 ACR
15106 3 B Co
15110 503 B Co
15112 501 C Co
15113 308 AHB
15116 2 ACR
15131 8 C Co
15134 501 B Co
15142 11 ACR
15152 501 B Co
15167 501 B Co
15173 501 B Co
15180 503 B Co
15208 503 C Co

FY66
15249 503 B Co
15250 2 ACR
15252 11 ACR
15254 2 ACR
15261 2 ACR
15263 8 B Co
15264 3 B Co
15266 2 ACR
15273 11 ACR
15275 503 C Co
15286 2 ACR
15289 8 B Co
15290 2 ACR
15292 8 C Co
15293 501 C Co
15295 2 ACR
15315 503 B Co
15316 3 C Co
15321 8 C Co
15322 501 B Co
15324 501 C Co
15328 503 B Co
15335 11 ACR
15348 3 C Co
15350 3 C Co
15356 11 ACR

FY67
15450 2 ACR
15452 8 C Co
15455 2 ACR
15456 501 C Co
15457 503 C Co
15459 2 ACR
15460 8 B Co
15470 11 ACR
15473 11 ACR
15475 11 ACR
15477 3 C Co
15479 3 B Co
15480 503 B Co
15489 8 B Co
15490 503 B Co
15491 8 C Co
15497 2 ACR
15506 3 B Co
15508 501 C Co
15512 3 B Co
15520 501 C Co
15522 3 B Co
15528 3 B Co
15530 3 B Co
15535 3 C Co
15540 8 C Co
15548 3 B Co
15551 501 C Co
15565 3 C Co
15571 8 B Co
15572 11 ACR
15587 501 C Co

Serial	
15593	11 ACR
15610	2 ACR
15613	8 C Co
15614	8 B Co
15617	503 B Co
15621	2 ACR
15624	501 B Co
15633	501 C Co
15642	8 C Co
15643	2 ACR
15650	503 B Co
15652	503 B Co
15658	11 ACR
15659	2 ACR
15662	11 ACR
15664	3 C Co
15665	8 C Co
15666	11 ACR
15675	11 ACR
15679	8 C Co
15682	8 B Co
15683	501 B Co
15689	2 ACR
15701	2 ACR
15710	503 B Co
15716	503 C Co
15717	3 B Co
15721	3 C Co
15736	3 C Co
15741	503 C Co
15745	8 B Co
15757	503 C Co
15762	501 B Co
15764	3 B Co
15769	8 C Co
15771	503 B Co
15772	8 B Co
15775	308 AHB
15776	503 C Co
15784	8 B Co
15789	501 C Co
15790	3 C Co
15805	501 B Co
15815	501 B Co
15822	2 ACR
15829	501 C Co
15833	8 C Co
15842	501 B Co
15852	308 AHB
15860	8 C Co
15863	3 C Co
FY70	
15947	501 C Co
15950	501 C Co
15951	503 C Co
15952	11 ACR
15958	11 ACR
15959	8 C Co
15961	8 C Co
15970	3 B Co
15971	3 C Co
15995	2 ACR
16012	3 C Co
16016	3 C Co
16048	3 C Co
16054	501 B Co
16091	501 B Co
FY69	
16411	3 C Co
16422	501 B Co
16426	2 ACR

Serial	
16429	3 B Co
16431	3 B Co
16432	503 B Co
16433	8 B Co
16434	503 B Co
16436	503 C Co
16439	11 ACR
16445	8 B Co
FY68	
17023	503 C Co
17028	503 B Co
17047	11 ACR
17049	8 B Co
17062	503 C Co
17063	503 B Co
17066	501 C Co
17067	501 C Co
17070	501 C Co
17074	503 C Co
17076	501 B Co
17078	8 B Co
17079	503 B Co
17082	503 C Co
17085	503 C Co
17087	501 C Co
17088	11 ACR
17092	503 B Co
17095	8 C Co
17100	501 B Co
17101	308 AHB
17104	501 B Co
17105	501 C Co
17108	501 C Co
17111	8 C Co
17112	503 B Co
FY71	
20998	11 ACR
21014	503 C Co
21028	503 C Co
21035	2 ACR
FY78	
23089	3 C Co
23095	11 ACR
23118	3 B Co
FY79	
23189	3 B Co
23190	3 B Co
23194	3 B Co
23199	3 C Co
23200	3 C Co
23235	3 C Co
FY81	
23526	11 ACR
23527	11 ACR
23528	8 C Co
23529	8 C Co
23530	8 C Co
23531	8 B Co
23532	8 C Co
23533	8 B Co
23534	8 B Co
23535	8 B Co
23536	8 B Co
23537	3 B Co
23538	3 B Co
23539	3 C Co
23540	3 B Co

Grumman V-1 Mohawk

†1MIB, Wiesbaden
‡2MIB, Stuttgart

Serial		
14239	(FY64)	RV-1D†
14244	(FY64)	RV-1D‡
14245	(FY64)	RV-1D†
14246	(FY64)	RV-1D‡
14248	(FY64)	RV-1D†
14256	(FY64)	RV-1D‡
14261	(FY64)	RV-1D†
14263	(FY64)	RV-1D†
14268	(FY64)	OV-1B‡
14269	(FY64)	RV-1D†
15900	(FY64)	OV-1D†
15930	(FY68)	OV-1D‡
15940	(FY68)	OV-1D†
15956	(FY68)	OV-1D‡
15960	(FY68)	OV-1D†
15962	(FY68)	OV-1D‡
16993	(FY68)	OV-1D†
16996	(FY68)	OV-1D‡
17004	(FY69)	OV-1D‡
17008	(FY69)	OV-1D‡
17021	(FY69)	OV-1D†
18900	(FY67)	OV-1D†
18908	(FY67)	OV-1D‡
18921	(FY67)	OV-1D†
25865	(FY62)	OV-1D†
25878	(FY62)	OV-1D†
25891	(FY62)	RV-1D‡
25897	(FY62)	RV-1D†
25902	(FY62)	OV-1D‡

Beech C-12A Super King Air ($=C-12C, †=RC-12D, ‡=C-12F)

25AvCo, Stuttgart;
HQ/USEUCOM;
56AvCo, Vicenza
207AvCo Heidelberg
Corps of Engineers, Wiesbaden
62AvCo, Wiesbaden
1MIB, Wiesbaden
2MIB/330 ASACo, Stuttgart

Serial		
22253	(FY73)	25AvCo
22254$	(FY73)	207AvCo
22255	(FY73)	HQ/USEUCOM
22260	(FY73)	Corps of Eng's
22261$	(FY73)	62AvCo
22262	(FY73)	Berlin Bgde
22556	(FY76)	56AvCo
22557	(FY76)	207AvCo
22564	(FY76)	56AvCo
22944	(FY77)	56AvCo
22950	(FY77)	207AvCo
23126$	(FY78)	207AvCo
23127$	(FY78)	207AvCo
23128$	(FY78)	207AvCo
23141†	(FY78)	1MIB
23142†	(FY78)	1MIB
23144†	(FY78)	2MIB/ 330ASA Co
23371†	(FY80)	2MIB/ 330ASA Co
23373†	(FY80)	2MIB/ 330ASA Co
23374†	(FY80)	2MIB/ 330ASA Co
23375†	(FY80)	1MIB
23376†	(FY80)	2MIB/ 330ASA Co

US Army (EUR based)

Serial

23377† (FY80) 1MIB
23378† (FY80) 2MIB/ 330ASA Co
23542† (FY81) 1MIB
24380† (FY84) 207AvCo
51264‡ (FY85) 1MIB

Beech U-21A King Air
***EU-21A**

18000* (FY66) 7th Sigs Bgde
18010 (FY66) 56 AvCo
18013* (FY66) 7th Sigs Bgde
18014 (FY66) 56th AvCo
18019 (FY66) 56th AvCo
18025 (FY66) 56th AvCo
18027* (FY66) 7th Sigs Bgde
18030 (FY66) 7th ATC
18049 (FY67) 14th AvCo
18058 (FY67) 5th Corps
18078 (FY67) 7th Corps
18080 (FY67) 56th AvCo
18116 (FY67) 56th AvCo

Boeing-Vertol
CH-47C Chinook

* 180AvCo, Schwabisch Hall;
† 205AvCo, Mainz-Finthen;
‡ 295AvCo, Coleman Barracks

15002 (FY70)*
15005 (FY70)†
15012 (FY70)‡
15020 (FY70)*
15829 (FY68)‡
15831 (FY68)‡
15838 (FY68)†
15846 (FY68)*
15847 (FY68)†
15849 (FY68)‡
15851 (FY68)†
15856 (FY68)*
15865 (FY68)*
15867 (FY68)*
15868 (FY68)*
15990 (FY68)‡
15995 (FY68)*
15997 (FY68)*
16005 (FY68)†
16006 (FY68)*
16008 (FY68)‡
16009 (FY68)†
17114 (FY69)‡
17116 (FY69)*
17117 (FY69)‡
17118 (FY69)*
17126 (FY69)†
18516 (FY67)‡
18531 (FY67)†
18533 (FY67)‡
18540 (FY67)*
18548 (FY67)*
20950 (FY71)†
20952 (FY71)†
20953 (FY71)†
20954 (FY71)‡
22277 (FY74)†
22281 (FY74)*
22283 (FY74)‡
22284 (FY74)‡
22285 (FY74)‡
22286 (FY74)†
22291 (FY74)‡

Serial

22293 (FY74)‡
22676 (FY76)†
22677 (FY76)‡
22678 (FY76)‡
22679 (FY76)‡
22681 (FY76)*
22683 (FY76)*
22684 (FY76)*
23394 (FY79)*
23395 (FY79)†
23396 (FY79)*
23398 (FY79)‡
24734 (FY85)
24735 (FY85)
24736 (FY85)
24737 (FY85)
24739 (FY85)
24740 (FY85)
24742 (FY85)

Boeing-Vertol CH-47D
Chinook

†205 AvCo, Mainz-Finthen

61671 (FY86)†
61672 (FY86)†
61673 (FY86)†
61674 (FY86)†

Sikorsky UH-60A
Blackhawk

3rd Aviation Battalion (Combat), 'D' Co and 'E' Co: Giebelstadt
8th Aviation Battalion (Combat), 'D' Co: Mainz-Finthen
4th Aviation Co: Wiesbaden
48th Aviation Co: Wiesbaden
203rd Aviation Co: Wertheim
205th AVIM Battalion: Hanau
207th Aviation Co: Heidelberg
57th Aviation Co: Hanau
21st Aviation Co: Giebelstadt
159th Med Det (HA), Lemwerder
15th Med Det (HA), Grafenwohr
63rd Med Det (HA), Landstuhl
236th Med Det (HA), Gablingen
357th Avn Det/SHAPE, Chievres
421st Medical Co: Nellingen
394th AVIM Battalion: Nellingen
421st Medical Co, 1st Platoon: Wiesbaden
421st Medical Co, 2nd Platoon: Schweinfurt
421st Medical Co, 3rd Platoon: Wiesbaden
421st Medical Co, 4th Platoon: Darmstadt
501st Aviation Battalion (Combat), 'D' Co and 'E' Co: Ansbach
503rd Aviation Battalion (Combat), 'D' Co and 'E' Co: Hanau

FY77

22723 159 Med Det
22727 63 Med Det

FY78

22969 63 Med Det
22986 236 Med Det
22990 159 Med Det
22991 421 Med Co

Serial

22995 63 Med Det
22996 236 Med Det
22997 159 Med Det
23000 159 Med Det
23001 63 Med Det
23003 159 Med Det

FY80

23425 3 E Co
23427 3 E Co
23428 3 E Co
23431 3 E Co
23432 3 E Co
23433 3 E Co
23434 236 Med Det
23436 3 E Co
23438 3 E Co
23439 3 E Co
23440 3 E Co
23441 3 E Co
23442 3 E Co
23443 3 E Co
23489 394
23490 394

FY81

23548 203
23551 159 Med Det
23568 205
23571 3 E Co
23572 205
23573 205
23575 48
23578 48
23579 48
23580 48
23581 503 E Co
23582 48
23583 503 E Co
23584 503 E Co
23585 357 Avn Det
23586 503 E Co
23587 48
23588 48
23589 48
23590 48
23591 48
23592 48
23593 48
23594 501 E Co
23595 501 E Co
23596 15 Med Det
23597 48
23598 48
23599 48
23602 57 Av Co
23603 503 E Co
23604 503 E Co
23605 57 Av Co
23606 503 E Co
23607 4
23608 501 E Co
23609 503 E Co
23610 503 E Co
23613 501 E Co
23614 503 E Co
23615 503 E Co
23616 4 E Co
23617 503 D Co
23618 503 E Co
23622 8 E Co
23623 8 D Co
23624 8 E Co

Serial		Serial		Serial	
23625	8 E Co	23705	203	*FY86*	
23626	8 E Co	23706	203	24498	357 Avn Det
		23707	203	24530	
FY82		23721	203	24531	
23660	501 E Co	23722	203	24532	
23661	501 E Co	23723	421 4 Pl	24544	207
23662	501 E Co	23726	63 Med Det	24550	63 Med Det
23663	501 E Co	23727	421 4 Pl	24552	48
23664	501 E Co	23729	15 Med Det	24553	48
23665	8 E Co	23730	421	24554	48
23666	8 E Co	23731	421 4 Pl	24551	15 Med Det
23667	8 E Co	23733	421 4 Pl	24555	421 Med Co
23668	4	23735	421	24579	48
23669	4	23736	421	24581	236 Med Det
23672	203	23737	421 4 Pl		
23673	203	23738	421 2 Pl	**McD AH-64A Apache**	
23674	203	23739	421 4 Pl	Ildesheim	
23675	421 4 Pl	23740	—		
23676	421 2 Pl	23741	421 2 Pl	*FY84*	
23682	4	23743	421 2 Pl	24218	
23683	8 E Co	23744	501 D Co	24257	
23684	8 E Co	23745	421	24258	
23685	4	23746	421 2 Pl	24259	
23686	4	23749	421	24260	
23690	501 E Co	23750	421	24262	
23691	501 E Co	23751	421	24263	
23692	501 E Co	23752	421	24290	
23693	501 E Co	23753	421	24291	
23694	501 E Co	23754	421	24292	
23695	203	23755	421	24293	
23696	203	23756	421	24294	
23697	203			24295	
23698	203			24296	
23699	203			24297	
23700	—	*FY85*		24298	
23701	207	24390		24299	
23702	207	24392		24302	
23703	203	24417		24303	
23704	203	24418	21	24304	

European based US Navy Aircraft

Serial

Grumman C-2A Greyhound
(VR-24 Sigonella)
162143 [JM23]
162144 [JM24]
162145 [JM25]
162146 [JM26]
162153 [JM21]
162155 [JM27]
162159 [JM20]

Lockheed EP-3E/*UP-3A Orion
(VQ-2: Rota)
148888 [JQ-23]
149668 [JQ-21]
149677 [JQ-20]*
150494 [JQ-25]
150502 [JQ-22]
150503 [JQ-26]
150505 [JQ-24]
151368 [JQ-27]

Beech UC-12B Super King Air
8C: NAF Sigonella;
8D: NAF Rota
1188 [8A] (161188)
1197 [8D] (161197)
1323 [8C] (161323)
1517 [8D] (161517)

NA CT-39G Sabreliner
(VR-24 Sigonella)
159361 [JM30]
159362 [JM31]
159363 [JM32]

Lockheed C-130F/KC-130F* Hercules
(VR-22: Rota)
148892 [JL 05]*
149790 [JL00]
149794 [JL01]
149797 [JL02]
149801 [JL03]
150687 [JL04]*

US based USAF Aircraft

The following aircraft are normally based in the USA but are likely to be seen visiting the UK from time to time. The types are in numerical order, commencing with the E-**3** and concluding with the C-**141**. The aircraft are listed in numerical progression by the serial actually carried externally. Fiscal year information is provided, together with details of mark variations and in some cases operating units.

The B-52H has been excluded from this edition as European sightings are now rare, but additional C-130 Hercules have been included in a revised format. The B-52G aircraft are being moved between Wings as the refurbishing programme continues. Changes are also occurring with the C-5, C-135 and C-141 as more C-5B and KC-10 aircraft are introduced and others are transferred to AFRES and ANG Units.

Serial	*Wing*
Boeing E-3 Sentry	
552 AW&CW	
963 AW&CS (bk)	
964 AW&CS(r)	
965 AW&CS(y)	
966 AW&CS(TS) (bl)	
00137 (FY80) E-3C y	
00138 (FY80) E-3A y	
00139 (FY80) E-3C y	
10004 (FY81) E-3A y	
10005 (FY81) E-3A y	
11407 (FY71) E-3B bk	
11408 (FY71) E-3A r	
20006 (FY82) E-3C y	
20007 (FY82) E-3C y	
30008 (FY83) E-3C bk	
30009 (FY83) E-3C y	
31674 (FY73) E-3C	
31675 (FY73) E-3B r	
50556 (FY75) E-3B r	
50557 (FY75) E-3B	
50558 (FY75) E-3B r	
50559 (FY75) E-3B r	
50560 (FY75) E-3A r	
61604 (FY76) E-3B r	
61605 (FY76) E-3A r	
61606 (FY76) E-3B r	
61607 (FY76) E-3B bk	
70351 (FY77) E-3A r	
70352 (FY77) E-3B bk	
70353 (FY77) E-3B bk	
70354 (FY77) E-3B bk	
70355 (FY77) E-3A bk	
70356 (FY77) E-3A bk	
80576 (FY78) E-3A bk	
80577 (FY78) E-3A r	
80578 (FY78) E-3A bk	
90001 (FY79) E-3A bl	
90002 (FY79) E-3A bl	
90003 (FY79) E-3A r	
Boeing E-4B	
1ACCS 55SRW	
31676 (FY73)	
31677 (FY73)	
40787 (FY74)	
50125 (FY75)	

Lockheed C-5A Galaxy
(*ANG, Air National Guard
†AFRES, Air Force Reserve)
60 MAW: Travis AFB, California
137 MAS/105 MAG*: Stewart AFB, New York
433 MAW/68 MAS†: Kelly AFB, Texas
433 MAW/337 MAS†: Westover AFB
436 MAW: Dover AFB, Delaware
443 MAW: Atlas AFB, Oklahoma

Serial	*Wing*
FY70	
00445	433 MAW†
00446	60 MAW
00447	436 MAW
00448	436 MAW
00449	60 MAW
00450	60 MAW
00451	60 MAW
00452	436 MAW
00453	436 MAW
00454	436 MAW
00455	436 MAW
00456	436 MAW
00457	60 MAW
00458	60 MAW
00459	60 MAW
00460	436 MAW
00461	60 MAW
00462	443 MAW
00463	436 MAW
00464	436 MAW
00465	436 MAW
00466	436 MAW
00467	436 MAW
FY66	
68304	436 MAW
68305	433 MAW†
68306	433 MAW†
68307	436 MAW
FY67	
70167	436 MAW
70168	433 MAW†
70169	60 MAW
70170	137 MAS/105 MAG*
70171	433 MAW†
70173	436 MAW
70174	436 MAW
FY68	
80211	60 MAW
80212	137 MAS/105 MAG*
80213	60 MAW
80214	436 MAW
80215	436 MAW
80216	60 MAW
80217	436 MAW
80219	60 MAW
80220	436 MAW
80221	60 MAW
80222	436 MAW
80223	60 MAW
80224	436 MAW
80225	60 MAW
80226	60 MAW
80228	60 MAW
FY69	
90001	443 MAW
90002	433 MAW†
90003	436 MAW
90004	436 MAW
90005	60 MAW
90006	439 MAW
90007	60 MAW
90008	137 MAS/105 MAG*
90009	60 MAW
90010	60 MAW
90011	60 MAW
90012	60 MAW
90013	60 MAW
90014	443 MAW
90015	137 MAS/105 MAG*
90016	433 MAW/68 MAS†
90017	436 MAW
90018	60 MAW
90019	436 MAW
90020	60 MAW
90021	436 MAW
90022	60 MAW
90023	60 MAW
90024	60 MAW
90025	60 MAW
90026	436 MAW
90027	436 MAW

Lockheed C-5B Galaxy

Serial	*Wing*
FY83	
31285	443 MAW
FY84	
40059	443 MAW
40060	443 MAW
40061	60 MAW
40062	60 MAW
FY85	
50001	436 MAW
50002	60 MAW
50003	436 MAW
50004	60 MAW
50005	436 MAW
50006	60 MAW
50007	436 MAW
50008	60 MAW
50009	436 MAW
50010	60 MAW
FY86	
60011	436 MAW
60012	60 MAW
60013	436 MAW
60014	60 MAW
60015	436 MAW

Serial	Wing
60016	
60017	
60018	
60019	
60020	
60021	
60022	
60023	
60024	
60025	
60026	
FY87	
70027	
70028	
70029	
70030	
70031	
70032	
70033	
70034	
70035	
70036	
70037	
70038	
70039	
70040	
70041	
70042	
70043	
70044	
70045	

McDonnell-Douglas KC-10A Extender

2 BW* 22 ARW† 68 ARW‡

20191 (FY82)†
20192 (FY82)‡
20193 (FY82)†

30075 (FY83)*
30076 (FY83)†
30077 (FY83)‡
30078 (FY83)†
30079 (FY83)*
30080 (FY83)†
30081 (FY83)*
30082 (FY83)*

40185 (FY84)†
40186 (FY84)*
40187 (FY84)†
40188 (FY84)*
40189 (FY84)†
40190 (FY84)*
40191 (FY84)†
40192 (FY84)*

50027 (FY85)†
50028 (FY85)*
50029 (FY85)‡
50030 (FY85)‡
50031 (FY85)‡
50032 (FY85)*
50033 (FY85)*
50034 (FY85)*

60027 (FY86)*
60028 (FY86)‡
60029 (FY86)‡
60030 (FY86)‡
60031 (FY86)‡
60032 (FY86)‡
60033 (FY86)‡
60034 (FY86)‡
60035 (FY86)‡
60036 (FY86)‡
60037 (FY86)‡
60038 (FY86)‡

70117 (FY87)†
70118 (FY87)†
70119 (FY87)†
70120 (FY87)
70121 (FY87)‡
70122 (FY87)
70123 (FY87)
70124 (FY87)

90433 (FY79)*
90434 (FY79)*

91710 (FY79)*
91711 (FY79)*
91712 (FY79)*
91713 (FY79)*

91946 (FY79)†
91947 (FY79)†
91948 (FY79)†
91949 (FY79)†
91950 (FY79)†
91951 (FY79)†

Boeing C-18A/EC-18B*

(Air Force Systems Command)

Serial	Wing
FY81	
10891*	4950 TW
10892	4950 TW
10893	
10894*	4950 TW
10895	4950 TW
10896*	
10897	
10898*	

Grumman C-20B Gulfstream III

89 MAW Andrews AFB

FY86

60200
60201
60202
60203
60204
60205
60206

60403

Boeing VC-25A

89 MAW Andrews AFB

(Air Force One)

FY86

68000

Boeing B-52G Stratofortress

Serial	Wing
FY57	
76468	BW
76469	320 BW
76470	BW
76471	BW
76472	2 BW
76473	BW
76474	BW
76475	2 BW
76476	BW
76477	BW
76478	BW
76480	93 BW
76483	2 BW
76484	42 BW
76485	BW
76486	93 BW
76487	BW
76488	SW
76489	BW
76490	BW
76491	93 BW
76492	93 BW
76495	BW
76497	BW
76498	BW
76499	BW
76500	BW
76501	410 BW
76502	93 BW
76503	BW
76504	BW
76505	2 BW
76506	2 BW
76508	BW
76509	BW
76510	42 BW
76511	93 BW
76512	2 BW
76513	BW
76514	93 BW
76515	BW
76516	BW
76517	BW
76518	BW
76519	BW
76520	BW
FY58	
80158	93 BW
80159	BW
80160	BW
80162	BW
80163	93 BW
80164	416 BW
80165	BW
80166	BW
80167	BW
80168	BW
80170	BW
80171	BW
80172	42 BW
80173	2 BW
80175	BW
80176	BW
80177	2 BW
80178	97 BW
80179	BW
80181	BW
80182	BW

USAF (US based)

Serial	Wing
80183	BW
80184	2 BW
80185	BW
80186	43 SW
80189	320 BW
80190	BW
80191	2 BW
80192	93 BW
80193	BW
80194	BW
80195	BW
80197	320 BW
80199	BW
80200	2 BW
80202	42 BW
80203	BW
80204	BW
80205	BW
80206	93 BW
80207	2 BW
80210	2 BW
80211	BW
80212	2 BW
80213	93 BW
80214	93 BW
80216	2 BW
80217	BW
80218	2 BW
80219	93 BW
80220	2 BW
80221	43 SW
80222	2 BW
80223	BW
80224	93 BW
80225	BW
80226	BW
80227	2 BW
80229	BW
80230	BW
80231	BW
80232	93 BW
80233	2 BW
80234	320 BW
80235	93 BW
80236	BW
80237	379 BW
80238	93 BW
80239	320 BW
80240	42 BW
80241	42 BW
80242	320 BW
80243	BW
80244	BW
80245	BW
80247	379 BW
80248	93 BW
80249	BW
80250	93 BW
80251	BW
80252	BW
80253	BW
80254	93 BW
80255	BW
80257	BW
80258	BW

FY59

Serial	Wing
92564	93 BW
92565	BW
92566	416 BW
92567	416 BW
92568	BW
92569	2 BW
92570	BW
92571	BW
92572	320 BW
92573	320 BW
92575	93 BW
92577	BW
92578	42 BW
92579	BW
92580	2 BW
92581	BW
92582	2 BW
92583	93 BW
92584	416 BW
92585	BW
92586	AFFTC
92587	BW
92588	2 BW
92589	BW
92590	2 BW
92591	BW
92592	320 BW
92593	320 BW
92594	93 BW
92595	93 BW
92596	42 BW
92598	BW
92599	93 BW
92601	416 BW
92602	BW

Lockheed SR-71A Blackbird

9SRW/99SRS No 4 Det:
RAF Mildenhall

FY64

17958
17959
17960
17961
17962
17963
17964
17967
17968
17971
17972
17973
17974
17975
17976
17979
17980

Lockheed C-130 Hercules

$ — EC-130 £ — HC-130
● — LC-130 § — MC-130
‡ — WC-130
* — ANG: Air National Guard
† — AFRES: Air Force Reserve

FY60: **C-130B**

Serial	Wing
00294	731 TAS†
00295	731 TAS†
00296	731 TAS†
00299	731 TAS†
00300	731 TAS†
00303	731 TAS†
00310	731 TAS†

FY80: **C-130H**

Serial	Wing
00320	158 TAS*
00321	158 TAS*
00322	158 TAS*
00323	158 TAS*
00324	158 TAS*
00325	158 TAS*
00326	158 TAS*
00332	158 TAS*

FY70: **C-130E**

Serial	Wing
01259	317 TAW
01260	435 TAW
01261	317 TAW
01262	317 TAW
01263	317 TAW
01264	435 TAW
01265	317 TAW
01266	317 TAW
01267	317 TAW
01268	317 TAW
01269	317 TAW
01270	317 TAW
01271	435 TAW
01272	317 TAW
01273	317 TAW
01274	435 TAW
01275	317 TAW
01276	317 TAW

FY81: **C-130H**

Serial	Wing
10626	700 TAS†
10627	700 TAS†
10628	700 TAS†
10629	700 TAS†
10630	700 TAS†
10631	700 TAS†

FY68: **C-130E**

Serial	Wing
10934	317 TAW
10935	435 TAW
10937	317 TAW
10938	435 TAW
10939	317 TAW
10940	317 TAW
10941	317 TAW
10942	317 TAW
10943	435 TAW
10945	317 TAW
10947	435 TAW
10948	314 TAW
10949	314 TAW
10950	314 TAW

FY61: **C-130B**

Serial	Wing
10948	731 TAS†
10949	156 TAS*
10950	156 TAS*
10951	757 TAS†
10952	164 TAS*
10954	303 TAS†
10956	303 TAS†
10957	303 TAS†
10958	303 TAS†
10959	757 TAS†
10960	303 TAS†
10961	164 TAS*
10963	164 TAS*
10964	757 TAS†
10966	187 TAS*
10968	303 TAS†

Serial	Wing
10969	303 TAS†
10971	757 TAS†

FY61: **C-130E**

Serial	Wing
12358	115 TAS*
12359	115 TAS*
12360‡	WRS
12361	314 TAW
12362	314 TAW
12363	314 TAW
12364	314 TAW
12365‡	53 WRS
12366‡	WRS
12367	115 TAS*
12368	314 TAW
12369	314 TAW
12370	115 TAS*
12371	314 TAW
12372	115 TAS*
12373	115 TAS*

FY61: **C-130B**

Serial	Wing
12634	135 TAS*
12635	187 TAS*
12636	156 TAS*
12638	156 TAS*
12639	135 TAS*
12640	156 TAS*
12643	187 TAS*
12645	135 TAS*
12647	303 TAS†

FY64: **C-130H**

Serial	Wing
14854‡	815 WRS†
14859$	41 ECS
14861‡	WRS
14866‡	815 WRS†

FY64: **C-130E**

Serial	Wing
17680	314 TAW
17681	435 TAW
18240	435 TAW

FY82: **C-130H**

Serial	Wing
20054	144 TAS*
20055	144 TAS*
20056	144 TAS*
20057	144 TAS*
20058	144 TAS*
20059	144 TAS*
20060	144 TAS*
20061	144 TAS*

FY72: **C-130E**

Serial	Wing
21288	374 TAW
21289	374 TAW
21290	374 TAW
21291	314 TAW
21292	314 TAW
21293	314 TAW
21294	314 TAW
21295	314 TAW
21296	314 TAW
21298	314 TAW
21299	374 TAW

FY62: **C-130E**

Serial	Wing
21784	130 TAS*
21786	109 TAS*
21787	109 TAS*
21788	130 TAS*
21789	337 TAS†
21790	184 TFS*
21792	115 TAS*
21793	115 TAS*
21794	337 TAS†
21795	109 TAS*
21798	154 TAS*
21799	115 TAS*
21801	115 TAS*
21803	337 TAS†
21804	130 TAS*
21806	96 TAS†
21807	337 TAS†
21808	337 TAS†
21810	337 TAS†
21811	115 TAS*
21812	109 TAS*
21816	337 TAS†
21817	109 TAS*
21819	7405 OS
21820	337 TAS†
21821	314 TAW
21822	7405 OS
21823	337 TAS†
21824	130 TAS*
21826	115 TAS*
21827	314 TAW
21828	7405 OS
21829	109 TAS*
21830	63 TAS†
21833	115 TAS*
21834	96 TAS†
21835	96 TAS†
21837	109 TAS*
21838	337 TAS†
21839	96 TAS†
21842	115 TAS*
21844	96 TAS†
21846	109 TAS*
21847	96 TAS†
21848	96 TAS†
21849	337 TAS†
21850	337 TAS†
21851	115 TAS*
21852	96 TAS†
21855	314 TAW
21856	109 TAS*
21857$	7 ACCS [KS]
21858	337 TAS†
21859	374 TAW
21860	337 TAS†
21862	115 TAS*
21863$	7 ACCS
21864	109 TAS*
21866	337 TAS†

FY62: **C-130B**

Serial	Wing
23487	757 TAS†
23493	757 TAS†
23495	135 TAS*
23496	303 TAS†

FY83: **C-130H**

Serial	Wing
30486	139 TAS*
30487	139 TAS*
30488	139 TAS*
30489	139 TAS*
30490●	139 TAS*
30491●	139 TAS*
30492●	139 TAS*
30493●	139 TAS*
31212§	AFFTC

FY73: **C-130H**

Serial	Wing
31580	374 TAW
31581$	41 ECS
31582	374 TAW
31583$	43 ECS [SB]
31584$	41 ECS
31585$	43 ECS [SB]
31586$	41 ECS
31587$	41 ECS
31588$	41 ECS [DM]
31590	374 TAW
31592$	41 ECS
31594$	43 ECS [SB]
31595$	43 ECS [SB]
31597	374 TAW
31598	374 TAW

FY53: **C-130A**

Serial	Wing
33132	95 TAS†
33135	64 TAS†

FY63: **C-130E**

Serial	Wing
37764	328 TAS†
37765	314 TAW
37767	314 TAW
37768	314 TAW
37769	314 TAW
37770	328 TAS†
37771	314 TAW
37773$	193 SOS* [RR]
37776	314 TAW
37777	374 TAW
37778	314 TAW
37779	345 TAS
37781	314 TAW
37782	
37783$	193 SOS* [RR]
37784	
37786	314 TAW
37788	
37790	314 TAW
37791	314 TAW
37792	
37793	314 TAW
37794	314 TAW
37795	314 TAW
37796	314 TAW
37799	314 TAW
37800	374 TAW
37803	374 TAW
37804	17 TAS
37805	328 TAS†
37806	314 TAW
37807	317 TAW
37808	314 TAW
37809	317 TAW
37811	374 TAW
37812	374 TAW
37813	317 TAW
37814	62 MAW
37815$	193 SOS* [EC]
37816$	193 SOS* [EC]
37817	328 TAS†
37818	345 TAS
37819	374 TAW

USAF (US based)

Serial	Wing
37820	314 TAW
37821	317 TAW
37822	328 TAS†
37823	317 TAW
37824	374 TAW
37825	374 TAW
37826	327 TAS†
37828$	193 SOS* [EC]
37829	317 TAW
37830	345 TAS
37831	345 TAS
37832	327 TAS†
37833	327 TAS†
37834	327 TAS†
37835	314 TAW
37836	314 TAW
37837	345 TAS
37838	314 TAW
37839	314 TAW
37840	374 TAW
37841	314 TAW
37842	
37845	317 TAW
37846	317 TAW
37847	314 TAW
37848	327 TAS†
37849	317 TAW
37850	314 TAW
37851	345 TAS
37852	328 TAS†
37853	327 TAS†
37854	62 MAW
37856	328 TAS†
37857	314 TAW
37858	62 MAW
37859	374 TAW
37860	314 TAW
37861	314 TAW
37863	328 TAS†
37864	314 TAW
37865	374 TAW
37866	314 TAW
37867	327 TAS†
37868	374 TAW
37869$	193 SOS*
37871	317 TAW
37872	345 TAS
37874	62 MAW
37876	314 TAW
37877	374 TAW
37879	374 TAW
37880	314 TAW
37881	374 TAW
37882	314 TAW
37883	327 TAS†
37884	317 TAW
37885	435 TAW
37887	314 TAW
37888	314 TAW
37889	374 TAW
37890	317 TAW
37891	
37892	327 TAS†
37893	
37894	314 TAW
37895	374 TAW
37896	314 TAW
37897	374 TAW
37898	314 TAW
37899	317 TAW
	317 TAW
	314 TAW
	314 TAW

Serial	Wing
39813	314 TAW
39814	314 TAW
39815	314 TAW
39816$	193 SOS* [CL]
39817$	193 SOS*
FY84: **C-130H**	
40204	700 TAS†
40205	700 TAS†
40206	142 TAS*
40207	142 TAS*
40208	142 TAS*
40209	142 TAS*
40210	142 TAS*
40211	142 TAS*
40212	142 TAS*
40213	142 TAS*
40475§	
40476§	
FY64: **C-130E**	
40495	317 TAW
40496	317 TAW
40497	374 TAW
40498	317 TAW
40499	317 TAW
40500	310 MAS
40501	317 TAW
40502	435 TAW
40503	374 TAW
40504	317 TAW
40510	
40512	
40513	314 TAW
40514	374 TAW
40515	374 TAW
40517	317 TAW
40518	314 TAW
40519	
40520	374 TAW
40521	
40523§	7 SOS
40524	
40525	317 TAW
40526	314 TAW
40527	435 TAW
40529	317 TAW
40530	314 TAW
40531	317 TAW
40533	314 TAW
40534	374 TAW
40535	314 TAW
40537	317 TAW
40538	314 TAW
40539	317 TAW
40540	317 TAW
40541	317 TAW
40542	317 TAW
40544	374 TAW
40550	435 TAW
40552‡	WRS
40553‡	53 WRS
40554‡	WRS
40555§	7 SOS
40556	374 TAW
40557	314 TAW
40560	314 TAW
40561§	7 SOS
40566§	7 SOS
40569	314 TAW
40570	317 TAW

Serial	Wing
FY54: **C-130A**	
41631	143 TAS*
41634	180 TAS*
41635	143 TAS*
41636	63 TAS†
41637	152 TFTS*
41638	95 TAS†
41639	155 TAS*
41640	105 TAS*
FY74: **C-130H**	
41658	17 TAS
41659	17 TAS
41660	463 TAW
41661	463 TAW
41662	463 TAW
41663	463 TAW
41664	463 TAW
41665	463 TAW
41666	463 TAW
41667	463 TAW
41668	17 TAS
41669	463 TAW
41670	463 TAW
41671	17 TAS
41673	463 TAW
41674	463 TAW
41675	463 TAW
41676	17 TAS
41677	463 TAW
41679	463 TAW
41680	463 TAW
41681	463 TAW
41682	463 TAW
41684	463 TAW
41685	463 TAW
41686	17 TAS
41687	463 TAW
41688	463 TAW
41689	463 TAW
41690	463 TAW
41691	463 TAW
41692	17 TAS
42061	463 TAW
42062	17 TAS
42063	463 TAW
42065	463 TAW
42066	17 TAS
42067	463 TAW
42069	463 TAW
42070	17 TAS
42071	17 TAS
42072	463 TAW
42130	463 TAW
42131	17 TAS
42132	463 TAW
42133	463 TAW
42134	463 TAW
FY55: **C-130A**	
50003	758 TAS†
50004	105 TAS*
50007	63 TAS†
50008	758 TAS†
50010	758 TAS†

Serial	Wing
50015	155 TAS*
50018	180 TAS*
50023	64 TAS†
50025	63 TAS†
50026	105 TAS*
50027	63 TAS†
50028	105 TAS*
50030	180 TAS*
50031	63 TAS†
50033	105 TAS*
50035	64 TAS†

FY85: **C-130H**

Serial	Wing
50011§	
50012§	
50035	357 TAS†
50036	357 TAS†
50037	357 TAS†
50038	357 TAS†
50039	357 TAS†
50040	†
50041	357 TAS†
50042	357 TAS†

FY65: **C-130H**

Serial	Wing
50962£	67 ARRS
50963‡	53 WRS
50964‡	815 WRS†
50966‡	53 WRS
50967‡	815 WRS†
50968‡	53 WRS
50969‡	815 WRS†
50972‡	815 WRS†
50976‡	54 WRS
50977‡	815 WRS†
50980‡	815 WRS†
50984‡	WRS
50985‡	53 WRS
50989$	41 ECS

FY85: **C-130H**

Serial	Wing
51361	181 TAS*
51362	181 TAS*
51363	181 TAS*
51364	181 TAS*
51365	181 TAS*
51366	181 TAS*
51367	181 TAS*
51368	181 TAS*

FY66: **C-130P**

Serial	Wing
60220£	67 ARRS

FY86: **C-130H**

Serial	Wing
60410	758 TAS†
60411	758 TAS†
60412	758 TAS†
60413	758 TAS†
60414	758 TAS†
60415	758 TAS†
60418	758 TAS†
60419	758 TAS†

FY56: **C-130A**

Serial	Wing
60468	105 TAS*
60471	105 TAS*
60473	64 TAS†
60475	
60478	143 TAS*
60479	95 TAS†
60483	180 TAS*
60485	105 TAS*
60487	
60493	155 TAS*
60494	155 TAS*
60495	155 TAS*
60496	95 TAS†
60498	155 TAS*
60500	64 TAS†
60503	105 TAS*
60507	95 TAS†
60508	63 TAS†
60511	180 TAS*
60517	105 TAS*
60518	105 TAS*
60522	64 TAS†
60523	105 TAS*
60524	155 TAS*
60525	356 TAS†
60529	105 TAS*
60531	180 TAS*
60536	758 TAS†
60537	64 TAS†
60543	105 TAS*
60544	180 TAS*
60547	105 TAS*
60550	180 TAS*
60551	

FY86: **C-130H**

Serial	Wing
61391	180 TAS*
61392	180 TAS*
61393	180 TAS*
61394	180 TAS*
61395	180 TAS*
61396	180 TAS*
61397	180 TAS*
61398	180 TAS*
61699§	

FY87: **C-130H**

Serial	Wing
70023§	
70024§	
70025	
70026	
70027	
70028	
70029	
70125§	
70126§	
70127§	

FY57: **C-130A**

Serial	Wing
70453	155 TAS*
70455	328 TAS†
70457	64 TAS†
70459	155 TAS*
70460	63 TAS†
70463	155 TAS*
70464	105 TAS*
70466	95 TAS†
70469	95 TAS†
70470	95 TAS†
70471	180 TAS*
70473	143 TAS†
70476	328 TAS†
70478	328 TAS†
70481	96 TAS†
70483	356 TAS†

FY57: **C-130D**

Serial	Wing
70487	139 TAS*

FY57: **C-130A**

Serial	Wing
70510	328 TAS†
70511	143 TAS*
70512	143 TAS*
70513	143 TAS*
70514	143 TAS*
70515	143 TAS*
70520	328 TAS†
70521	328 TAS†
70524	143 TAS*

FY57: **C-130B**

Serial	Wing
70525	167 TAS*
70529	167 TAS*

FY58: **C-130B**

Serial	Wing
80711	135 TAS*
80714	187 TAS*
80715	135 TAS*
80720	187 TAS*
80723	731 TAS†
80725	167 TAS*
80726	164 TAS*
80727	167 TAS*
80728	156 TAS*
80729	181 TAS*
80731	181 TAS*
80732	167 TAS*
80733	164 TAS*
80734	181 TAS*
80735	167 TAS*
80736	164 TAS*
80738	731 TAS†
80740	167 TAS*
80741	167 TAS*
80742	181 TAS*
80744	187 TAS*
80746	156 TAS*
80747	167 TAS*
80749	164 TAS*
80751	181 TAS*
80752	167 TAS*
80753	167 TAS*
80754	187 TAS*
80755	135 TAS*
80757	731 TAS†
80758	181 TAS*

FY78: **C-130H**

Serial	Wing
80806	185 TAS*
80807	185 TAS*
80808	185 TAS*
80809	185 TAS*
80810	185 TAS*
80811	185 TAS*
80812	185 TAS*
80813	185 TAS*

FY79: **C-130H**

Serial	Wing
90473	130 TAS*
90474	183 TAS*
90475	130 TAS*
90476	130 TAS*
90477	130 TAS*
90478	130 TAS*
90479	130 TAS*
90480	130 TAS*

USAF (US based)

FY59: C-130B

Serial	Type	Wing
91524		757 TAS†
91525		164 TAS*
91526		731 TAS†
91527		731 TAS†
91528		156 TAS*
91529		167 TAS*
91530		731 TAS†
91531		731 TAS†
91532		757 TAS†
91533		156 TAS*
91535		757 TAS†
91536		135 TAS*
91537		731 TAS†

FY69: **C-130N**

Serial	Type	Wing
95820£		67 ARRS
95823£		67 ARRS
95826£		67 ARRS
95827£		67 ARRS
95831£		67 ARRS

FY59: **C-130B**

Serial	Type	Wing
95957		187 TAS*

FY69: **C-130E**

Serial	Type	Wing
96566		435 TAW
96579		314 TAW
96580		317 TAW
96582		435 TAW
96583		435 TAW

Boeing C-135 Stratotanker

* Air National Guard:
- 108 ARS Illinois ANG
- 116 ARS Washington ANG
- 117 ARS Kansas ANG
- 126 ARS Wisconsin ANG
- 132 ARS Maine ANG
- 133 ARS New Hampshire ANG
- 145 ARS Ohio ANG
- 147 ARS Pennsylvania ANG
- 150 ARS New Jersey ANG
- 151 ARS Tennessee ANG
- 168 ARS Alaska ANG
- 191 ARS Utah ANG
- 197 ARS Arizona ANG

† AFRES, Air Force Reserve:
- 72 ARS bl Grissom AFB, In
- 314 ARS r Mather AFB, Ca
- 336 ARS y March AFB, Ca

FY60

Serial	Type	Wing
00313	KC-135A	410 BW
00314	KC-135A	410 BW
00315	KC-135A	2 BW
00316	KC-135A	22 ARW
00317	KC-135A	379 BW
00318	KC-135A	416 BW
00319	KC-135A	93 BW
00320	KC-135A	379 BW
00321	KC-135R	28 BW
00322	KC-135R	19 ARW
00323	KC-135A	319 BW
00324	KC-135A	7 BW
00325	KC-135A	379 BW
00326	KC-135A	379 BW
00327	KC-135A	376 SW
00328	KC-135A	7 BW
00329	KC-135R	93 BW
00331	KC-135A	93 BW
00332	KC-135A	320 BW
00333	KC-135A	319 BW
00334	KC-135A	96 BW
00335	KC-135Q	380 BW
00336	KC-135Q	376 SW
00337	KC-135Q	380 BW
00339	KC-135Q	9 SRW
00341	KC-135R	
00342	KC-135Q	9 SRW
00343	KC-135Q	380 BW
00344	KC-135Q	376 SW
00345	KC-135Q	9 SRW
00346	KC-135Q	9 SRW
00347	KC-135R	19 ARW
00348	KC-135A	416 BW
00349	KC-135A	509 BW
00350	KC-135A	
00351	KC-135A	305 ARW
00353	KC-135R	19 ARW
00355	KC-135A	416 BW
00356	KC-135A	305 ARW
00357	KC-135A	305 ARW
00358	KC-135A	410 BW
00359	KC-135R	19 ARW
00360	KC-135A	93 BW
00362	KC-135A	305 ARW
00363	KC-135A	92 BW
00364	KC-135A	410 BW
00365	KC-135R	28 BW
00366	KC-135A	410 BW
00367	KC-135R	28 BW
00371	NC-135A	4950 TW
00372	C-135E	4950 TW
00374	EC-135E	4950 TW
00375	C-135E	4950 TW
00376	C-135E	8 TDCS/ CinC SC
00377	C-135A	4950 TW
00378	C-135E	55 SRW

FY61

Serial	Type	Wing
10261	EC-135L	305 ARW
10262	EC-135A	28 BW
10263	EC-135L	305 ARW
10264	KC-135A	42 BW
10266	KC-135A	97 BW
10267	KC-135A	97 BW
10268	KC-135A	379 BW
10269	EC-135L	305 ARW
10270	KC-135A	410 BW
10271	KC-135A	5 BW
10272	KC-135R	340 ARW
10274	EC-135H	6 ACCS
10275	KC-135A	97 BW
10276	KC-135R	384 BW
10277	KC-135A	97 BW
10278	EC-135A	28 BW
10279	EC-135L	305 ARW
10280	KC-135A	380 BW
10281	KC-135A	93 BW
10282	EC-135H	513 ACCW
10283	EC-135L	305 ARW
10284	KC-135A	22 ARW
10285	EC-135H	513 ACCW
10286	EC-135H	513 ACCW
10287	EC-135A	28 BW
10288	KC-135A	97 BW
10289	EC-135A	28 BW
10290	KC-135A	97 BW
10291	EC-135H	
10292	KC-135R	384 BW
10293	KC-135R	384 BW
10294	KC-135R	28 BW
10295	KC-135R	93 BW
10297	EC-135A	28 BW
10298	KC-135A	379 BW
10299	KC-135A	410 BW
10300	KC-135A	22 ARW
10302	KC-135A	93 BW
10303	KC-135A	97 BW
10304	KC-135R	384 BW
10305	KC-135A	305 ARW
10306	KC-135R	384 BW
10307	KC-135R	384 BW
10308	KC-135R	384 BW
10309	KC-135R	319 BW
10310	KC-135R	384 BW
10311	KC-135R	93 BW
10312	KC-135R	384 BW
10313	KC-135R	93 BW
10314	KC-135R	19 ARW
10315	KC-135R	384 BW
10317	KC-135R	384 BW
10318	KC-135R	384 BW
10320	KC-135A	42 BW
10321	KC-135A	410 BW
10323	KC-135A	376 SW
10324	KC-135R	384 BW
10325	KC-135A	42 BW
10326	EC-135E	4950 TW
10327	EC-135E	4950 TW
10329	EC-135E	4950 TW
10330	EC-135E	4950 TW

Serial	Type	Wing
12662	RC-135S	6 SW
12663	RC-135S	6 SW
12665	WC-135B	55 WRS
12666	WC-135B	55 WRS
12667	WC-135B	55 WRS
12668	C-135C	89 MAW
12669	C-135C	4950 TW
12670	WC-135B	55 WRS
12671	C-135C	89 MAW
12672	WC-135B	55 WRS
12673	WC-135B	55 WRS
12674	WC-135B	55 WRS

FY64

Serial	Type	Wing
14828	KC-135A	509 BW
14829	KC-135A	42 BW
14830	KC-135A	5 BW
14831	KC-135A	5 BW
14832	KC-135A	96 BW
14833	KC-135A	97 BW
14834	KC-135A	340 ARW
14835	KC-135A	93 BW
14836	KC-135A	376 SW
14837	KC-135A	319 BW
14838	KC-135A	97 BW
14839	KC-135A	19 ARW
14840	KC-135A	380 BW
14841	RC-135V	55 SRW
14842	RC-135V	55 SRW
14843	RC-135V	55 SRW
14844	RC-135V	55 SRW
14845	RC-135V	55 SRW
14846	RC-135V	55 SRW
14847	RC-135U	55 SRW

Serial	Type	Wing
14848	RC-135V	55 SRW
14849	RC-135U	55 SRW
FY62		
23497	KC-135A	416 BW
23498	KC-135A	93 BW
23499	KC-135R	19 ARW
23500	KC-135A	380 BW
23501	KC-135A	42 BW
23502	KC-135A	509 BW
23503	KC-135A	42 BW
23504	KC-135A	319 BW
23505	KC-135A	509 BW
23506	KC-135R	19 ARW
23507	KC-135R	93 BW
23508	KC-135R	340 ARW
23509	KC-135A	509 BW
23510	KC-135R	
23511	KC-135R	384 BW
23512	KC-135R	93 BW
23513	KC-135A	416 BW
23514	KC-135A	416 BW
23515	KC-135A	410 BW
23516	KC-135A	93 BW
23517	KC-135A	7 BW
23518	KC-135A	340 ARW
23519	KC-135A	416 BW
23520	KC-135A	340 ARW
23521	KC-135A	93 BW
23523	KC-135R	19 ARW
23524	KC-135A	380 BW
23525	KC-135A	93 BW
23526	KC-135A	416 BW
23527	KC-135A	410 BW
23528	KC-135A	96 BW
23529	KC-135A	509 BW
23530	KC-135R	
23531	KC-135R	340 ARW
23532	KC-135A	509 BW
23533	KC-135R	384 BW
23534	KC-135R	19 ARW
23537	KC-135A	376 SW
23538	KC-135A	509 BW
23539	KC-135A	340 ARW
23540	KC-135R	28 BW
23541	KC-135A	340 ARW
23542	KC-135A	7 BW
23543	KC-135R	19 ARW
23544	KC-135A	2 BW
23545	KC-135A	380 BW
23546	KC-135R	
23547	KC-135A	42 BW
23548	KC-135A	93 BW
23549	KC-135A	416 BW
23550	KC-135R	19 ARW
23551	KC-135A	93 BW
23552	KC-135R	19 ARW
23553	KC-135A	42 BW
23554	KC-135A	319 BW
23555	KC-135A	410 BW
23556	KC-135R	
23557	KC-135R	19 ARW
23558	KC-135A	376 SW
23559	KC-135A	379 BW
23560	KC-135A	93 BW
23561	KC-135R	340 ARW
23562	KC-135A	410 BW
23563	KC-135A	96 BW
23564	KC-135R	
23565	KC-135A	305 ARW
23566	KC-135A	22 ARW
23567	KC-135A	340 ARW
23568	KC-135A	509 BW
23569	KC-135A	19 ARW
23570	EC-135G	28 BW
23571	KC-135A	410 BW
23572	KC-135A	416 BW
23573	KC-135A	42 BW
23574	KC-135A	305 ARW
23575	KC-135A	42 BW
23576	KC-135A	2 BW
23577	KC-135A	305 ARW
23578	KC-135A	42 BW
23579	EC-135G	28 BW
23580	KC-135A	28 BW
23581	EC-135C	55 SRW
23582	EC-135C	28 BW
23583	EC-135C	55 SRW
23584	EC-135J	9 ACCS
23585	EC-135C	55 SRW
24125	C-135B	58 MAS
24126	C-135B	89 MAW
24127	C-135B	89 MAW
24128	RC-135X	6 SW
24129	C-135B	89 MAW
24130	C-135B	89 MAW
24131	RC-135W	55 SRW
24132	RC-135W	55 SRW
24133	TC-135S	6 SW
24134	RC-135W	55 SRW
24135	RC-135W	55 SRW
24138	RC-135W	55 SRW
24139	RC-135W	55 SRW
26000	VC-137C	89 MAW
FY72		
27000	C-137C	89 MAW
FY63		
37976	KC-135A	93 BW
37977	KC-135R	19 ARW
37978	KC-135A	305 ARW
37979	KC-135A	93 BW
37980	KC-135A	305 ARW
37981	KC-135A	319 BW
37982	KC-135A	379 BW
37983	KC-135A	305 ARW
37984	KC-135R	384 BW
37985	KC-135A	42 BW
37986	KC-135A	416 BW
37987	KC-135A	410 BW
37988	KC-135A	509 BW
37990	KC-135A	305 ARW
37991	KC-135R	28 BW
37992	KC-135A	93 BW
37993	KC-135A	319 BW
37994	EC-135G	305 ARW
37995	KC-135R	19 ARW
37996	KC-135A	305 ARW
37997	KC-135R	384 BW
37998	KC-135A	380 BW
37999	KC-135R	384 BW
38000	KC-135A	22 ARW
38001	EC-135G	28 BW
38002	KC-135R	19 ARW
38003	KC-135A	93 BW
38004	KC-135A	379 BW
38005	KC-135A	2 BW
38006	KC-135A	305 ARW
38007	KC-135A	379 BW
38008	KC-135R	19 ARW
38009	KC-135A	305 ARW
38010	KC-135A	22 ARW
38011	KC-135A	410 BW
38012	KC-135A	93 BW
38013	KC-135A	340 ARW
38014	KC-135A	22 ARW
38015	KC-135A	416 BW
38016	KC-135A	416 BW
38017	KC-135A	22 ARW
38018	KC-135A	410 BW
38019	KC-135A	22 ARW
38020	KC-135R	19 ARW
38021	KC-135A	5 BW
38022	KC-135A	416 BW
38023	KC-135A	2 BW
38024	KC-135R	384 BW
38025	KC-135A	340 ARW
38026	KC-135A	22 ARW
38027	KC-135A	42 BW
38028	KC-135A	305 ARW
38029	KC-135A	380 BW
38030	KC-135A	305 ARW
38031	KC-135A	305 ARW
38032	KC-135R	28 BW
38033	KC-135A	305 ARW
38034	KC-135A	5 BW
38035	KC-135A	93 BW
38036	KC-135R	19 ARW
38037	KC-135A	2 BW
38038	KC-135A	93 BW
38039	KC-135A	379 BW
38040	KC-135R	384 BW
38041	KC-135A	2 BW
38043	KC-135A	42 BW
38044	KC-135A	7 BW
38045	KC-135A	92 BW
38046	EC-135C	55 SRW
38047	EC-135C	28 BW
38048	EC-135C	55 SRW
38049	EC-135C	55 SRW
38050	EC-135C	55 SRW
38051	EC-135C	28 BW
38052	EC-135C	55 SRW
38053	EC-135C	55 SRW
38054	EC-135C	55 SRW
38055	EC-135J	9 ACCS
38056	EC-135J	9 ACCS
38057	EC-135J	9 ACCS
38058	KC-135D	305 ARW
38059	KC-135D	305 ARW
38060	KC-135D	305 ARW
38061	KC-135D	305 ARW
38871	KC-135A	305 ARW
38872	KC-135A	509 BW
38873	KC-135A	320 BW
38874	KC-135A	319 BW
38875	KC-135A	7 BW
38876	KC-135A	93 BW
38877	KC-135A	5 BW
38878	KC-135A	5 BW
38879	KC-135A	22 ARW
38880	KC-135A	509 BW
38881	KC-135A	380 BW
38883	KC-135A	305 ARW
38884	KC-135A	376 SW
38885	KC-135A	410 BW

USAF (US based)

Serial	Type	Wing
38886	KC-135A	96 BW
38887	KC-135A	93 BW
38888	KC-135A	410 BW
39792	RC-135V	55 SRW
FY55		
53118	EC-135K	8 TDCS
53119	NKC-135A	55 SRW
53120	NKC-135A	4950 TW
53122	NKC-135A	4950 TW
53123	NKC-135A	4950 TW
53124	NKC-135A	4950 TW
53125	EC-135Y	CinC CC
53127	NKC-135A	4950 TW
53128	NKC-135A	4950 TW
53129	EC-135P	6ACCS
53130	KC-135A	7 BW
53131	NKC-135A	4950 TW
53132	NKC-135A	4950 TW
53134	NKC-135A	USN/FEWSG
53135	NKC-135A	4950 TW
53136	KC-135A	22 ARW
53137	KC-135A	2 BW
53139	KC-135A	92 BW
53141	KC-135E	116 ARS*
53142	KC-135A	93 BW
53143	KC-135E	197 ARS*
53145	KC-135E	314 ARS†
53146	KC-135E	145 ARS*
FY85		
56973	C-137C	89 MAW
56974	C-137C	89 MAW
FY56		
63591	KC-135A	380 BW
63592	KC-135A	380 BW
63593	KC-135E	133 ARS*
63594	KC-135A	93 BW
63595	KC-135A	22 ARW
63596	NKC-135A	USN/FEWSG
63600	KC-135A	2 BW
63601	KC-135A	93 BW
63603	KC-135A	2 BW
63604	KC-135E	117 ARS*
63606	KC-135E	132 ARS*
63607	KC-135E	151 ARS*
63608	KC-135A	340 ARW
63609	KC-135E	151 ARS*
63610	KC-135A	92 BW
63611	KC-135E	145 ARS*
63612	KC-135E	126 ARS*
63614	KC-135A	93 BW
63615	KC-135A	320 BW
63616	KC-135A	96 BW
63617	KC-135A	340 ARW
63619	KC-135A	2 BW
63620	KC-135A	5 BW
63621	KC-135A	7 BW
63622	KC-135E	132 ARS*
63623	KC-135E	336 ARS†
63624	KC-135A	42 BW
63625	KC-135A	305 ARW
63626	KC-135E	147 ARS*
63627	KC-135A	2 BW
63630	KC-135E	. ARS*
63631	KC-135E	117 ARS*
63632	KC-135A	92 BW
63633	KC-135A	509 BW

Serial	Type	Wing
63634	KC-135A	96 BW
63635	KC-135A	96 BW
63636	KC-135A	376 SW
63637	KC-135A	42 BW
63638	KC-135E	197 ARS*
63639	KC-135A	96 BW
63640	KC-135E	132 ARS*
63641	KC-135E	117 ARS*
63642	KC-135A	92 BW
63643	KC-135E	151 ARS*
63644	KC-135A	92 BW
63645	KC-135A	93 BW
63646	KC-135A	92 BW
63647	KC-135A	305 ARW
63648	KC-135E	145 ARS*
63649	KC-135A	2 BW
63650	KC-135E	133 ARS*
63651	KC-135A	92 BW
63652	KC-135A	42 BW
63653	KC-135A	92 BW
63654	KC-135E	132 ARS*
63656	KC-135A	93 BW
63658	KC-135E	117 ARS*
FY57		
71418	KC-135A	93 BW
71419	KC-135A	92 BW
71420	KC-135A	7 BW
71421	KC-135E	116 ARS*
71422	KC-135E	72 ARS†
71423	KC-135A	92 BW
71425	KC-135E	151 ARS*
71426	KC-135E	. ARS*
71427	KC-135A	93 BW
71428	KC-135E	133 ARS*
71429	KC-135E	117 ARS*
71430	KC-135A	92 BW
71431	KC-135E	126 ARS*
71432	KC-135A	92 BW
71433	KC-135E	197 ARS*
71434	KC-135E	116 ARS*
71435	KC-135A	92 BW
71436	KC-135A	5 BW
71437	KC-135A	92 BW
71438	KC-135E	72 ARS†
71439	KC-135A	92 BW
71440	KC-135R	319 BW
71441	KC-135A	92 BW
71443	KC-135E	132 ARS*
71445	KC-135E	145 ARS*
71447	KC-135A	93 BW
71448	KC-135E	. ARS*
71450	KC-135E	132 ARS*
71451	KC-135A	2 BW
71452	KC-135E	197 ARS*
71453	KC-135A	7 BW
71454	KC-135A	376 SW
71455	KC-135E	151 ARS*
71456	KC-135A	340 ARW
71458	KC-135E	108 ARS*
71459	KC-135A	93 BW
71460	KC-135E	117 ARS*
71461	KC-135A	376 SW
71462	KC-135R	28 BW
71463	KC-135E	117 ARS*
71464	KC-135E	145 ARS*
71465	KC-135E	. ARS*
71467	KC-135A	93 BW
71468	KC-135E	336 ARS†
71469	KC-135A	42 BW

Serial	Type	Wing
71470	KC-135A	376 SW
71471	KC-135A	19 ARW
71472	KC-135A	93 BW
71473	KC-135R	384 BW
71474	KC-135A	509 BW
71475	KC-135E	197 ARS*
71476	KC-135A	305 ARW
71477	KC-135A	340 ARW
71478	KC-135E	151 ARS*
71479	KC-135E	336 ARS†
71480	KC-135E	108 ARS*
71481	KC-135E	. ARS*
71482	KC-135E	117 ARS*
71483	KC-135R	93 BW
71484	KC-135E	197 ARS*
71485	KC-135E	151 ARS*
71486	KC-135A	22 ARW
71487	KC-135A	93 BW
71488	KC-135A	2 BW
71490	KC-135A	7 BW
71491	KC-135E	145 ARS*
71492	KC-135A	2 BW
71493	KC-135A	7 BW
71494	KC-135E	168 ARS*
71495	KC-135E	197 ARS*
71496	KC-135E	197 ARS*
71497	KC-135A	92 BW
71499	KC-135A	93 BW
71501	KC-135E	116 ARS*
71502	KC-135R	319 BW
71503	KC-135E	151 ARS*
71504	KC-135E	72 ARS†
71505	KC-135E	132 ARS*
71506	KC-135A	42 BW
71507	KC-135E	145 ARS*
71508	KC-135R	28 BW
71509	KC-135E	147 ARS*
71510	KC-135E	191 ARS*
71511	KC-135E	314 ARS†
71512	KC-135E	336 ARS†
71514	KC-135A	376 SW
72589	KC-135E	55 SRW
72590	KC-135A	
72591	KC-135A	410 BW
72592	KC-135A	5 BW
72593	KC-135A	96 BW
72594	KC-135E	108 ARS*
72595	KC-135E	147 ARS*
72596	KC-135A	5 BW
72597	KC-135A	92 BW
72598	KC-135E	336 ARS†
72599	KC-135A	319 BW
72600	KC-135E	116 ARS*
72601	KC-135A	97 BW
72602	KC-135A	7 BW
72603	KC-135E	336 ARS†
72604	KC-135E	126 ARS*
72605	KC-135A	93 BW
72606	KC-135E	150 ARS*
72607	KC-135E	147 ARS*
72608	KC-135E	147 ARS*
72609	KC-135A	320 BW
FY58		
80001	KC-135A	93 BW
80003	KC-135E	108 ARS*
80004	KC-135A	379 BW
80005	KC-135A	93 BW
80006	KC-135E	191 ARS*

Serial	Type	Wing
80008	KC-135E	145 ARS*
80009	KC-135A	5 BW
80010	KC-135A	93 BW
80011	KC-135A	305 ARW
80012	KC-135E	191 ARS*
80013	KC-135E	72 ARS†
80014	KC-135A	93 BW
80015	KC-135A	320 BW
80016	KC-135A	92 BW
80017	KC-135E	145 ARS*
80018	KC-135A	305 ARW
80019	EC-135P	6 ACCS
80020	KC-135E	116 ARS*
80021	KC-135A	340 ARW
80022	EC-135P	6 ACCS
80023	KC-135A	340 ARW
80024	KC-135E	126 ARS*
80025	KC-135A	340 ARW
80027	KC-135A	97 BW
80028	KC-135A	410 BW
80029	KC-135A	97 BW
80030	KC-135A	42 BW
80032	KC-135E	150 ARS*
80033	KC-135A	305 ARW
80034	KC-135A	410 BW
80035	KC-135A	93 BW
80036	KC-135A	19 ARW
80037	KC-135A	410 BW
80038	KC-135A	93 BW
80040	KC-135E	150 ARS*
80041	KC-135E	72 ARS†
80042	KC-135Q	380 BW
80043	KC-135E	191 ARS*
80044	KC-135A	19 ARW
80045	KC-135Q	380 BW
80046	KC-135Q	380 BW
80047	KC-135Q	380 BW
80049	KC-135Q	380 BW
80050	KC-135Q	380 BW
80051	KC-135A	93 BW
80052	KC-135E	336 ARS†
80053	KC-135E	314 ARS†
80054	KC-135Q	9 SRW
80055	KC-135Q	376 SW
80056	KC-135A	92 BW
80057	KC-135E	108 ARS*
80058	KC-135E	314 ARS†
80059	KC-135A	5 BW
80060	KC-135Q	380 BW
80061	KC-135Q	380 BW
80062	KC-135Q	9 SRW
80063	KC-135A	93 BW
80064	KC-135E	314 ARS†
80065	KC-135Q	380 BW
80066	KC-135A	19 ARW
80067	KC-135E	108 ARS*
80068	KC-135E	108 ARS*
80069	KC-135Q	376 SW
80070	KC-135A	376 SW
80071	KC-135Q	9 SRW
80072	KC-135Q	376 SW
80073	KC-135A	96 BW
80074	KC-135Q	9 SRW
80075	KC-135A	93 BW
80076	KC-135A	96 BW
80077	KC-135Q	9 SRW
80078	KC-135E	150 ARS*
80079	KC-135A	376 SW
80080	KC-135E	191 ARS*
80081	KC-135A	42 BW
80082	KC-135E	116 ARS*
80083	KC-135A	509 BW
80084	KC-135Q	9 SRW
80085	KC-135E	336 ARS†
80086	KC-135Q	9 SRW
80087	KC-135E	150 ARS*
80088	KC-135Q	9 SRW
80089	KC-135Q	9 SRW
80090	KC-135E	314 ARS†
80091	KC-135A	5 BW
80092	KC-135A	379 BW
80093	KC-135A	93 BW
80094	KC-135Q	9 SRW
80095	KC-135Q	9 SRW
80096	KC-135E	314 ARS†
80097	KC-135A	93 BW
80098	KC-135R	93 BW
80099	KC-135Q	9 SRW
80100	KC-135A	7 BW
80102	KC-135A	93 BW
80103	KC-135Q	9 SRW
80104	KC-135A	92 BW
80105	KC-135A	92 BW
80106	KC-135A	22 ARW
80107	KC-135E	191 ARS*
80108	KC-135E	314 ARS†
80109	KC-135A	96 BW
80110	KC-135A	319 BW
80111	KC-135E	126 ARS*
80112	KC-135Q	9 SRW
80113	KC-135A	96 BW
80114	KC-135A	96 BW
80115	KC-135E	150 ARS*
80116	KC-135A	96 BW
80117	KC-135Q	9 SRW
80118	KC-135A	509 BW
80119	KC-135A	5 BW
80120	KC-135R	384 BW
80121	KC-135A	93 BW
80122	KC-135A	92 BW
80123	KC-135A	379 BW
80124	KC-135A	305 ARW
80125	KC-135Q	9 SRW
80126	KC-135A	305 ARW
80128	KC-135A	5 BW
80129	KC-135Q	9 SRW
80130	KC-135A	7 BW
86970	VC-137B	89 MAW
86971	VC-137B	89 MAW
86972	VC-137B	89 MAW
FY59		
91444	KC-135A	92 BW
91445	KC-135E	116 ARS*
91446	KC-135R	28 BW
91447	KC-135E	72 ARS†
91448	KC-135E	133 ARS*
91449	KC-135A	22 ARW
91450	KC-135E	133 ARS*
91451	KC-135E	72 ARS†
91452	KC-135E	116 ARS*
91453	KC-135R	93 BW
91454	KC-135A	319 BW
91455	KC-135R	28 BW
91456	KC-135E	126 ARS*
91457	KC-135E	147 ARS*
91458	KC-135R	319 BW
91459	KC-135R	28 BW
91460	KC-135Q	376 SW
91461	KC-135A	92 BW
91462	KC-135Q	380 BW
91463	KC-135A	376 SW
91464	KC-135Q	376 SW
91466	KC-135R	319 BW
91467	KC-135Q	380 BW
91468	KC-135Q	9 SRW
91469	KC-135A	380 BW
91470	KC-135Q	9 SRW
91471	KC-135Q	376 SW
91472	KC-135A	97 BW
91473	KC-135E	191 ARS*
91474	KC-135Q	9 SRW
91475	KC-135A	319 BW
91476	KC-135A	319 BW
91477	KC-135E	72 ARS†
91478	KC-135R	19 ARW
91479	KC-135E	126 ARS*
91480	KC-135Q	9 SRW
91482	KC-135R	384 BW
91483	KC-135A	93 BW
91484	KC-135E	147 ARS*
91485	KC-135E	150 ARS*
91486	KC-135A	5 BW
91487	KC-135E	108 ARS*
91488	KC-135A	319 BW
91489	KC-135E	191 ARS*
91490	KC-135Q	9 SRW
91492	KC-135A	319 BW
91493	KC-135A	319 BW
91494	KC-135E	133 ARS*
91495	KC-135R	319 BW
91496	KC-135A	7 BW
91497	KC-135E	150 ARS*
91498	KC-135A	92 BW
91499	KC-135E	133 ARS*
91500	KC-135A	319 BW
91501	KC-135A	92 BW
91502	KC-135A	319 BW
91503	KC-135A	42 BW
91504	KC-135Q	9 SRW
91505	KC-135E	133 ARS*
91506	KC-135E	147 ARS*
91507	KC-135A	93 BW
91508	KC-135A	410 BW
91509	KC-135E	133 ARS*
91510	KC-135Q	376 SW
91511	KC-135A	42 BW
91512	KC-135Q	9 SRW
91513	KC-135Q	9 SRW
91514	KC-135E	55 SRW
91515	KC-135R	384 BW
91516	KC-135A	379 BW
91517	KC-135R	28 BW
91518	EC-135K	8 TDCS
91519	KC-135E	126 ARS*
91520	KC-135Q	9 SRW
91521	KC-135R	
91522	KC-135A	410 BW
91523	KC-135Q	9 SRW

Lockheed C-141B Starlifter
(*ANG, Air National Guard
†AFRES, Air Force Reserve)
60 MAW: Travis AFB, California
62 MAW: McChord AFB, Washington
63 MAW: Norton AFB, California
172 MAG*: Jackson Field AFB, Mississippi
437 MAW: Charleston AFB, S Carolina
438 MAW: McGuire AFB, New Jersey
443 MAW: Altus AFB, Oklahoma
459 MAW†: Andrews AFB, Maryland

FY61

Serial	Wing
12778	438 MAW

FY63

Serial	Wing
38075	60 MAW
38076	438 MAW
38078	437 MAW
38079	437 MAW
38080	438 MAW
38081	62 MAW
38082	62 MAW
38083	438 MAW
38084	63 MAW
38085	63 MAW
38086	62 MAW
38087	63 MAW
38088	60 MAW
38089	443 MAW
38090	438 MAW

FY64

Serial	Wing
40609	62 MAW
40610	437 MAW
40611	437 MAW
40612	437 MAW
40613	437 MAW
40614	172 MAG*
40615	437 MAW
40616	438 MAW
40617	63 MAW
40618	437 MAW
40619	63 MAW
40620	459 MAW†
40621	438 MAW
40622	438 MAW
40623	438 MAW
40625	438 MAW
40626	438 MAW
40627	438 MAW
40628	438 MAW
40629	437 MAW
40630	437 MAW
40631	437 MAW
40632	172 MAG*
40633	438 MAW
40634	63 MAW
40635	62 MAW
40636	443 MAW
40637	60 MAW
40638	438 MAW
40639	438 MAW
40640	172 MAG*
40642	60 MAW
40643	60 MAW
40644	437 MAW
40645	459 MAW†
40646	437 MAW
40648	60 MAW
40649	437 MAW
40650	438 MAW
40651	437 MAW
40653	63 MAW

FY65

Serial	Wing
50216	459 MAW†
50217	437 MAW
50218	437 MAW
50219	60 MAW
50220	437 MAW
50221	438 MAW
50222	438 MAW
50223	438 MAW
50224	438 MAW
50225	63 MAW
50226	459 MAW†
50227	62 MAW
50228	62 MAW
50229	62 MAW
50230	60 MAW
50231	60 MAW
50232	62 MAW
50233	60 MAW
50234	60 MAW
50235	62 MAW
50236	438 MAW
50237	62 MAW
50238	60 MAW
50239	60 MAW
50240	62 MAW
50241	62 MAW
50242	60 MAW
50243	62 MAW
50244	62 MAW
50245	60 MAW
50246	60 MAW
50247	60 MAW
50248	62 MAW
50249	60 MAW
50250	60 MAW
50251	60 MAW
50252	60 MAW
50253	62 MAW
50254	60 MAW
50255	62 MAW
50256	60 MAW
50257	60 MAW
50258	62 MAW
50259	60 MAW
50260	60 MAW
50261	438 MAW
50262	443 MAW
50263	62 MAW
50264	62 MAW
50265	60 MAW
50266	437 MAW
50267	437 MAW
50268	60 MAW
50269	437 MAW
50270	437 MAW
50271	459 MAW†
50272	437 MAW
50273	437 MAW
50275	437 MAW
50276	437 MAW
50277	62 MAW
50278	443 MAW
50279	437 MAW
50280	443 MAW
59397	443 MAW
59398	443 MAW
59399	62 MAW
59400	63 MAW
59401	437 MAW
59402	63 MAW
59403	60 MAW
59404	63 MAW
59405	443 MAW
59406	63 MAW
59408	437 MAW
59409	438 MAW
59410	60 MAW
59411	438 MAW
59412	438 MAW
59413	438 MAW
59414	63 MAW

FY66

Serial	Wing
60126	438 MAW
60128	63 MAW
60129	62 MAW
60130	172 MAG*
60131	437 MAW
60132	438 MAW
60133	438 MAW
60134	63 MAW
60135	437 MAW
60136	63 MAW
60137	63 MAW
60138	63 MAW
60139	63 MAW
60140	438 MAW
60141	62 MAW
60142	62 MAW
60143	63 MAW
60144	438 MAW
60145	62 MAW
60146	438 MAW
60147	60 MAW
60148	60 MAW
60149	443 MAW
60150	63 MAW
60151	60 MAW
60152	437 MAW
60153	63 MAW
60154	438 MAW
60155	438 MAW
60156	63 MAW
60157	438 MAW
60158	62 MAW
60159	459 MAW†
60160	437 MAW
60161	62 MAW
60162	438 MAW
60163	437 MAW
60164	172 MAG*
60165	62 MAW
60166	438 MAW
60167	437 MAW
60168	437 MAW
60169	438 MAW
60170	443 MAW
60171	63 MAW
60172	63 MAW
60173	438 MAW
60174	459 MAW†
60175	63 MAW
60176	62 MAW
60177	63 MAW

Serial	*Wing*
60178	437 MAW
60179	63 MAW
60180	63 MAW
60181	63 MAW
60182	63 MAW
60183	438 MAW
60184	63 MAW
60185	60 MAW
60186	443 MAW
60187	437 MAW
60188	60 MAW
60189	443 MAW
60190	172 MAG*
60191	60 MAW
60192	63 MAW
60193	63 MAW
60194	437 MAW
60195	437 MAW
60196	437 MAW
60197	62 MAW
60198	63 MAW
60199	438 MAW
60200	63 MAW
60201	63 MAW
60202	437 MAW
60203	437 MAW
60204	438 MAW
60205	63 MAW
60206	62 MAW
60207	443 MAW
60208	63 MAW
60209	437 MAW
67944	60 MAW
67945	437 MAW
67946	63 MAW
67947	437 MAW
67948	438 MAW
67949	63 MAW
67950	438 MAW
67951	62 MAW
67952	63 MAW
67953	438 MAW
67954	438 MAW
67955	437 MAW
67956	437 MAW
67957	63 MAW
67958	63 MAW
67959	63 MAW
FY67	
70001	63 MAW
70002	437 MAW
70003	443 MAW
70004	437 MAW
70005	63 MAW
70007	438 MAW
70009	63 MAW
70010	437 MAW
70011	437 MAW
70012	437 MAW
70013	438 MAW
70014	437 MAW
70015	63 MAW
70016	437 MAW
70018	62 MAW
70019	438 MAW
70020	438 MAW
70021	438 MAW
70022	63 MAW
70023	63 MAW
70024	438 MAW
70025	443 MAW
70026	437 MAW
70027	438 MAW
70028	63 MAW
70031	60 MAW
70164	62 MAW
70165	438 MAW
70166	443 MAW

Civil Registered Aircraft in Military Service

Serial

Boeing 747SP
(Omani Government)
A40-SO

Boeing B-727
(Government of Saudi Arabia)
HZ122

Grumman Gulfstream III
(Government of Saudi Arabia)

HZ103
HZ108
HZ-MS3

Lockheed C-130H Hercules
(Government of Saudi Arabia)

MS019
HZ114
HZ115
HZ116
HZ117

Lockheed P-3 Orion
(NOAA)
N42RF (159773) WP-3D
N43RF (159875) WP-3D

North American Sabre 75A
(Federal Aviation Administration)

N51
N52
N53
N54
N55
N56
N57
N58
N59
N60
N61
N62
N63
N64
N65

North American F-100F Super Sabre
(Flight Refuelling Ltd, Hurn/ Flight Systems, Decimomannu)
N416FS
N417FS
N418FS

Dassault Falcon 20DC
(Flight Refuelling Ltd/FRADU, Hurn)

N900FR
N901FR
N902FR
N903FR
N904FR
N905FR
N906FR
N907FR
N908FR
N909FR
G-FRAE (N910FR)
G-FRAF (N911FR)

YUGOSLAVIA
(Yugoslav Government)
Antonov AN.12
YU-AIC/73311
YU-AID/73312

Addenda

Note: The following additional information is correct to 31 January.

Notes	*Serial*	*Type (code/other identity)*	*Owner, Operator, Location or Fate*
	D7889	Bristol F2b Fighter (G-AANP/ BAPC166)	Privately owned, St Leonards
	WD355	DH Chipmunk T10 PAX (8099M)	Scrapped at Tilehurst, Berks, October 1987
	WG308	DH Chipmunk T10 [W]	RAF No 7 AEF, Newton
	WG469	DH Chipmunk T10 [X]	RAF No 7 AEF, Newton
	WG478	DH Chipmunk T10 [L]	RAF EFTS, Swinderby
	WK626	DH Chipmunk T10 PAX (8213M)	No 358 Sqn ATC, Welling, London
	WK642	DH Chipmunk T10 [M]	RAF No 3 AEF, Filton
	WP784	DH Chipmunk T10 PAX	Privately owned, Tilehurst, Berks
	WP844	DH Chipmunk T10	RAF No 11 AEF, Teesside
	WZ877	DH Chipmunk T10	RAF No 7 AEF, Newton
	XE793	Slingsby Cadet TX3	RAF St Athan — instructional use
	XJ607	DH Sea Vixen FAW2 (8171M)	Privately owned, Southampton
	XM474	Hunting Jet Provost T3 (8121M)	No 1330 Sqn ATC, Warrington
	XN386	WS55 Whirlwind HAR9 [435/ED]	Privately owned, Squires Gate
	XN493	Hunting Jet Provost T3 (nose only)	No 1075 Sqn ATC, Camberley
	XN734	EE Lightning F2A (G-BNCA)	Privately owned, Cranfield
	XP535	HS Gnat T1	Privately owned, Leavesden
	XP694	EE Lighting F3	RAF Binbrook decoy
	XP701	EE Lightning F3 (8924M)	Kent Battle of Britain Museum, Hawkinge
	XP702	EE Lightning F3	RAF Binbrook decoy
	XP706	EE Lightning F3 (8925M)	Lincolnshire Lightning Preservation Society, Louth
	XP991	BAC Gnat T1	Privately owned, Leavesden
	XR527	WS58 Wessex HC2	RAF WSF, Benson
	XR528	WS58 Wessex HC2	RAF WSF, Benson
	XS903	EE Lightning F6 [BA]	RAF No 11 Sqn, Binbrook
	XT614	WS Scout AH1 [C]	AAC No 660 Sqn, Sek Kong
	XT624	WS Scout AH1 [D]	AAC No 660 Sqn, Sek Kong
	XT628	WS Scout AH1 [E]	AAC No 660 Sqn, Sek Kong
	XT636	WS Scout AH1 [F]	AAC No 660 Sqn, Sek Kong
	XV229	HS Nimrod MR2P	RAF No 42 Sqn, St Mawgan
	XV251	HS Nimrod MR2	RAF No 42 Sqn, St Mawgan
	XV258	HS Nimrod MR2	RAF No 42 Sqn, St Mawgan
	XV281	HS Harrier GR3	RAF Wittering
	XV341	HS Buccaneer S2A	RAF Lossiemouth Fire Section
	XV466	McD Phantom FGR2 [R]	RAF No 56 Sqn, Wattisham
	XV473	McD Phantom FGR2 [K]	RAF No 56 Sqn, Wattisham
	XV699	WS61 Sea King HAS5 [134]	RN No 826 Sqn, Culdrose
	XV705	WS61 Sea King HAS5 [821]	RN No 771 Sqn, Culdrose
	XV712	WS61 Sea King HAS5 [583]	RN No 706 Sqn, Culdrose
	XW612	WS Scout AH1 [A]	AAC No 660 Sqn, Sek Kong
	XW613	WS Scout AH1 [B]	AAC No 660 Sqn, Sek Kong
	XW797	WS Scout AH1 [G]	AAC No 660 Sqn, Sek Kong
	XW798	WS Scout AH1 [H]	AAC No 660 Sqn, Sek Kong
	XX241	HS Hawk T1	Collided and crashed 16 November 1987, Welton, Lincs
	XX259	HS Hawk T1A	Collided and crashed 16 November 1987, Welton, Lincs
	XX629	SA Bulldog T1 [V]	RAF, Northumbrian UAS, Leeming
	XX631	SA Bulldog T1 [W]	RAF, Northumbrian UAS, Leeming
	XX633	SA Bulldog T1 [X]	RAF, Northumbrian UAS, Leeming
	XX636	SA Bulldog T1 [Y]	RAF, Northumbrian UAS, Leeming
	XX666	SA Bulldog T1 [V]	RAF No 1FTS, Topcliffe
	XX701	SA Bulldog T1 [02]	RAF, Southampton UAS, Lee-on-Solent
	XX705	SA Bulldog T1 [05]	RAF, Southampton UAS, Lee-on-Solent
	XX706	SA Bulldog T1 [01]	RAF, Southampton UAS, Lee-on-Solent
	XX707	SA Bulldog T1 [04]	RAF, Southampton UAS, Lee-on-Solent
	XX708	SA Bulldog T1 [03]	RAF, Southampton UAS, Lee-on-Solent
	XZ229	WS Lynx HAS3 [402/BX]	RN No 829 Sqn, Portland
	XZ248	WS Lynx HAS3 [345/NC]	RN No 815 Sqn, Portland
	XZ493	BAe Sea Harrier FRS1 [006/R]	RN No 801 Sqn, Yeovilton
	ZA373	Panavia Tornado GR1R [BR-60]	RAF TTTE, Cottesmore

Serial	Type (code/other identity)	Owner, Operator, Location or Fate	Notes
ZD324	BAe Harrier GR5 [B]	RAF No 233 OCU, Wittering	
ZD326	BAe Harrier GR5 [D]	RAF No 233 OCU, Wittering	
ZD900	Panavia Tornado F2T	MoD(PE) A&AEE Boscombe Down	
ZD901	Panavia Tornado F2T [AB]	RAF St Athan	
ZE207	Panavia Tornado F3 [AK]	RAF No 229 OCU/65 Sqn, Coningsby	
ZE253	Panavia Tornado F3T [AB]	RAF No 229 OCU/65 Sqn, Coningsby	
ZE292	Panavia Tornado F3 [CA]	RAF No 5 Sqn, Coningsby	
ZE293	Panavia Tornado F3T [AC]	RAF No 5 Sqn, Coningsby	
ZE294	Panavia Tornado F3 [CB]	RAF No 5 Sqn, Coningsby	
ZE295	Panavia Tornado F3 [CC]	RAF No 5 Sqn, Coningsby	
ZE296	Panavia Tornado F3T [AM]	RAF No 229 OCU/65 Sqn, Coningsby	
ZE338	Panavia Tornado F3 [CD]	RAF No 5 Sqn, Coningsby	
ZE339	Panavia Tornado F3 [CE]	RAF No 5 Sqn, Coningsby	
ZE340	Panavia Tornado F3T [AG]	RAF No 229 OCU/65 Sqn, Coningsby	
ZE341	Panavia Tornado F3 [CF]	RAF No 5 Sqn, Coningsby	
ZE342	Panavia Tornado F3 [CG]	RAF No 5 Sqn, Coningsby	

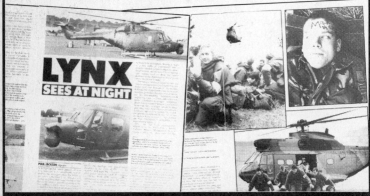